Orientation and Mobility Techniques

A Guide for the Practitioner

Second Edition

Diane L. Fazzi
and
Janet M. Barlow

A revised edition of the Hill and Ponder classic

American Foundation for the Blind

Printed in the United States of America

Library of Congress Cataloging-in-Publication Data

Names: Fazzi, Diane L., author. | Barlow, Janet M., author. | Hill, Everett. Orientation and mobility techniques. | Ponder, Purvis. Orientation and mobility techniques.
Title: Orientation and mobility techniques : a guide for the practitioner / by Diane L. Fazzi and Janet M. Barlow.
Description: Second Edition. | New York : AFB Press, American Foundation for the Blind, [2017] | Revised edition of Orientation and mobility techniques, 1976. | A Revised Edition of the Hill and Ponder Classic. | Includes bibliographical references.
Identifiers: LCCN 2017001186 (print) | LCCN 2017014641 (ebook) | ISBN 9780891287889 (online subscription) | ISBN 9780891287896 (ePub) | ISBN 9780891287902 (mobi) | ISBN 9780891287919 (PDF) | ISBN 9780891286844 (pbk. : alk. paper)
Subjects: LCSH: Blind—Orientation and mobility.
Classification: LCC HV1598 (ebook) | LCC HV1598 .F39 2017 (print) | DDC 362.4/18—dc23
LC record available at https://lccn.loc.gov/2017001186

The American Foundation for the Blind removes barriers, creates solutions, and expands possibilities so people with vision loss can achieve their full potential.

It is the policy of the American Foundation for the Blind to use in the first printing of its books acid-free paper that meets the ANSI Z39.48 Standard. The infinity symbol that appears above indicates that the paper in this printing meets that standard.

Contents

Italics indicate techniques with step-by-step descriptions.

Chapter 8   **Transportation Systems   *172***

Chapter 9   **Special Situations   202**

Chapter 10   **Travel Techniques for Learners Who Have Low Vision   225**

Foreword

The First Edition

More than five years ago, at an AFB Leadership Conference, Natalie Hilzen, then editor in chief of AFB Press, came to me and asked, "After more than 35 years, should we continue publishing the Hill and Ponder textbook on mobility techniques or is it obsolete?" The answer to that question was a difficult one for me since so many in the discipline of orientation and mobility (O&M) consider the "Blue Book," as it is affectionately known, to be the "Bible" of the field. The book had changed the field and improved learning, yet the material within the text had become somewhat dated and did not completely address changes in the discipline of O&M or the challenges of the current environment. I finally came to the conclusion that a major revision of the text was necessary.

The first edition of *Orientation and Mobility Techniques: A Guide for the Practitioner*, by Everett "Butch" Hill and Purvis "Perky" Ponder, holds a special place in our hearts and minds. Generations of O&M specialists were weaned on that book, and it standardized the various approaches to independent travel in the United States and across the world. It was a staple in many university training programs. Often, when there was a dispute regarding the best technique to employ, instructors returned to that book for guidance and inspiration. Prior to the publication of the first edition, all O&M students would have to write down the techniques in their own notebooks to document the procedures taught to them in their visual occlusion and simulation mobility classes. This was a difficult task and one that did not always result in a comprehensive compendium of skills.

Early on, when O&M was just gaining a foothold as a profession, many in the field did not want to see the development of a readily available textbook that contained the various techniques and rationale for their use. Many feared that such a textbook would be taken up by those without the prerequisite knowledge and experience to provide a safe and effective training program. At that time, the American Foundation for the Blind recognized that the development of any profession is based on a foundation of literature and a means of sharing that foundation with its practitioners. The publication of the first comprehensive textbook of O&M techniques became an integral building block in the professionalization of the discipline. Each university program now had a textbook with standardized procedures that formed the basis of practice.

The Significance of the Texts

We must look back upon the history that led to the first edition to understand the significance of that text. Since the beginning of recorded history people who were blind were traveling independently using various techniques that helped protect them from danger while at the same time allowing them to explore what lay ahead. These skills evolved through trial and error and were passed down from one generation to the next by word of mouth and demonstration. In more modern times the two World Wars led to a dramatic increase in the number of individuals who experienced vision loss. As a result of the influx of blinded veterans from World War II, a more systematic approach was needed. Sargent Richard Hoover, serving at Valley Forge General Hospital, chose a team of "orientors"—selected from the newly developed department of Corrective Therapy in the Veterans Administration (VA)—to pioneer a series of techniques called "foot travel." After the war, with the help of Warren Bledsoe, the VA established the Blindness Center at Hines Veterans Administration Hospital outside of Chicago. The techniques pioneered by the original "orientors" were further refined by the first six mobility specialists: John Malamazian, Stanley Suterko, Alfred Dee Corbett, Edward Thuis, Lawrence Blaha, and Edward Mees. Oversite and further development was provided by Russell C. Williams, chief of the Blindness Center, with Richard Hoover serving as a consultant.

The early university training programs seized upon this body of knowledge and incorporated the techniques into their training of practitioners. When I was department chair at Western Michigan University (WMU), I interviewed George Mallinson, dean of the graduate school, and learned that the O&M program at the university was created by taking the content of the training provided at Hines and giving course numbers to the various components. Hill was an early graduate of this program and an assistant professor in the Department of Blind Rehabilitation at WMU when the first edition of the book was published. The influence of the Hines program on the writing of *Orientation and Mobility Techniques* was demonstrable. During the 15 years between the establishment of the first university programs and the publication of the first edition, Hill and Ponder incorporated some modifications of the techniques into the book, although it still tended to concentrate on skills for adults who were totally blind.

While the early pioneering techniques were found to be successful, they were developed through trial and error and were not subject to experimental research designed to determine the most effective approaches. Over the years graduates of the various university programs conducted practice-based research to test the efficacy of many of the accepted procedures. They explored such topics as methods of crossing streets, new cane materials, types of cane tips, various cane lengths, techniques to use with vision, and adaptations for children and for those with additional disabilities.

The first edition of *Orientation and Mobility Techniques* was written based on the techniques that had been developed for adults and for those with no usable vision. With the success of these techniques, it was clear that the techniques and their modifications could also be used to help children. Over the years much work has been done to tailor these techniques for use by children who are blind. Additional adaptive mobility devices have been developed to further assist children in the early stages of their instruction. And with the overwhelming majority of individuals who have useful vision, a growing emphasis arose as to how to teach them to best use their vision.

The built environment is different today than when the book was first written and techniques have had to change to keep up with those differences. Back when the first edition of the book was written, intersections were controlled by mechanisms that provided a consistent timing for light changes. Actuated and semi-actuated traffic controls were not in the picture. Accessible pedestrian signals had not yet become prominent in large cities. Roundabouts were a curiosity rather than a reality in the United States. Various phasing cycles at complex intersections were not encountered on a regular basis.

Equipment has also changed since that time. Travelers were taught to use a touch technique using a one-piece cane that had a pencil-type tip at the end. Today we find that learners use a variety of travel instruments based on their unique needs and the environment in which they are traveling. Folding canes are the norm and are used with a variety of tips. The constant-contact technique has been shown to provide advantages over the touch technique and is used in combination with the touch technique or as a replacement. The interior layout of buses has changed and hybrid and electric cars present unique issues. Travelers today are using their smartphones equipped with GPS to gather information about their surroundings and to plan travel routes.

As a result of changes to the environment, the growing emphasis on the use of low vision, expansion of services to children, and studies conducted by practitioners, the practice of O&M has evolved from where it was at the time of the publication of the first edition of this book. The textbook did not always address the procedures that were needed to manage these new realities. Many of these topics were missing or not treated adequately in the previous text and thus it became critical to refresh the book.

The first edition of *Orientation and Mobility Techniques* was unique in the way it was constructed. Hill and Ponder conceptualized the text to be one that an instructor could pick up, quickly identify a specific procedure, and understand the rationale and the possible variations that would be useful. To accomplish that task, they used a landscape format that allowed them to list the steps on the left side and show the rationale and observations on the right side. This made it easy for the practitioner to integrate practice with theory. Other textbooks later followed but many did not have the detail presented in *Orientation and Mobility Techniques.*

The Development of the New Edition

While many other texts provided information relating to the changes previously mentioned, *Orientation and Mobility Techniques* remained rooted in the past. However, this new edition contains a fresh look at the travel needs of children and adults with vision loss and addresses the techniques that are needed in today's environment. The book contains information on crossing today's complex intersections, including the use of accessible pedestrian signals, traffic-light timing, signal phasing, and crossing roundabouts.

When thinking about a new team to carry on the Hill and Ponder tradition, the choice was easy. Diane Fazzi, with her years of experience as a faculty member and expertise with children, would add a broader perspective to the book. Janet Barlow, with her advocacy and experience in environmental accessibility, would be able to address the changes in the environment that have required new street-crossing approaches. It was an added benefit that Janet Barlow had been one of Hill and Ponder's students and contributed to the writing of the original text.

The philosophy of the book is communicated through a description of its structure at the very beginning. The content is based on teaching principles and models of instruction. The format of the book has changed but the principles have been retained to provide the features that made the original book so useful. While the new book could not be printed in landscape format, the same elements of the original text were incorporated into a portrait layout. There is a section called Procedure at a Glance, which provides simplified versions of the techniques for easy reference. Each step is also clearly

articulated with a follow-up rationale providing the underpinnings for the procedures. At the end of each technique there is an area for final considerations that apply to teaching the technique. At the end of major units there is a section called Tips for Teaching. Under this heading the reader will find information relating to orientation, positioning of the instructor, strategies to be used, modifications for learners with low vision, application to individuals of different ages, modifications for people with additional disabilities, and a section on self-advocacy.

The text of the new edition is also organized in a slightly different way. Instead of taking the learner through each step as it might unfold in a classic training program, it groups techniques together according to similarities. Thus, there are chapters specifically focused on cane techniques, block travel, and street crossings. This reorganization encourages flexibility in sequencing based on the environment and the needs of the learner rather than on a predetermined schedule. The book also adds a wealth of new information that had been missing from the original text or that was treated only briefly in that text. For example, topics such as crossing a slope, intersection analysis, and street-corner familiarization are treated thoroughly in the new edition. The book also has a chapter dedicated to travel for learners who have low vision.

I believe that the new edition of *Orientation and Mobility Techniques* presents the most comprehensive treatment of the techniques and their theoretical underpinnings found anywhere in literature. It calls upon best practices and current research, and has an organizational structure that makes it easy to digest. I believe it is destined to become the new Bible for the field of orientation and mobility.

William R. Wiener, PhD
Brenda Brodie Endowed Chair
Department of Curriculum and Instruction
School of Education
North Carolina Central University
Durham, North Carolina

Acknowledgments

This revision of the classic *Orientation and Mobility Techniques: A Guide for the Practitioner* is our first collaboration. We consider it an honor and a tremendous responsibility to revise the pioneering work of Everett Hill and Purvis Ponder. We hope these giants in the field would have approved of the final product, which attempts to hold true to their format while updating the content in a meaningful way.

We are very grateful to our families who gave us the time and space we needed to work collaboratively on this project, as well as for the unlimited texting plans that allowed us to stay connected from over 2,000 miles away. Thanks to the many orientation and mobility specialists who have contributed their knowledge to the field through books, articles, and presentations from which we drew upon while revising the content of this book. Special thanks to Kathryn, Vince, Brenda, Jacob, Ronan, and the O&M students and staff at California State University, Los Angeles who posed for photos multiple times as we tried to get just the right position of various techniques. A special thank you also goes to Brenda Naimy for her numerous contributions to the book, including training handouts that we borrowed from generously.

Kudos to the team at AFB Press, starting with Natalie Hilzen and Ellen Bilofsky and finishing with George Abbott and Alina Vayntrub, for their tremendous support throughout the process. Thanks also goes to Bill Wiener for writing the foreword. Everyone involved provided insight that was invaluable to the successful completion of this book.

Important Notice

Dear reader of *O&M Techniques,* Second Edition,

The American Foundation for the Blind has developed an online learning center to accompany this book. Access to the AFB Learning Center is complimentary for purchasers of the book, but registration is required. If you purchased an online subscription of this book, you will be able to access the full text through the Learning Center as well.

Registration for the AFB Learning Center is fast and simple. Just follow these steps:

- Go to www.afb.org/OMT2Register

- Complete the short registration form by entering your name and e-mail address, creating a username and password, and entering the code **OMT2**.
- Submit the form.

To access the AFB Learning Center once you have registered, go to www.afb.org/OMT2. Choose the link to log in and enter the username and password you created during registration.

If you experience technical problems or have any questions, contact AFB at afbpress@afb.net.

Introduction

The history of the profession of *orientation and mobility* (O&M) is rich with anecdotes that detail the first instances of travel for individuals who are blind, whether with the assistance of others; independently with a rod, staff, short or long cane; or with a dog guide. That history has been shaped by many factors, including

- the complexity of environments to be traveled in, from rural streets to busy metropolitan areas;
- the availability and ingenuity of human-made materials to make canes and other travel devices;
- the development of accessible technologies that could be incorporated for both mobility and orientation;
- the changes in the automotive industry and public- and private-transportation networks;
- the needs and demands of consumers of O&M services and the dedication and creativity of service providers;
- the advent of blind rehabilitation centers, university training programs, private- and public-service agencies, schools for the blind, and public-school programming;
- the introduction of federal legislation addressing education, rehabilitation, employment, environmental design, and transportation; and
- the evolution of research into evidence-based practices for teaching techniques to use for travel in home, school, work, and community environments.

There are many important milestones in the progression of the O&M profession (see Wiener, Welsh, & Blasch, 2010, for a thorough review of the history, development, progression, and research in the field). First and foremost is Everett Hill and Purvis Ponder's groundbreaking work, *Orientation and Mobility Techniques: A Guide for the Practitioner* (1976), which provided one of the first resources, with de-

tailed techniques and considerations in working with students, for O&M specialists.

At that time there were many individuals in the field who thought a detailed description of techniques should not be published because it would provide untrained individuals with an opportunity to pick up a book and attempt to teach O&M without proper foundational knowledge or clinical experience. However, Hill and Ponder firmly believed that for O&M to grow as a profession, "we who are in it have a responsibility to document what we already know" (Hill & Ponder, 1976, p. 1). From 1970 to 1974, Florida State University students developed the text, describing and numbering the procedures, rationales, and observations in their individual notebooks and working with professors Hill and Ponder to refine the descriptions. The coauthor of this book, Janet Barlow, was one of those students. She remembers Hill and Ponder's absolute dedication to completing the book and getting it published. Everett (Butch) Hill's insistence on the detailed formatting with a rationale for each step remains etched in her mind. In 1975, Barlow also heard some of the concerns expressed by others at an Association for the Education of the Visually Handicapped (AEVH) conference, suggesting that the publication of such a book would be the end of the profession. Despite those doubts, Hill and Ponder persevered and published their book, which was followed by many others that expanded and redefined the O&M profession. In working on this revision, some of those earlier conversations echoed in Ms. Barlow's head. She is immensely honored to take part in this updated second edition.

After 40 years of the well-used and well-loved original edition of *Orientation and Mobility Techniques: A Guide for the Practitioner*, the changes in what the profession teaches, how the profession teaches, and where the profession teaches O&M necessitated an update to the classic text. Research, whether collected from a network of practicing

O&M specialists (Wall Emerson & De l'Aune, 2010) or learned through classical research—including controlled experiments, single-subject design, surveys, and qualitative studies—has helped the authors approach the O&M techniques from a more informed perspective. It is fully expected that the updates for techniques presented here will also need to be revised as the knowledge base of the profession grows. The demands of the travel environments in which O&M specialists teach continue to challenge the profession to reflect on what defines best practice as well as how to appropriately individualize and adapt current knowledge to ensure that each learner has the best opportunity to learn to travel safely, and as independently as is desired and possible. Practicing O&M specialists, engaged in lifelong learning and accountable to their students, will continue to be a driving force in shaping the future of the O&M profession. The authors hope that this revision of the classic text will provide another step forward in the practice of teaching orientation and mobility.

Several chapters of the third edition of *Foundations of Orientation and Mobility* (Wiener et al., 2010) are heavily referenced in this work, as they provide an in-depth examination of the foundational content that O&M practitioners should possess in order to design and implement O&M lessons for the wide range of learners they serve. That same level of detail cannot be duplicated in this book if it is to maintain its ultimate purpose of providing O&M specialists with thorough descriptions of techniques in an easy to reference, portable format.

In This Edition

Through surveys of the field, the authors of this updated edition have worked diligently to maintain the essence of the original text that professionals loved, and have retained the step-by-step approach complete with behavioral descriptions of techniques. The Procedure at a Glance feature was added for each technique for quick reference and overview. However, the Procedure at a Glance is not to be used as a substitute for the complete and detailed Method section included for each technique, which also describes the rationale and possible variations. The new layout is intended to make the book a quick and easy reference for both preservice and active O&M practitioners.

Throughout this book the term "learner" will be used to refer to anyone receiving O&M instruction, typically a person with a visual impairment, although it may also be a preservice professional learning O&M techniques in a university program. This term was chosen because learners may be of any age and not necessarily young or in school, as the term "student" might imply. "O&M specialist" will be used to refer to a professional who specializes in teaching travel skills to individuals who are blind or who have low vision in home, school, and community environments, including the use of sensory and cognitive skills, specialized techniques, travel with guides, and use of technology. In addition, to avoid awkward language, the gender of the learner and the O&M specialist will be different in each chapter. Lastly, italicized phrases throughout the chapters will be used to signify important terms readers should know, with definitions provided in a glossary located at the back of the book.

The book begins with a short overview chapter on basic teaching principles and models of instruction for consideration in planning O&M instruction. Similar in approach to Hill and Ponder's first edition, the general conceptual content related to orientation is dealt with in a separate chapter (Chapter 2). This chapter provides the reader with a detailed discussion of associated principles, processes, and concepts, as well as the understanding that O&M instruction must be fully integrated in order to promote purposeful movement and independent travel that is safe, efficient, and satisfying for each individual. Somewhat different from Hill and Ponder's organization of the techniques, this book deals with groups of techniques rather than dividing the content by indoor versus outdoor and residential versus commercial environments. Chapter 3 covers guide techniques, Chapter 4 contains hand trailing and protective techniques, and Chapter 5 discusses cane techniques. Rather than including some cane techniques in a chapter addressing indoor travel and some in a different chapter on residential travel, the cane techniques have been combined in one chapter for easy access and reference.

The techniques have also been grouped together based on the understanding that different O&M specialists may introduce techniques in a variety of sequences that may or may not follow a specific environmental sequence. The sequence of instruction may be based on the types of environments readily available to the learner, that individual's learning style, or the immediate needs for travel. Using this method of grouping techniques will allow for easy reference and encourage O&M specialists to consider the best sequence for individual learners. It is also important to note that the earlier placement of guide techniques and hand trailing and protective techniques should not be considered an indication that they are prerequisites to the introduction of cane techniques. To the contrary, the authors strongly support the earliest possible introduction of the long cane to learners who can benefit from use of the long cane for purposeful movement and travel.

Chapter 6 focuses on block travel and discusses basic techniques that can be applied to both residential and business areas. The treatment of street crossings in Chapter 7 addresses the complexity of computer-controlled signals and quieter vehicles, and separates the task of crossing into a series of techniques that can be used for a variety of intersection geometries and controls in diverse environments. The inclusion of intersection analysis as a technique is intended to ensure that O&M specialists work with learners to think critically and systematically about crossings prior to making timing and crossing decisions.

Chapter 8 covers transportation, including bus travel, light rail, and other forms of public transportation. Chapter 9 addresses special situations such as elevators, escalators, shopping districts, and rural areas.

A brand-new addition to the text is Chapter 10, which focuses on travel techniques for individuals who have low vision. Considerations for these individuals are incorporated throughout the book, but Chapter 10 provides more in-depth coverage on visual techniques and the use of low vision devices for the purposes of O&M.

Similar to the original book, rationales and variations for the techniques are found throughout the chapters. New elements include increased emphasis on strategies, sequencing, positioning of the instructor, self-advocacy, and general strategies for working with learners of different ages and with additional disabilities.

The authors hope that this revision of the original groundbreaking work pays appropriate tribute to the pioneers who authored *Orientation and Mobility Techniques: A Guide for the Practitioner* while providing appropriate updates and a refreshed contribution to the field.

This book will be useful to both preservice and in-service O&M specialists. For preservice specialists, it will provide a foundational tool for learning the techniques, while in-service specialists will find this to be an essential reference guide. If university personnel preparation programs elect to adopt this book for use in training future O&M specialists and teachers of students with visual impairments, the following suggestions are offered for how the book might be incorporated into training.

Strategies for University Personnel Preparation

Personnel preparation programs may elect to use and adopt this book as a source of training for O&M specialists or teachers of students with visual impairments in the techniques of O&M. The traditional approach to teaching O&M skills involves practicing the techniques through simulation using a blindfold (sleep shade) or simulator goggles. For preservice O&M specialists, learning to teach the technique and monitor the application of the technique in a variety of dynamic settings is as important as developing and applying the technique appropriately.

Groupings

Personnel preparation programs use a variety of groupings to teach O&M techniques. The basic skills can be taught in larger groups of six to twelve, especially when being introduced and practiced in a contained area. More advanced skills are typically taught in smaller groups of two to four learners per experienced instructor. The rationale behind working in smaller groups for more advanced skills includes, but is not limited to, the following:

- Smaller groups afford more time for individual technique practice in rotation, which supports greater mastery of the techniques being learned.
- Smaller groups afford more individual teaching time in rotation, which supports the development of teaching skills to be used later in applied practice.
- Smaller groups ensure that the faculty or experienced instructor is able to provide direct and timely feedback about techniques, teaching, and monitoring as needed.

■ Smaller groups enable the faculty or experienced instructor to maintain greater control over the learning environment and maintain safety for the learners.

When working with preservice teachers of students with visual impairments, some chapters of the book can be used to teach techniques while other chapters may be assigned as a future reference. In instances in which O&M specialists and teachers of students with visual impairments are being taught on the same university campus, preservice O&M specialists can be assigned to prepare instructional units or segments to teach newly learned skills to their classmates who are preservice teachers. This provides an opportunity for collaborative learning and practice in preparing in-service training that can be useful in working with families and school, community, and medical teams that support individuals who are blind or who have low vision.

Emphasis

There are many O&M techniques and potential variations and considerations for preservice O&M specialists to learn. It can be helpful to work within a predetermined sequence of training at the university, incorporating in-person or online seminars that provide an overview of the techniques or a series of related techniques or foundational content, so that the preservice O&M specialists can develop a whole-picture understanding of the approach. From that big picture, preservice O&M specialists can then more readily integrate the specific steps, variations, and considerations within an overall understanding of the technique so that they will be able to reference materials later as part of a review or retrieve them easily from memory.

Special emphasis may be placed on having preservice students in O&M university programs clearly and accurately verbalize the techniques so that they are confident in their ability to do so prior to initial fieldwork. It is also of critical importance that these future professionals understand and can explain the rationale for each technique so that they may be able to share this information with their future learners and effectively adapt aspects of techniques when necessary, not haphazardly, for given individuals.

Future O&M specialists will also benefit from practicing correct positions with regard to their learners who are visually impaired that will ensure safety without impeding their learners' interactions with the community and travel environment. Preservice students engaging in early fieldwork may err on the side of maintaining an instructor position that is somewhat closer to the learner than that of an experienced O&M specialist. However, it is still expected that the student understand which relative position should be maintained, for example, alongside and slightly below a beginning learner during stair travel or off the shoulder opposite the near-lane-parallel traffic during alignment for street crossings. While there is a valid progression of decreasing proximity based on knowledge of the abilities of the learner who is visually impaired, complexity of the travel environment, physical capabilities of the learner and instructor, and experience and reaction time of the instructor, the appropriate position for the O&M specialist is gauged on an individual basis for every learner, every lesson, and every dynamic learning situation.

Once preservice O&M specialists have mastered the content and rationale for the techniques, are able to clearly describe and explain both, and establish and maintain good instructor positioning, they are prepared to design effective lessons for supervised fieldwork that incorporates models of instruction and strategies that will enable their learners to understand and grow.

CHAPTER

Basic Teaching Principles

While the primary purpose of this technique book is to provide a foundation for preservice orientation and mobility (O&M) specialists and serve as a reference guide for practicing O&M specialists, the authors are mindful that the techniques described will be applied to O&M instruction with an extremely heterogeneous population of learners who have visual impairments. O&M specialists work with learners from early childhood to older adulthood and learners who have either *congenital* (present at birth) or *adventitious* (occurring later in life) visual impairment with differing degrees and types of vision loss and levels of previous training, and the context and environment under which the techniques may be taught will vary greatly. As a result, the sequencing and emphasis of techniques and lessons may shift according to the *learning styles* of individuals being taught and learner or family priorities. O&M specialists, with strong rationale and careful consideration, will use creativity to adapt the techniques described in this book to meet the demands of various travel environments and the needs of individual learners, including those who have additional disabilities.

Assessment and Goal Setting

The key to knowing how to apply O&M techniques with an individual learner is to conduct a thorough assessment of the learner's present level of travel,

needs, abilities, prior experiences, interests, and goals. A complete O&M assessment will also include input from learners, families, teachers, and other specialists in the event that the learner is receiving other services. Ideal assessments are collaboratively planned, and for younger learners must include an assessment of family priorities. For techniques that may require repetition, daily use of the techniques and consistent monitoring are essential to develop and refine skills for younger children. An important aspect of the assessment process will be to determine the key members of the team who will be able to provide support and reinforcement of the techniques to be learned and applied in daily living. The team established during this assessment and planning process will also need to receive updates from the O&M specialist as new techniques are introduced.

For older learners, especially those for whom vision loss is a more recent experience, the assessment process will include developing a picture of previous content knowledge and experience that can be mapped onto the O&M instruction in order to make it readily accessible to the learner throughout the learning and adjustment process. The assessment process will likely include a trip to the school, college, workplace, home, and community environments to assess the learner's more salient travel needs. While the end goal for most learners will be to learn the full complement of O&M techniques to generalize across a myriad of unfamiliar and *familiar environments,* prioritizing the learner's immediate needs can be crucial for learners who may have work and family obligations or limited access to training hours.

Models of Instruction

Once O&M specialists determine the skills and techniques learners need, define the optimum *sequence for instruction* (the steps or order of skills taught), and prioritize goals for their learners based on individualized assessment, *models of instruction* can then be selected. Models of instruction are frameworks or broad sets of approaches to instruction that stem from a particular learning theory. O&M specialists can design individual and unit lessons, incorporating instructional strategies from the model accordingly. These models are not intended to be static. They are blueprints from which to plan and adjust instruction in a manner that is explicit and clear to learners. Models of instruction have been characterized by theorists and grouped by pedagogical experts in a variety of ways and can be summarized as follows:

- **Information-processing** models of instruction are based on the *cognitive-learning theory* that learning is a result of mental connections and associations that can result in conceptual understanding, generalizations, and critical thinking. Cognitive reasoning, application of logic, and storage and retrieval of information are all important foci of this model for teaching. While the general goal of the model is to design lessons that focus on learning specific information, organizing sets of information or data, solving specific problems using data, and developing *concepts* and language, the model also values individual learning styles and promotes metacognition in which learners are also expected to understand how they learn and the best strategies for processing new information and accessing previously learned information. Information-processing models of instruction include the use of advanced organizers, opportunities for critical thinking, scientific and inquiry-based learning, metacognitive strategies for memorization, and practice and application of learning.
- **Behavioral** models of instruction, or *behavioral-learning theory,* emphasize the focus on specific observable behaviors or skill sets, including the role of reinforcement in learning. Behavioral models include clearly identified learning outcomes and highly structured approaches to teaching such as direct instruction, skill drill

and practice, direct training, desensitization, and simulation. Hunter's (2004) clearly structured approach to lesson planning with anticipatory set, direct instruction, *guided practice*, independent practice, and feedback loop is one such example of a model to support direct instruction. Behavior analysis and principles of reinforcement can also be applied within these models. Assessing antecedents, behaviors, and their consequences helps teachers to understand the functional communication underlying learner behaviors and develop positive support and strategies to optimize learning.

- **Social** models of instruction, or *social-learning theory,* involve structures in which learners share information and responsibility for learning with one another, including collaborative learning, cooperative learning, role-playing, and group inquiry. Social models of instruction reflect how humans learn in social contexts through observation, modeling, and social exchanges. These models are aimed at building communities among learners and can result in multiple gains in learning and social networking.
- **Problem-based** models of instruction incorporate authentic tasks or projects to engage learners in new learning. The approach combines cognitive- and social-learning theories to encourage learners to construct new knowledge based on prior understanding and social interaction. Other descriptors, including project-based or *discovery learning,* in which material to be learned is uncovered while solving a problem or completing a task, can also fit within this model of instruction, which promotes application of knowledge in real-world contexts that can support community engagement and active learning.

While there are a variety of frameworks that can be used to design instruction for various aspects of the skills and techniques for *orientation* (the process of using information received through the senses to know one's location and destination in relation to significant objects in the environment) and *mobility* (the process of a learner moving from a current location to a desired new location in the environment), Table 1.1 provides sample focus areas and strategies that may fit within each of the four major models described.

O&M specialists may select a model of instruction based on the primary objective of the lesson. While an initial lesson on learning how to gather information for planning a bus *route* (a path fol-

Table 1.1   Models of Instruction Focus Areas and Strategies for O&M Lessons

Instruction Model	Sample Mobility Focus Areas and Strategies	Sample Orientation Focus Areas and Strategies	Sample Integrated Focus Areas and Strategies
Information Processing (Cognitive Learning)	A learner uses critical thinking to determine when to use the congested area technique. A learner uses a mnemonic to memorize the steps for intersection analysis.	A learner compares the layout of one shopping mall to another to identify similarities. A learner selects aspects of Jacobson's (2013) five-point travel system to maintain orientation in an office building.	A learner gathers sensory information to determine his or her location and which cane technique to use during a drop-off lesson. A learner keeps a journal of travel successes and challenges.
Behavioral Learning	A learner refines cane technique through drill and practice. Relaxation techniques are used prior to O&M lessons to reduce anxiety for street crossings.	A learner is reinforced when making accurate 90-degree turns during route travel. Direct instruction is used to introduce the concepts of the address system with learner-guided practice on identifying the location of various addresses on a map.	A learner reviews a route's O&M components each time before practicing it. A learner earns tokens for bringing her cane and completing campus routes independently.
Social Learning	A younger learner acquiring new O&M techniques spends time observing the skills of a more advanced traveler. A small group of learners completes a treasure hunt using low vision devices.	A learner solicits information to gather directions after becoming disoriented. A small group of learners co-plan a route to the mall.	A buddy system is established to learn a new school campus route while practicing cane skills together. A small group of learners debriefs about lessons learned after traveling to a city together.
Problem Based	A learner travels to a new destination utilizing appropriate cane techniques and strategies. A learner considers if it would be beneficial to install an accessible pedestrian signal at a given intersection. A learner or group of learners designs an adapted mobility device for a younger learner.	A learner considers different routes to reach a destination, and determines most efficient route. A learner designs an accessible map for a large school campus. A learner designs a mobile app for campus orientation.	A learner determines travel options for a possible community internship opportunity. A learner or group of learners work on a community service project to make a community garden accessible.

lowed to reach a destination) might incorporate a behavioral model of direct instruction that has a clear introduction, presentation of key information, and opportunity for guided and then independent practice, a future unit of lessons focused on developing confidence for bus travel might use a social-learning model by pairing two learners to work together to plan and execute a series of simple bus routes in a familiar area. Eventually, if the overall lesson goal is for the learner to be able to apply the skills previously learned for bus travel independently in newer travel areas, then a problem-based model of instruction could be designed to enable the learner to plan a series of connected bus routes as part of a project to learn the bus system in a new city in which he intends to attend college.

Learning Components

To effectively apply O&M techniques in a wide range of travel environments, individuals who are blind or who have *low vision* must draw on a vast array of intuitive and learned skills and concepts. O&M specialists should be mindful that the mechanics of O&M techniques are more than *motor* skills that are practiced and automatically incorporated in independent travel. In fact, some preservice O&M specialists may be surprised to find that individuals may be reluctant to use various techniques either at the appropriate time, in certain surroundings, or at all. It may be helpful to think about each of the techniques contained in this book as having motor, cognitive, and affective components.

Motor Component

The *motor component* of O&M is the physical ability to demonstrate or execute a technique properly. The component includes the strength, balance, *coordination*, and stamina required to repeat a physical movement. For use in travel it requires the physical ability to do all of these things in a range of environments, such as along different walking surfaces and levels, in various weather conditions, and among competing distractions for the traveler's attention. As is true of learning any physical skill, learning O&M skills requires clear instruction, opportunities for guided and independent practice, and application in diverse conditions. Examples of motor components of techniques that can be found later in this book include:

- The ability to *grasp* a guide's arm for an extended period of time
- The ability to move the cane from side to side in a consistent *arc* (semicircle created when the tip of the cane is moved from one side to the other)
- The ability to step off a curb at the beginning of a street crossing

When O&M specialists note that, despite effective instruction and ample practice an individual is unable to exert the physical ability to demonstrate a technique, they may choose to adapt the technique or tool to ensure its safe use. In some instances, O&M specialists will want to consult with *occupational* or *physical therapists*—professionals who specialize in the development and functioning of fine and gross motor skills—for further recommendations.

Cognitive Component

While it is one thing to be able to physically master a technique, it is another to understand why, when, and where the technique should be used during travel. This understanding of the *cognitive component* is not limited to knowledge of the technique (e.g., the *constant-contact cane technique* provides more consistent detection of *drop-offs* than does the *two-point-touch technique*), but extends to an understanding of an ever-changing environment and determination of what situations may call for the application of a different technique (e.g., switching from one cane technique to another because the walking surface begins to slope downward). To learn the "why" of a technique, the learner needs to be given a clear rationale for the technique, an opportunity for first-hand or discovery experience that the technique is effective in a given circumstance, and self-reflection and instructional feedback during application of the technique in the environment. The following are examples of a few cognitive components of techniques that can be found later in this book:

- Understanding where to grasp a guide's arm for moving through doorways together
- Understanding how far to move the cane from side to side in a consistent arc
- Understanding the difference between a blended curb and a typical curb in order to prepare for the step-off at the beginning of a street crossing

When O&M specialists note that, despite effective instruction, discovery, and ample practice, an individual is unable to understand why, when, or where to apply a technique, then they may choose to incorporate instructional prompts or memory aids, or adapt the technique or tool to make it possible to develop travel habits that will aid in safe movement in given environments.

Affective Component

An individual may be able to understand why a technique is important and physically do the technique, but simply choose not to use the technique. The *affective component* relates to the individual's feelings about the technique or psychological comfort in using the technique. O&M specialists may find that a learner is able to properly use a technique in correct instances during O&M lessons, but that the learner does not freely use the technique elsewhere. For example, travelers may have adapted their own versions of how they like to travel with a guide, use the *long cane,* or manage travel on public transportation. The reasons for why an individual may stray from or vary a technique are probably similar to those of novice and experienced drivers not adhering to the rules of the road and expected driving behaviors. In some instances, it can be related to risk-taking behavior, notions of social differences, or even perceptions of personal safety. For example, a teenager may think it is not necessary to wait until the next available light to initiate a street crossing and feels quite comfortable with the level of perceived risk. Or a child may not wish to use a low vision device while on the school campus because he feels it makes him look different, or an adult who lost his vision as the result of a gunshot wound may feel that using a long cane in his neighborhood will make him appear to be vulnerable. The following are a few examples of affective components that can be found later in this book:

- Feeling comfortable to grasp a friend's arm to travel together as a guide team
- Choosing to use the long cane while walking in a home neighborhood
- Choosing to practice a local bus route on the weekend

Issues related to the affective domain can be more complicated to address than those that are physical or cognitive; they can be more challenging for the O&M specialist to influence because they are related to comfort, feelings, and internal motivation. O&M specialists may want to introduce learners who are acquiring new O&M techniques to experienced travelers to promote positive feelings about O&M and independent travel. In instances in which learners lack intrinsic motivation to practice or apply skills outside of O&M lessons, a challenge or positive behavior plan can be established, such as allowing an elementary-school-age student to earn points for practicing cane skills at family weekend outings and cashing in the points for an O&M outing during school to a highly motivating location such as a computer store.

When O&M specialists consider all three components associated with learning a technique that can be used correctly on a daily basis to help an individual travel independently, they can prepare lessons that will address each component. Research on brain function and research in teaching and learning will continue to expand the tools and perspectives O&M specialists can use to effectively teach O&M to learners with visual impairments. O&M specialists can stay abreast of current research that supports evidence-based practices through reading scholarly articles, attending professional conferences, and participating in action research projects.

CHAPTER

2

Orientation for Mobility

Chapters 3 through 10 of this book are intended to provide the orientation and mobility (O&M) specialist with the techniques that can be used to teach learners with visual impairments how to travel from one place to another in an informed, efficient, and safe manner. The procedures in these chapters focus on what are considered to be mobility techniques. In order to move purposefully in the environment, however, individuals must also have concepts and skills related to orientation so that they know how to get from a current location to a desired new location in the environment. Orientation and mobility are inextricably interrelated, and O&M instruction must include a balance of concepts and skills for both mobility and orientation, and integrate the two in a fluid manner. This chapter is intended to provide basic definitions and principles, ideas for application of specific orientation skills in travel, as well as some basic teaching tips related to orientation. Although orientation concepts are dealt with separately in this chapter of the book, O&M specialists should work with their learners to continually integrate these areas of O&M for purposeful movement in the environment.

Each element of orientation offers its own foundational knowledge and experiences that may include aspects of academic content covered in schools, content covered as part of the *expanded core curriculum (ECC),* or past travel experiences. For example, the following skills and concepts covered in academic content in schools are foundational to applying the use of measurements in establishing landmarks and understanding and applying orientation to indoor and outdoor numbering or address systems:

- Ability to count, add, or subtract
- Concepts of relative value of numbers
- Concepts of greater than, less than, and equal to
- Knowledge of standardized measurement units
- Concepts of odd and even numbers
- Ordering, sequencing, and patterns
- Ability to identify 90-degree and 180-degree angles and turns
- Understanding and use of cardinal directions

Similarly, the following foundational elements, which help a learner to identify distinguishable characteristics of objects to be used as landmarks for orientation in a variety of environments, may be addressed as part of the expanded core curriculum:

- Sensory memory
- Awareness of basic spatial relationships
- Concepts of movable and fixed objects
- *Sound localization* (ability to orient oneself to the environment through hearing)
- Use of compass directions
- Ability to complete *systematic search patterns* (a set pattern used to visually or tactilely search for an item of interest)

Experiential knowledge from past travel experiences can contribute to orientation. For example:

- Prior experience as a taxi driver contributes to understanding of community layouts, address systems, and directions that can readily be transferred to travel situations
- Prior experience in the military may lead to increased ability to use accurate turns for maintaining orientation along a complex route
- Living in a high-rise apartment may lead to basic knowledge of common building arrangements
- Riding the bus increases familiarity with and orientation to bus-route patterns

The reader is also encouraged to seek out additional readings in this important area, including emerging peer-reviewed research on brain function, *perception,* and giving meaning to sensory information; and foundational texts such as the two volumes of *Foundations of Orientation and Mobility,* which include several chapters on orientation. In addition, numerous books and articles describe strategies for teaching orientation to learners of all ages (see, for example, Allman & Lewis, 2014; Fazzi & Petersmeyer, 2001; Griffin-Shirley & Bozeman, 2016; Jacobson, 2013; Pogrund & Fazzi, 2002).

Orientation

Orientation is the process of perceiving and using sensory information and conceptual understanding of body and environmental space to determine one's current location, location of a desired destination, and relative position to other significant objects and features in the environment, while stationary or moving. The ability to keep track of and adjust understanding of current location and position in relation to other environmental features while moving is commonly referred to as *spatial updating.* One's current location can be perceived as an approximate distance and direction from a known object or location (e.g., I am a few steps in front of the main entrance of the grocery store). The location of a desired destination can be described in relation to the individual's current location, *self-to-object spatial relationships* (e.g., the pharmacy is ahead of me and on my right side); in relation to other known objects or locations,—*object-to-object spatial relationships* (e.g., the pharmacy is next to the gas-station parking lot); or a combination of both.

Foundational Knowledge and Experiences

Bozeman and McCulley (2010) describe *spatial orientation* as existing along a continuum from "concrete person-centered knowledge to a more abstract understanding of space, or a combination of both" (p. 28). Before attempting to orient himself within his environment, the learner must have a concept of "self." This concept is referred to as *body image*—an awareness and knowledge of body parts, their full range of movements, and their functions. The learner must also have an understanding of the environment. Within an *egocentric frame of reference*, the learner uses his own body as a *reference point* from which to understand the location of other objects or areas in the environment. The process of orientation begins as the learner relates position of self to position of key features and objects in the environment (e.g., I am standing next to the drinking fountain. It is on my right side, which means that my classroom door is across the hall to my left side.) An *allocentric frame of reference* (also commonly referred to as a survey-level *cognitive map*) helps the individual to understand the locations of objects or places as related to one another; it is based on the external environment and not dependent on one's current location. For example, a given park is located north of the river regardless of the location of the individual, but the park is only on the individual's right side when he is on the west side of the park and facing north. Within a *survey-level* or allocentric frame of reference, the learner connects the location of one place to another in a manner that increases orientation across a larger geographic span and allows for flexible *route planning*—selecting a path to follow to reach a given destination—and travel (Long & Giudice, 2010). While the location of the learner as he moves changes the self-to-object relationships, object-to-object relationships of permanently fixed locations are consistent. Long and Giudice (2010) emphasize the importance of helping learners to think about the environment in terms of object-to-object relationships so that an allocentric frame of reference is further refined and applied to establishing and maintaining orientation in a variety of changing contexts.

O&M specialists may work with learners to develop their orientation skills in tandem with mobility techniques, but they will also need to focus on the conceptual and perceptual knowledge, experience, and practice required for learners to become oriented, recognize when they are no longer on an intended path, and take action to regain orientation after experiencing disorientation. (See Bozeman & McCulley, 2010, and Long & Giudice, 2010, for more in-depth coverage of the emerging research, theoretical underpinnings, and practical approaches to developing orientation skills for learners with visual impairments.)

Mental and Physical Readiness Levels

In addition to the foundational knowledge and experiences required for the orientation process, learners must also exhibit basic readiness, both mental and physical. Mental readiness for orientation may include intellectual ability, developmental level, prior life and learning experience, frustration level, attention span, concentration level, and the ability to apply abstract concepts to individual situations. The orientation process also requires that the learner integrate *sensory information* received from the environment to plan for and execute specific patterns of movement to achieve desired objectives. Guth, Rieser, and Ashmead (2010) explore models of *sensory integration*—the neurological process that organizes sensory input from one's body and the environment to support effective movement—that emphasize the importance of using multiple points of relevant sensory information. O&M specialists can work with learners to develop skills and ensure ample practice so learners are able to determine which perceptual clues or cues are most relevant and reliable in a given situation. Roughly described, a *clue* is information that can be used by a person to help figure out his location or the location of objects in the environment. In slight contrast, a *cue* is a signal that something is about to happen or a certain location or object is about to be reached. (Also see LaGrow, 2010, for strategies for improving perception as related to independent orientation and mobility.)

Physical readiness level may also vary among learners. Factors such as level of vision, hearing, and tactile perception can impact the amount and type of sensory inputs available for analyzation for orientation purposes. To use orientation skills effectively, the learner must be proficient in performing basic movement behaviors; that is, maintaining a straight line of travel, making precise turns, and adjusting body movements to sustain a stable *posture* while moving on uneven surfaces. (See Rosen, 2010a, 2010b, for approaches to improving sensorimotor functioning for orientation and mobility.)

Principles of Orientation

The following three questions address the three key elements of establishing orientation that individuals must consider:

1. Where am I?
2. Where is my desired destination?
3. How do I get there?

These questions require that the learner knows or can surmise

- the general layout or specific features of the environment;
- where he is in the environment in relation to his understanding of the layout or specific features of the environment;
- where the desired destination is in the environment and in relation to his current location; and
- a way of integrating this knowledge in an organized and sequential manner so that the learner can plan what he must do to get from his present location to his destination goal. As the learner works to answer these three questions, he is going through a cognitive mental process that involves gathering and analyzing sensory information in order to make accurate determinations about location and travel directions.

Establishing and Maintaining Orientation

The cognitive process of establishing and maintaining orientation can be described as a continuous cycle of five steps that the learner uses to perform orientation tasks. The steps interact with one another and can be repeated as needed to confirm a location or choice of travel route. The process may take only a short moment or a considerable amount of time depending on the learner's abilities and experience level or the relative complexity of, or familiarity with, the environment. O&M specialists can encourage learners to go through the complete process, integrating information along the way.

The five steps of the *cognitive orientation process* are as follows:

1. **Perception:** The process of gathering and integrating sensory information from the environment may include:

   a. smelling odors

   b. hearing sounds

   c. feeling terrain changes

   d. detecting movement or kinesthetic perceptions

   e. noticing changes in brightness level

2. **Analysis:** The process of organizing information, determining whether the information is relevant, and making meaning of perceived sensory information based on the features of the environment being traveled in and conceptual and experiential knowledge may include the following:

   a. determining if the information perceived is consistent with expectations for the area, such as hearing prominent echoes in a hallway with low ceilings

   b. identifying the possible sources of a sloping walkway in the area

   c. considering if there is sensory information missing that is expected, such as the smell of fresh baked bread at an early hour

   d. remembering, if the information is familiar

   e. guessing the possible source of the sensory information received

3. **Selection:** The process of choosing relevant information that has been analyzed to help inform orientation choices in the present environmental situation may include:

   a. paying attention to the downward sloping pavement rather than people's voices in the distance to determine that a step or ramp is fast approaching

   b. choosing to attend to the reflected sound from a nearby brick wall together with the pattern of pedestrian traffic to help maintain a desired line of travel

4. **Planning:** The process of designing a course of action or next steps based on the sensory data selected as most relevant to the present environmental situation may include:

   a. hearing an elevator tone, which helps the individual know that the desired office destination is across the hallway and it is time to cross to the other side

   b. despite the unexpected slope encountered along the walkway, the consistent sound of the *perpendicular* (intersecting) traffic indicates that the best plan of action is to maintain a straight line of travel until the perpendicular traffic is close enough to make further analysis

5. **Action:** The process of performing the planned course of action (e.g., following a unique wooden fence to locate a desired walkway to a friend's house).

A decision to act (e.g., to stop, continue, or change direction) occurs when the learner has analyzed the sensory information together with the conceptual understanding of the area and deemed it to be of some value for navigation purposes. Sensory information is constantly perceived by the learner, but it is through the process of analysis that the learner selects the information that is most relevant to the situation. If the information is determined to be irrelevant (such as a baby crying in the mall in an area with many shoppers), it is discarded and new sensory information is then perceived and analyzed. Learners will also refine decision making as they experience and learn from detection errors (e.g., the learner stops because he thinks he has reached the curb ramp, when in fact it was a minor slope caused by an older sidewalk mid-block crossing). Further analysis of perceptual information and guided practice can reduce such perceptual errors (Guth et al., 2010). During the selection, planning, or action stage the learner may perceive new sensory data that will alter or confirm the strategy.

One way to be certain that learners are thoroughly attending to each step in the process is to ask them to describe out loud what is happening as they work through the steps. Bozeman and McCulley (2010) refer to this approach as "self-talk." It is also often referred to as "say-aloud." Having learners talk through what they are perceiving and how that information is informing their orientation and decisions about next steps provides the O&M specialist with the opportunity to point out possible gaps in thinking and provide support for unfamiliar or unclear information.

Orientation Terminology and Concepts

This section defines additional terms and concepts in orientation and their use in travel.

Cognitive Mapping

The ability to develop a mental image of a physical space, specific location, geographic area, or travel route is commonly referred to as *cognitive mapping*. Cognitive maps are updated as the individual perceives new information, develops an expanded concept of the area, or changes location. The accuracy of a cognitive map is dependent on the individual's conceptual understanding of the area, prior experience and familiarity with the area, access to sensory information, and ability to apply meaning to sensory information related to that understanding of the area. For example, a learner may perceive a plethora of sensory information in a commercial area, but if he has no conceptual understanding of block layouts or prior experiences in the specific area, the sensory information cannot be readily applied to form a cognitive map of the area.

Cognitive mapping can be used to

- provide context for sensory information,
- generalize spatial layouts for similar areas or buildings (e.g., gas stations, shopping malls, or fast-food restaurants),
- assist with travel along a set route and planning routes and detours, and
- give directions to others, including any potential guides.

Spatial Updating

As noted earlier, spatial updating is the ability to keep track of one's current location and of changes in distance and direction in relation to objects or places (Long & Giudice, 2010), and adjusting that understanding in relation to other environmental features while moving. An important aspect of the integration of orientation and mobility concepts and techniques during route travel is that of *environmental flow*, or how the movement of the learner changes the manner in which he perceives the environment. While vision is useful for keeping track of many objects at one time as the learner moves, hearing can also be used to perceive sounds coming from all angles, including behind the learner. (See Guth et al., 2010, for a full discussion of concepts related to environmental flow and refined development of spatial updating.)

Spatial updating is a crucial part of orientation. Without the ability to adjust perspectives, the learner is limited in his ability to anticipate the presence or absence of environmental features along a path or in an area and to problem solve to recover from instances of *disorientation*.

Spatial updating can be used in travel to

- maintain orientation along a travel route,
- increase awareness of the environment while walking with a guide,
- provide driving directions while riding as a passenger in a car,
- keep track of the progression of a bus route while riding as a passenger, and
- understand how to use *global positioning system (GPS)* features on assistive and mainstream technology.

Time-Distance Estimation

The ability to judge distance (e.g., the distance between the office and the restroom in a C-wing hallway) based on the time it takes to travel between two points is commonly referred to as *time-distance estimation*. Time-distance estimation is established through repetition of travel between two points at consistent rates of walking. The estimation can be affected by elements in the environment that may alter this rate, such as walking more slowly due to pedestrian congestion. Learners may use other sensory information to complement their general understanding of the distances to be traveled. O&M specialists focus on the development of time-distance estimation with learners to support travel with greater efficiency and decreased reliance on tactile landmarks, which can be cumbersome. For example, when a learner establishes good time-distance estimation he is better able to anticipate turns to *intersecting sidewalks* without having to follow a grass line with his cane, thus increasing the rate of travel.

Time-distance estimation can be used in travel to

- help organize attention to sensory information along a route in a sequential order,
- increase travel efficiency,
- decrease reliance on tactile landmarks for orientation purposes,
- anticipate expected drop-offs so that walking speed can be adjusted accordingly,
- recognize and correct for veering or misalignment during street crossings, and
- anticipate public transportation stops based on time traveled.

Spatial Concepts

Mental representations or ideas about how people, places, and things are positioned and located in the environment are commonly referred to as *spatial concepts*. Spatial concepts, which can include self-to-object or object-to-object relationships, are often represented in positional terms such as next to, in front of, right side, or north facing.

Spatial concepts are used in travel to

- describe relative locations of people, places, and things in the environment (e.g., the dog is behind the fence that is on your right);
- order segments of a route (e.g., the route to the cafeteria comes before the turn to the office);
- provide an egocentric frame of reference for spatial updating (e.g., I just passed the drinking fountain so the office should be on my left);
- understand the layout of a *map*; and
- learn mobility techniques that require specific body positions.

Landmarks

Any familiar object, sound, odor, temperature, or tactile or visual clue that is easily recognized, is constant, has a known, permanent location in the environment, and provides specific information to the traveler about location in the environment can be a *landmark*. Long and Giudice (2010) further distinguish between *primary landmarks,* which are readily encountered along the travel path, and *secondary landmarks,* which may possibly be missed while traveling due to their location or size.

Landmarks are constant and permanent. A landmark's use is dependent on knowledge of at least one direction or one object in the environment in relation to it. A landmark has at least one unique characteristic to differentiate it from other objects in the environment. Landmarks may be recognizable by their visual, tactile, olfactory, kinesthetic, or auditory characteristics or a combination thereof.

Points of Information or Clues

A *point of information* (Long & Giudice, 2010) or clue (Jacobson, 2013) is any perceived auditory, olfactory, tactile, kinesthetic, or visual stimulus that can be used by the learner to determine position or line of direction. Unlike a landmark, which gives the learner automatic location details, a clue needs to be paired with additional sources of information to provide meaningful location or directional informa-

tion. The functional use of a clue depends on its familiarity to the learner. For example, the sound of a copier is not useful unless the learner knows its source (e.g., office machinery) and additional information about the possible offices located in the hallway (e.g., there are only two offices located in the hallway). With this contextual information, the learner can pair the location of the office with the copier to the classroom being sought.

Landmarks and points of information or clues can be used in travel to

- establish and maintain directional orientation,
- provide a reference point for travel and orientation (e.g., when my back is against this door I am facing east),
- establish and maintain distance relationships between self and objects or between environmental features,
- locate specific destinations,
- orient or reorient oneself to an area,
- form a perpendicular or *parallel* alignment for straight line of travel, and
- obtain information about a corresponding area, such as a floor above, using transferability of such landmarks as elevators, stairs, or drinking fountains.

Numbering Systems (Indoor and Outdoor)

The systematic patterning or arrangement of numbers of locations within a specific indoor or outdoor area is commonly referred to as a *numbering system*. (Numbers or addresses may be used to identify classrooms, offices, houses, or commercial buildings, for example.) Not all buildings incorporate systematic numbering systems and those with random or irregular patterns will not be as helpful to learners for the purposes of orientation. In outdoor areas, using GPS with updated maps can assist with locating businesses or other points of interest in an area lacking a systematic *address system*. Learners can determine whether an area has a systematic numbering system through exploration or by asking others.

Room numbers are often located on the wall on the handle side of a door. Store numbers or addresses within a shopping center or mall are usually located near main entrances, but can be positioned in a variety of locations. House numbers can be found along the curb in front of a home; on a mailbox or gate; or on, above, or beside the front door.

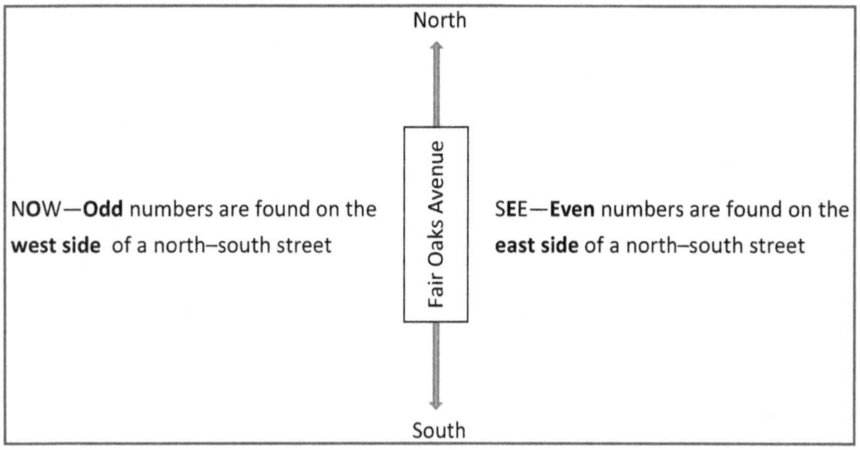

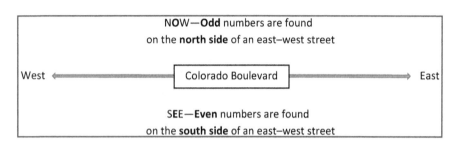

North

Fair Oaks Avenue

NOW—**Odd** numbers are found on the **west side** of a north–south street

SEE—**Even** numbers are found on the **east side** of a north–south street

South

Figure 2.1

NOW and SEE System of Numbering on a North–South Street

NOW—**Odd** numbers are found on the **north side** of an east–west street

West ← Colorado Boulevard → East

SEE—**Even** numbers are found on the **south side** of an east–west street

Figure 2.2

NOW and SEE System of Numbering on an East–West Street

Odd numbers are usually on one side of a hallway or street and even numbers on the other, but exceptions can be found in many locations. The North-Odd-West (NOW) and South-Even-East (SEE) system can be used in some traditional street grids in which odd numbers are found on the north side of east–west streets and the west side of north–south streets, and even numbers are found on the south side of east–west streets and the east side of north–south streets. However, numbering systems can vary greatly in different areas of the country. Indoor numbers may progress from the focal point in sequences of twos, while outdoor numbers may have greater variance in progressions including increases by twos, fifties, or even hundreds on the same side of the street. Possible ranges of numbers on any given floor might be 0 to 99 in the basement or on the first floor, 100 to 199 on the first floor, 200 to 299 on the second floor, and so on.

In commercial or light business travel areas, it may be helpful to determine the central dividing streets for north–south and east–west. See Figures 2.1 and 2.2 for a sample of the NOW and SEE systems of numbering found along north–south and east–west streets. The numbering system then extends in a pattern from the central dividing streets. For example, if Colorado Boulevard (an east–west street) and Fair Oaks Avenue (a north–south street) intersect at the center of Pasadena, California, then addresses will start with the number 100 north and south of Colorado Boulevard, and likewise, building numbers will begin with 100 east and west of Fair Oaks Avenue.

While the conceptual understanding of the numbering system used in an indoor or outdoor environment is useful for orientation, the availability of digital maps, *geographic information systems (GIS)*, and GPS is changing the manner in which this knowledge can ultimately be used for determining current and desired locations. Advances in assistive and mainstream technology enable learners to use a wide variety of tools to determine the address and location of specific points of interest or to scan the area for favorite restaurants, businesses, or services. (See Bentzen & Marston, 2010a, 2010b; Penrod, Smith, Haneline, & Corbett, 2010, for strategies for teaching the use of *electronic orientation aids [EOAs]*.)

Numbering systems can be used in travel to

- familiarize oneself with a given building, shopping center, or community,
- assist in efficiently locating specific points or objects,

- generalize room locations and addresses to other floors, buildings, or streets, and
- assist in understanding and verbally describing the location of specific points or objects.

Route Shapes and Reversals

The description of a travel route according to a basic shape, such as I, L, U, or Z-shaped, is commonly referred to as a *route shape*. Route shapes can help a learner to conceptualize the route of travel in a means that is easy to retain, map cognitively, and reverse as needed. *Route reversals* provide a means for thinking about how to return from a destination by applying turns in reverse. For example, if a learner travels an L-shaped route from the mailbox to the bus stop that required a left turn, the route reversal of the L-shaped route will require a right turn. In cardinal direction terms, the route from the mailbox to the stop sign required traveling south for half a block and a left turn to walk one block east. The route reversal would be to walk one block west and make a right turn to walk half a block north.

Route shapes and route reversals can be used in travel to

- remember routes,
- create cognitive maps,
- keep track of turns (e.g., L-shaped routes have only one turn; U-shaped routes have two turns, both to the same side with either two right turns or two left turns; and Z-shaped routes have two turns, both to the opposite side with one right and one left turn), and
- stack two or more route shapes together to conceptualize segments of a more complex route of travel (e.g., travel an L-shaped route to the bus stop and from there travel a U-shaped route to the elementary school).

Types of Measurement

Measurement is the act or process of determining the exact or approximate dimensions of an object or space using a given unit. Everything in the environment is measurable. *Linear measurements* are constant and are expressed using standard increments or units. Units of measurement commonly used indoors are inch (or centimeter in metric systems), foot and yard (meter), and any fraction or approximation thereof. Standard units of measurement have fixed, defined, and interchangeable relationships to each other (12 inches = 1 foot), and appropriate units should be chosen based on the distance to be measured (e.g., use feet to measure the length of a table but inches to measure the length of a pencil). *Comparative measurements* correlate the length or distance of two or more things (e.g., longer than, wider than, less than). Linear measurement is applied to the three basic dimensions of length, width, and height. Standard or nonstandard units may be used for approximate measurements (e.g., approximately 7 yards, waist-high, 3 paces).

Measurement can be used in travel to

- approximate the dimensions of a travel area to assist in orientation,
- assist in distance estimation,
- identify landmarks based on relative size or location,
- gain an accurate concept of particular objects and positional relationships between or among them, and
- form a clear concept of the size of an area or object in relation to body size.

The learner can use standard measuring tools, such as rulers, dividers, or measuring tape, to obtain an exact measure of an object, area, or distance. Becoming familiar with common sizes of items in the environment (e.g., 12-inch floor tiles or 5-foot sidewalk slabs) may help the learner to better estimate distances. The learner can use various techniques to obtain approximate measurements, such as using arm span; comparative measures such as knee-high and waist-high; counting paces; using the cane as a unit of measurement; and using object perception or the ability to interpret auditory input (such as echoes) to determine the approximate dimensions of a room or hallway.

Compass Directions

A direction is a line along which something moves, is pointed or aimed toward, or is facing. *Compass directions*, also known as cardinal or polarcentric directions, are dictated by the magnetic polar fields of the earth. The four main compass directions are cardinal points, and are spaced at 90-degree intervals around the circle of the compass: north, east, south, and west. In addition, intermediate directions, including northwest, northeast, southwest, and southeast, can be used for orientation purposes.

Compass directions are constant and transferable from one environment to another. Compass directions allow the learner to relate to the distant environment. They also allow the learner to relate the environment to environmental concepts in a more positive and definitive manner. Not only can polarcentric information be used to describe a direction of travel (e.g., I am walking south), it can also be used to describe the side of a street (e.g., I am walking along the north side of Broadway) or the side of a block (e.g., the post office is on the south side of the block). Initially it can be confusing for some learners to conceptualize multiple polarcentric pieces of information at once. For example, a learner might be walking east along the north side of Broadway to locate the post office, which is on the south side of his residential block. Despite the initial complexity of interconnecting multiple concepts, understanding them can aid in refined orientation, route planning, and independent travel. Intermediate cardinal points are commonly used to describe corners or an intersection during *intersection analysis*. For example, if a learner is preparing to make a clockwise crossing while standing on the southeast corner of an intersection, he is going to locate the first car heard or seen in the near-lane-parallel traffic to align with the southwest corner for his crossing.

Basic compass-direction principles are as follows:

- East and west are opposites.
- North and south are opposites.
- An east–west line of direction is perpendicular and at a right angle to a north–south line.
- All east–west lines are parallel.
- All north–south lines are parallel.
- Travel may occur in either an eastward or westward direction on an east–west line and in a northward or southward direction on a north–south line.
- Not all travel lines such as hallways, roads, or highways are aligned to exact north–south or east–west directions, and some may curve and change directions in a significant manner.

Compass directions are used in travel to

- provide a constant reference for orientation,
- provide explicit and consistent directions, especially when covering greater travel distances,
- provide a systematic means for maintaining orientation during travel,
- describe or follow a line of direction or given route destination,
- design alternate routes to a destination,
- facilitate communication concerning the location of an object or place position between people,
- establish and make optimum use of landmarks or points of reference, and
- form relationships between points (objects or places) in the environment or between oneself and points in the environment (e.g., the market is east of the post office or I am walking north along Vermont Avenue).

Labels

A *label* is a name given to an object or place so that different individuals can consistently identify the same item or area. The names of a location, hallway, or street are examples of labels that are used for orientation. Some labels are assigned seemingly randomly to an environment, while others may have a theme or pattern that can be helpful for orientation. For example, a large residential community may use tree names (e.g., Oak and Palm) for all north–south streets and ordinal numbers (e.g., First, Second, Third, and so on) for all east–west streets. Learning label patterns, where available, can be a valuable orientation tool for learners.

Labels are used in travel to

- create a common reference for describing an area or giving specific directions,
- apply knowledge of label patterns to assist with orientation,
- increase awareness of the environment while walking with a guide,
- maintain orientation along an indoor or outdoor travel route,
- provide driving directions while riding as a passenger in a car,
- keep track of the progression of a bus route while riding as a passenger, and
- understand how to use GPS features on assistive and mainstream technology.

Teaching Tips

Skills and concepts for orientation can be taught using a variety of formats. Separate lessons involving concept development, map usage, orientation games, and learning activities can be developed to establish foundational knowledge for later application and practice during O&M lessons. A variety of teaching approaches and manipulatives can be incorporated in creative ways. Some orientation skills may be readily introduced and taught within the context of an O&M lesson that involves travel in the community or a shopping area. Typically, a combination of several approaches will be most effective.

The following specific tips can be used to teach various orientation skills and concepts:

- *Mnemonics* such as "Never Eat Soggy Waffles" or "Never Eat Sour Watermelons" can be used to teach the orders of north, east, south, and west in a clockwise direction.

- Motor activities can be incorporated along with orientation concepts to make learning more effective and motivating, such as a game of beanbag toss using cardinal directions for learners who have low vision.

- Scavenger and treasure hunts for learners of all ages can be developed to practice following route directions and increasing orientation within the community in a highly motivating fashion in which both orientation and mobility are integrated.

- Building maps with learners can help to strengthen understanding of relative positions among key features in a given environment.

- Teaching map basics promotes general orientation concepts that can be applied in travel and for use in assistive and mainstream technology with directional information such as a GPS system developed for use by individuals who are blind or auditory features that access commercially available map systems.

- Practice independent route planning using maps that are made by learners, made or adapted by teachers, or are commercially or digitally available. Highlight traveled routes on a "master map" to represent the learner's progress by keeping a record of all of the areas in which the learner has traveled.

- Community exploration lessons can incorporate measurements using either measuring tools (such as rulers, measuring tape, or measurement wheels) or informal comparisons, using the learner's long cane to select landmarks, become familiar with a new area, or learn measurement concepts (e.g., in the residential area near an elementary school a learner can measure which fences were taller or shorter than his cane).

- Incorporate orientation devices, such as a compass, a smartphone or tablet with accessibility and navigation features, or a GPS system, into O&M lessons whenever appropriate.

- Engage in role-playing in a safe environment to practice *soliciting assistance* (obtaining information from another individual) for orientation purposes. Role-playing can be practiced with the O&M specialist or with other learners when possible. The ability to solicit assistance for travel-related information is an important skill for learners to develop.

- Using smartphone technology, create a list of interesting destinations and have the learner call each of the businesses to gather information such as address, nearest cross street, side of the street, and potential landmarks.

- Using brailled address cards, have the learner organize them in order of location according to the address system in the local business area.

- Create a recipe box full of interesting destinations and select from the box for the learner to design his own route.

- Tables can be arranged in a lunchroom or gymnasium to form an interactive *model* of blocks and intersections to allow learners (or small groups of learners) to travel between them as "cars." Creating close proximity between the "streets" allows for hands-on movement of the activity and helps learners better understand the traffic patterns and general "rules of the road."

- Engage in games of "I Spy" or "What Do I Hear?" to increase the learner's interest in attending to and giving meaning to various sensory stimuli.

- Use or create audio recordings of highly salient sounds to practice identifying sounds and their associated meanings.

(For additional teaching tips on orientation concepts and skill development for learners of various ages see Allman & Lewis, 2014; Bentzen & Marston, 2010b; Fazzi & Petersmeyer, 2001; Griffin-Shirley & Bozeman, 2016; Jacobson, 2013; Pogrund & Fazzi, 2002.)

Combining Mobility and Orientation for Purposeful Movement

Perceiving, exploring, and processing sensory information for orientation in travel is inextricably intertwined with the physical aspects of exploration and the conceptual aspects related to understanding the environment. Even when O&M lessons are initially designed to focus on *mobility techniques* to develop skills that will become automatic, such as cane skills, spatial concepts such as left and right or *arc width* (distance between furthest points of contact for the cane tip) coverage are fully embedded. As the learner practices the techniques associated with the use of the long cane, he is still perceiving sensory information and attending to changes in the environment as he walks forward. While an instructional unit on spatial concepts related to traveling around a block can be packaged together, these concepts cannot be fully learned without hands-on exploratory experiences that will be further facilitated through mobility processes.

Route Travel

Both natural environments and simulated travel experiences can help learners integrate their newly acquired mobility skills with skills for orientation for use in future route travel. Perceptual-motor learning occurs with practice through actual travel, such as learning how to manage the passenger-side door and entering the car without bumping one's head on the top of the car. It simply takes practice, exposure to, and experience with, a variety of vehicles before it becomes second nature. Natural learning occurs along routes that are part of the learner's daily routine as he learns to attend to relevant *environmental features* along the route that enable him to maintain his line of travel, make changes in direction when needed, apply specific cane techniques at appropriate times, and eventually reach his desired destination. The O&M specialist can also set up situations along a route that challenge the learner to make decisions about which environmental features are most important for orientation, so that he can increasingly generalize his skills in new environments (Guth et al., 2010). The learner can adopt various approaches for remembering key environmental features of regularly traveled routes and strategies for unfamiliar routes, such as making and keeping braille notes, making audio recordings, or learning a sequence of features using mnemonics.

While learners may have mastered mobility techniques, O&M specialists may observe a backslide in adherence to good technique in situations in which the learner is attending to or making decisions about relevancy of or analyzing sensory information for orientation purposes. It should be stressed to learners that good cane techniques are always important, but never more so than when a learner is thinking about orientation and is in the process of acting on perceived information. It is likely that both experienced and inexperienced travelers will make detection errors on occasion and the properly used cane will provide good coverage and additional sensory information from which the learner can adjust the plan of action.

Jacobson (1993, 2013) describes a five-point travel system that learners can use to organize their thinking around orientation:

1. Route shapes: I-shape, L-shape, U-shape, and Z-shape (or zigzag) routes
2. Compass directions
3. Naming walls in a room (e.g., coatrack wall, window wall, north wall), hallways in a building, or streets in the community
4. Landmarks along the route
5. The reversal of route shapes, compass directions, names and labels, and landmarks upon a return route

Using Jacobson's five-point travel system provides learners with a consistent structure in which to organize orientation information. O&M specialists can review the five points prior to introducing a route and as a review after the route has been completed.

Familiarization to New Places

It is important that O&M specialists provide learners with opportunities to familiarize themselves with indoor and outdoor environments. While an O&M specialist may be gifted at orienting a learner to an area that the learner needs to travel in, such as a home neighborhood, work environment, college campus, or school, she also needs to teach the learner how to initiate the orientation process so that he will be able to familiarize himself with a variety of environments long after he is finished receiving O&M instruction. While more research is needed to determine the optimal evidence-based approach to orienting oneself to a new area, the following approaches provide some general guidelines and accepted practices.

Indoor *familiarization* encompasses individual rooms and other areas in buildings. Jacobson (2013) provides a clearly delineated procedure for independent room-familiarization using a *perimeter pattern* and a *gridline pattern* for exploration. The door or other salient room feature provides the reference point from which the learner explores the perimeter of the room, recalling the order of important objects found along the wall (e.g., window, closet). Walls can be labeled according to their most memorable features (e.g., the whiteboard wall) or by using cardinal directions (e.g., the east wall). The gridline pattern encourages the learner to explore the interior of the room using a systematic pattern. The gridline pattern can be challenging to use in rooms that are cluttered with furniture. Both approaches are intended to help the learner understand object-to-object relationships within the room for future reference while moving about the room.

While most rooms have a clearly defined square or rectangle shape that allows individuals to learn spatial relationships for orientation, building layouts may be more complex and include multiple floors. While many buildings generally have consistent layouts for upper floors, building lobbies may be somewhat different due to large entrance and receiving areas.

The main entrance to a building provides a logical starting place for familiarization to a building. The learner can take the following steps:

1. Identify the entrance door's directional position (e.g., the door is located on the southeast corner of the building).

2. Note any easily identifiable characteristics about the entrance that would establish it as a landmark. Also note any clues that may aid in relocation.

3. Determine the position of the entrance door relative to the lobby or main corridor. Also identify the direction of the main corridor, if one exists.

4. Explore the lobby or entrance area to select landmarks or clues such as stairs, elevators, water fountains, restrooms, or the sound of automatic or revolving doors to use as reference points for orientation.

5. Explore the main corridor or connecting hallways as needed, classifying environmental information into clues or landmarks and establishing the positional relationship between each location and the main entrance. (The use of directional concepts—such as east–west hallway—can help the learner to understand the overall shape of the building layout and which hallways may be parallel or perpendicular to one another.)

6. Identify landmarks or clues that can be generalized to another floor in the same building (e.g., water fountains, stairs, restrooms, elevators).

7. Determine the numbering system in the building, where applicable, by checking braille or print room numbers or by asking someone. The numbering system can provide the learner with additional details to use for orientation and destination travel.

8. Steps 1 through 7 can be repeated until the learner is familiar with the full building layout.

Self-familiarization to residential or commercial blocks and corners is addressed in Chapter 6 and intersection analysis is covered in Chapter 7.

Drop-Off Lessons

Drop-off lessons provide the O&M specialist with one approach to teach and assess the full integration of orientation and mobility skills and concepts. Depending on the learner's ability and maturity level, drop-off lessons can be planned for familiar areas. The learner must use his knowledge of the area and information-gathering and problem-solving skills to determine where he has been "dropped off" and how to reach his desired destination. The size of the drop-off area can be adjusted based on the learner's level. The drop-off lesson can be monitored quietly from as short or long a distance as needed. A more advanced drop-off lesson, in which the O&M specialist takes the learner to an unfamiliar area, can be used to help the learner practice the application of O&M skills from a familiar area to an unfamiliar area. This type of drop-off lesson is typically conducted with confident, adult travelers; however, a simulated drop-off lesson in an unfamiliar area can also be conducted with less experienced or younger learners and turned into a game by giving the learner one "phone a friend" card to use with the O&M specialist as needed. The O&M specialist remains close enough for safety monitoring but perceptually distant from the learner to simulate independent travel in an unfamiliar environment. More information on drop-off lessons is provided in Chapter 9.

Similar to using drop-off lessons for teaching the integration of orientation and mobility skills and concepts in familiar and unfamiliar environments, drop-off lessons can be used to assess the attainment of these same skills for future travel. A drop-off lesson can be the concluding lesson for an instructional unit on the address system, with the learner being asked to apply the concepts to reach an assigned destination.

Summary

Research on sensory and orientation processes for individuals with visual impairments will continue, and O&M specialists can benefit by staying abreast of emerging evidence-based practices in this area as a part of their professional practice. Considering the foundational elements, guiding principles, and practical application of spatial knowledge and information gathering will help O&M specialists plan for lessons that fully integrate orientation and mobility for purposeful movement.

Guide Techniques

This chapter is intended to provide preservice orientation and mobility (O&M) specialists, teachers of students with visual impairments, and other professionals in the related fields of education and rehabilitation with the techniques to both serve as a guide and to simultaneously teach, support, and monitor their learners' travels with guides. The section on *self-advocacy* describes how to prepare learners to monitor their own techniques and travel with inexperienced guides.

The techniques described include information for using the long cane with a guide, which aligns with the belief that it is essential to introduce a mobility tool as early as possible. O&M specialists may choose to sequence instruction beginning with *guide techniques* or with cane techniques, depending on what best meets the needs of their individual learners and their given circumstances. O&M specialists may also find value in combining the content from this chapter and Chapter 5 on cane techniques as needed.

BASIC GUIDE TECHNIQUE

Purpose: To enable the learner to be an active participant while walking with a guide.

PROCEDURE AT A GLANCE

1. The guide verbally offers an arm and makes contact with the learner's lower arm with the back of his hand.
2. The learner trails her hand up the guide's arm into position just above the elbow.
3. The learner grasps the guide's arm just above the elbow with the thumb positioned on the lateral side and the fingers on the medial side, creating a secure grasp.
4. The learner's upper arm is positioned parallel and close to the side of her body.
5. The learner's upper arm and lower arm form an approximate 90-degree angle.
6. The shoulder of the learner's grip arm is aligned directly behind the shoulder of the guide's arm.
7. The learner remains approximately one half-step behind the guide as they walk together.
8. To signal the end, the guide rotates his arm outward and the learner releases her grasp.

METHOD

STEP 1 The learner asks to walk with the guide, or the guide verbally offers, and the learner accepts. The guide offers an arm and makes contact with the learner's lower arm with the back of his hand.

Rationale The initiation of travel with a guide should be made through a verbal request of the learner or verbal offer of the guide. Making physical contact with the back of the hand provides a nonverbal way for the guide to initiate contact, eliminating the need for the learner to search for the guide's arm. The use of the back of the hand is less intrusive, allowing the learner to proactively grasp the guide's arm correctly when she is ready.

STEP 2 The learner trails her hand up the guide's arm into position just above the elbow.

Rationale This approach helps the *guide team* efficiently initiate correct positioning while reducing the need for the learner to search for the guide's elbow. The grasp position above the elbow maximizes tactile information and frees the guide's lower arm and hand for carrying items or opening doors.

Variations The grasp position on the guide's arm can be adjusted for differences in height between the guide and the learner. A very young child may grasp the guide at the wrist or on extended fingers as needed. An older adult may use an interlocking finger grasp as needed for minor balance support.

Diane L. Fazzi

STEP 3 The learner grasps the guide's arm above the elbow with the thumb on the lateral side (nearest the learner) and the fingers on the medial side (nearest the guide) in a grasp that is secure yet comfortable for the guide. The position is similar to that of holding a cup. The wrist remains straight.

Rationale With the wrist straight and the fingers and thumb positioned to resemble the grasp of a cup, the learner has a secure grasp that can give tactile information about movement, including starting, stopping, turning, and *ascending* or *descending*. The secure grasp ensures that contact is not lost, especially during turns, changes in level, and in crowded areas.

STEP 4 The learner's upper arm is positioned parallel and close to the side of her body.

Rationale The learner's consistent arm position helps keep the guide team at a close and uniform width and makes it easier for the guide to judge distances to potential *obstacles* and freely move around them. When the arm is not held parallel and close to the side of the body, learners may unconsciously move away from the guide and increase the chance of grazing obstacles to the side, especially during turns when the learner is on the outside of the turn.

STEP 5 The learner's upper arm and lower arm form an approximate 90-degree angle.

Rationale While the exact angle of the learner's upper arm and *forearm* will vary according to height differences between guide and learner, approximating a 90-degree angle in combination with the grasp and arm positioning as described in the previous steps helps the learner maintain an appropriate distance behind the guide. A consistent position also provides the learner with tactile information about movement, including stops, starts, turns, and changes in level.

STEP 6 The shoulder of the learner's grip arm is aligned directly behind the shoulder of the guide's arm. (With the exception of a partial switch or narrow passageway, described in techniques later in this chapter, the aligned shoulders are always opposite sides [right shoulder of learner behind left shoulder of guide or left shoulder of learner behind right shoulder of guide].)

Diane L. Fazzi

Rationale The alignment of opposite shoulders minimizes the width of the guide team as they walk together and ensures that the guide reaches obstacles or important environmental features, such as stairs or open doorways, first. Consistent alignment provides the team with more predictable space between them and objects in their path, making it easier to negotiate a wide variety of travel environments.

STEP 7 The learner remains approximately one half-step behind the guide as they walk together.

Rationale Maintaining a distance of approximately one half-step behind the guide enables the learner to interpret movements in a consistent manner and gives the learner adequate time to react to stops, turns, and steps.

STEP 8 To signal the end, the guide rotates the guide arm outward and the learner releases her grasp.

Rationale The outward rotation of the arm provides a discreet, nonverbal, and natural manner of informing the learner that contact is to be broken.

Variations Breaking contact may be accomplished by the guide giving a verbal cue in the context of a conversation. The learner may initiate breaking contact by simply releasing the grip. Before breaking contact it may be helpful to place the learner in contact with, or in close proximity to, a stationary object for orientation purposes.

CONSIDERATIONS FOR BASIC GUIDE TECHNIQUE

- The learner's grasp can be affected by many factors, including general *grip strength*, size of the guide's arm in comparison to the size of the learner's hand, cultural and personal comfort with physical contact, and bulkiness of clothing, such as a winter coat worn by the guide or thick gloves worn by the learner. If the learner is unable to maintain a secure grasp, the guide or learner may need to adapt the technique. A slower pace may be needed when a secure grasp is difficult to maintain.
- A guide may feel more comfortable holding his arm slightly away from his side to avoid inadvertent contact with the torso or chest area.
- Some learners may exhibit initial apprehension about traveling with a guide and the experienced guide should look for indications of learner anxiety, including an overextended arm position, leaning backward on the heels, a sense of pulling on the guide's arm, or very slow walking pace. The anxiety can be addressed directly through positive encouragement and practice. The O&M specialist can provide the learner with a comparison of how it feels to walk with hesitancy by exaggerating a slower pace and then how it feels to walk with confidence by encouraging the learner to walk quickly in a quiet and open space together. Doing so may help the learner to build confidence. With an inexperienced guide,

learners may need to advocate to ensure that the guide is traveling in a manner that the learner feels is safe and comfortable.

- For a variety of reasons, including overextension of the learner's arm or a more relaxed positioning alongside the guide, learners may swing wide, especially during turns. When serving as the instructor, the guide must monitor and give feedback and guidance to correct the positioning. An experienced guide who is walking with an individual who is not a learner may simply adjust his position or pace to accommodate. This situation may also occur when peers serve as guides, and they must learn to pay extra attention to the width of the guide team during turns to avoid unnecessary contact with obstacles. To travel safely with a variety of guides, learners must pay attention to their own positioning and make corrections as necessary so they do not become dependent on input from guides.

- When a learner notices that a guide is making a turn, she may need to increase her pace slightly when positioned on the outside of the turn as there will be a slightly larger space to cover. Conversely, her pace may need to be slightly slower when she is positioned on the inside of the turn and there is a shorter distance to cover.

- When either the guide or learner wishes to break contact, the guide and learner are responsible for making sure that the learner has her bearings before the guide leaves. For example, when a learner asks a guide for assistance in locating a bus stop, she should make sure that she knows the location of the bus pole or bench before allowing the guide to leave. Similarly, at a social gathering, it is typical to release the grasp of the guide when engaging in conversation with others, but the guide should make it clear to the individual when he is preparing to leave.

- Familiar guides, including parents, spouses, and friends, may have developed a more casual grasp and position when guiding and may walk arm in arm or hand in hand or even push from behind as if steering. Some individuals may prefer to put their hand on the guide's shoulder. While the learner receives less information about the travel environment in these settings, it may be an acceptable social practice in some instances. O&M specialists can teach individuals to make sure that family members and close friends are aware of the differences in information that will be provided and help to develop a work-around that is comfortable for everyone. For example, for a romantic couple that wishes to walk arm in arm, early detection of drop-offs might be missed and the couple should be encouraged to use a verbal or agreed-upon nonverbal alternative cue to signal an upcoming drop-off while still being able to enjoy a relaxing stroll. For children who may still be learning the guide techniques, O&M specialists may choose to encourage parents and caregivers to practice the techniques whenever possible. However, it is simply natural for parents and young children to walk hand in hand and O&M specialists may work with the family to make adaptations accordingly.

DIAGONAL CANE TECHNIQUE WHILE TRAVELING WITH A GUIDE

This section provides information on using a cane while traveling with a guide. Chapter 5 describes cane techniques in greater depth.

Purpose: **To enable the learner to manage and make optimum use of the long cane while walking with a guide.**

> **PROCEDURE AT A GLANCE**
>
> **1** The learner holds the cane in her free hand, using the *diagonal technique*.
>
> **2** The learner's elbow is slightly bent and she holds the cane diagonally across her body, but with the cane tip extended just beyond her body *midline* while walking with the guide.

METHOD

STEP 1 The learner holds the cane in her free hand, using the diagonal cane technique. The diagonal cane technique also provides the learner with additional information about the travel environment.

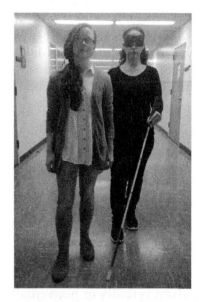

Rationale The diagonal cane technique provides the learner with added information about travel surfaces and low-lying objects in the learner's path while traveling with a guide.

Variations The learner may determine that the appropriate cane technique to use while walking with the guide is the *congested-area technique* with touch technique (see section on Two-Point-Touch Cane Technique in Chapter 5). This technique will provide the learner with additional information about the travel environment, and when used correctly, will not interfere with the guide's footsteps. Using touch technique is especially helpful when walking with an inexperienced guide who may miss certain nuances in the travel environment. Learners may find it valuable to always use this technique while traveling with a guide, regardless of experience level, because it provides learners with important information about the environment so they are active participants during travel experiences.

Some learners will prefer to walk with a familiar and experienced guide with the cane held in a "not-in-use" position. The learner holds the cane in her free hand, with the fingers and thumb wrapped around the grip. Depending on the length of the cane and the height of the learner, it may be more convenient to grasp the cane slightly below the grip to maintain greater control over the cane and to reduce the possibility of having the bottom portion of the cane inadvertently swing toward the guide and become entangled with the guide's footsteps.

Diane L. Fazzi

STEP 2 The learner's elbow is slightly bent and she holds the cane diagonally across her body, but with the cane tip extended just beyond her body midline while walking with the guide. With the shoulders of the guide and learner in alignment, the cane tip should be positioned about midway between the learner's midline and her opposite side foot to avoid extending in front of the guide's foot.

Rationale The bent elbow helps the learner to position the cane slightly beyond the midline and slightly to the side, closer to her opposite side foot, but not beyond so as not to impede the footsteps of the guide. The position of the cane tip provides additional information about the travel surface, complementary to the information obtained from traveling with the guide. The cane is held to the side and repositioned as needed.

CONSIDERATIONS FOR DIAGONAL CANE TECHNIQUE WHILE TRAVELING WITH A GUIDE

The learner may find the *pencil grasp* works best in this situation. If using the *thumb grasp* or *index finger grasp*, it may be necessary to adjust the grasp further down the cane shaft to shorten the cane. See Chapter 5 for a full description of the various grasps that can be used with the diagonal cane technique.

REVERSING DIRECTION WITH A GUIDE: 180-DEGREE TURN

Purpose: To enable the learner and guide to make a 180-degree turn in a limited space.

PROCEDURE AT A GLANCE

1 The guide indicates the need to reverse direction and starts to turn toward the learner.

2 The guide and learner turn 90 degrees toward each other. The guide initiates contact with his free hand for the learner to grasp the guide's free arm, then releases the original grasp.

3 The guide and learner then complete the rest of the 180-degree turn until they are facing the opposite travel direction.

METHOD

STEP 1 The guide indicates the need to reverse direction and starts to turn toward the learner. The signal to reverse direction can be given verbally or nonverbally.

Rationale The guide's indication that the team needs to reverse direction prepares the learner for the subsequent steps and enables the learner to update her orientation in the environment.

Diane L. Fazzi

STEP 2 Both the guide and learner turn 90 degrees toward each other, maintaining the guide grasp until they are facing each other. The guide initiates contact with the back of his free hand for the learner to grasp the free arm, then releases the original grasp (Jacobson, 2013).

Rationale By maintaining contact through the turn, the learner maintains a clear point of reference supporting an accurate 90-degree turn and smooth approach to initiating contact on the other arm for the remainder of the 180-degree turn.

Diane L. Fazzi

STEP 3 The guide and learner smoothly complete the rest of the 180-degree turn until they are facing the opposite travel direction.

Rationale The second half of the turn can be made without losing contact and provides the learner with a consistent point of reference for an accurate turn. The technique can be completed in a very limited area of space such as a crowded elevator, auditorium, or social gathering.

Variation The guide team can reverse direction and make the 180-degree turn by releasing the original grasp and making independent turns. The 180-degree turn can be initiated after the team comes to a stop and the guide can reinitiate contact after the turn has been made. The learner may need practice to make an accurate 180-degree turn independently. This variation may work especially well for a learner who has low vision and is able to maintain visual contact with the guide.

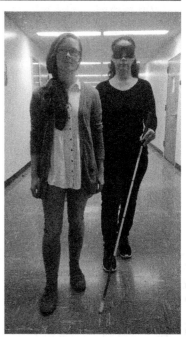

Diane L. Fazzi

NEGOTIATING NARROW PASSAGEWAYS WITH A GUIDE

Purpose: To enable the guide team to maintain contact while walking through a narrow area.

PROCEDURE AT A GLANCE

1	The guide moves his arm behind and toward the small of his back.
2	The learner extends her arm and moves directly behind the guide.
3	The guide returns his arm to his side, signaling the end of the narrow passage, and the learner returns to her original position.

METHOD

STEP 1 The guide moves his arm behind and toward the small of his back.

Rationale This movement provides a *nonverbal cue* that the team is approaching a narrow passageway.

STEP 2 The learner extends her arm and moves directly behind the guide.

Rationale By extending her arm, the learner increases the distance between herself and the guide, thereby reducing the chance of stepping on the guide's heels. The learner moving directly behind the guide reduces the width of the team, enabling them to walk through the narrow space.

Variation For some guides or learners it may be easier if the grasp is shifted from just above the elbow down to the wrist. This position can be easier for the guide if he cannot extend his upper arm comfortably behind his back. The wrist grasp can also make it easier for the learner to maximize the distance between herself and the guide and to more smoothly and directly align herself behind the guide.

Diane L. Fazzi

STEP 3 Once the team clears the narrow passage, the guide returns his arm to his side, signaling to the learner to return to the original position.

Rationale This movement provides a nonverbal cue that the team has completed the narrow passage.

CONSIDERATIONS FOR NEGOTIATING NARROW PASSAGEWAYS WITH A GUIDE

- A combination of verbal and nonverbal cues or a somewhat exaggerated arm movement on the part of the guide may be necessary early on for the learner to recognize the nonverbal cue for moving into the narrow-passageway position.
- Changes in elements of the guide technique, such as transitioning from basic guide technique to a narrow passageway, may result in disruption of the learner's *stride length* (the distance between successive steps of the same foot) or width and create awkward movement. Maintaining a consistent walking pace is important to making smooth transitions.
- The learner can initiate the transition to a narrow passageway when traveling with an inexperienced guide if she anticipates an upcoming narrow passageway.
- Time spent in the narrow-passageway position should be minimized to avoid discomfort on the part of both guide and learner.

SWITCHING (TRANSFERRING) SIDES WITH A GUIDE

Purpose: To enable the learner to switch sides from one arm of the guide to the other as needed or preferred while walking together.

PROCEDURE AT A GLANCE

1. The guide or learner indicates a need or desire to switch sides and transfer to the guide's opposite arm.

2. The learner grasps the guide's arm with her free hand, just above the existing grasp, and extends her arm while the team continues to walk forward.

3. The learner releases the initial grasp and with the back of that hand lightly trails across the guide's back to locate the elbow of the guide's opposite arm.

4. The guide moves his free arm back slightly in order to make it easier for the learner to locate his elbow, especially while moving.

5. Once contact is made with the guide's opposite arm, the learner releases her grasp on the original arm and brings her hand over to grasp the new arm.

METHOD

STEP 1 The guide or learner may verbally indicate a need or desire to switch sides and transfer to the guide's opposite arm.

Rationale A verbal cue to switch sides prepares the guide team for the steps to follow.

STEP 2 The learner grasps the guide's arm with her free hand, just above the existing grasp. The learner extends her arm to create enough distance between herself and the guide. The guide team continues to walk forward during this process. A slower pace of walking during the transfer of sides may be helpful for some learners.

Rationale The new grasp enables the learner to release her initial grasp in order to trail across the guide's back to locate the opposite arm in Step 3. The extended arm and slightly slower pace of the learner help to create added distance between the learner and guide—to avoid the possibility of stepping on the guide's heels. When the guide slows down, it can lead to a decrease in distance between the guide and the learner, causing the learner to inadvertently step on his heels.

Variation with the Long Cane The learner transfers the cane to the hand that is grasping the guide's arm between the thumb and the guide's arm, raising the cane into a vertical position so it is grasped below the grip. The learner simultaneously grasps the guide's arm with her newly freed hand just above the existing grasp, extending the arm to create enough distance between herself and the guide.

STEP 3 The learner releases the initial grasp and with the back of that hand lightly trails across the guide's back to locate the elbow of his opposite arm. The trailing hand should be cupped slightly to avoid catching on the guide's hair or clothing.

Rationale When the learner lightly trails across the guide's back while maintaining her grasp on the guide's initial arm with an extended arm, it helps the learner to find the guide's opposite arm while moving and reduces the chance of stepping on the guide's heels or losing contact with the guide.

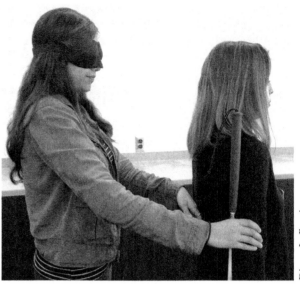

Variation with the Long Cane Keeping the cane in a vertical position grasped below the grip, the learner may continue to hold the cane while lightly trailing across the guide's back. Maintaining the distance between the guide and the learner is especially important when using a cane so that the shaft does not become intertwined with the guide's legs.

STEP 4 The guide moves his free arm back slightly in order to make it easier for the learner to locate it, especially while moving.

Rationale The guide facilitates the smooth transfer, making it easier for the learner to locate the guide's arm and form the grasp on the new side.

Variation Some guide teams may prefer to stop briefly in order to switch sides. This allows the learner to trail across the guide's back without maintaining contact with the original arm.

STEP 5 Once contact is made with the guide's opposite arm, the learner releases her grasp on the original arm and brings her hand over to grasp the new arm. Shoulders are then realigned on the new side and the team continues forward.

Rationale Upon contacting the guide's opposite arm, the learner releases her grasp on the initial guide arm to properly grasp the opposite arm. If the learner starts on the guide's right arm with a left-hand grasp, then the completed move will result in right-hand grasp of the guide's left arm. Shoulders should be aligned as the guide team proceeds forward.

Variation with the Long Cane When the learner completes the transfer she positions the cane properly in her free hand on the new side.

CONSIDERATIONS FOR SWITCHING SIDES WITH A GUIDE

- When guides anticipate the best side for a learner to be on in advance of a particular door, staircase, handrail, or obstacle-ridden area, the switching of sides can be done in advance so that the transition is not rushed.
- Stepping on the heel of the guide is a somewhat common experience when switching sides and often occurs when either the guide slows down too much while the learner is making the switch or if the learner does not extend her arm sufficiently.

NEGOTIATING DOORS WITH A GUIDE

Purpose: To enable the guide team to safely negotiate a variety of doorways in a coordinated manner.

	PROCEDURE AT A GLANCE
1	The guide approaches the door squarely and describes the door to the learner.
2a	For doors that **open on the same side as the learner**, the guide opens the door with a push or pull motion, depending on if it is opening toward or away from the guide team. The learner places her free hand in a modified upper-body protective technique position with the palm facing outward, keeping her fingers relaxed and together in preparation to receive the opening door.
2b	For doors that **open on the opposite side of the learner**, the guide opens the door with a push or pull motion, depending on if it is opening toward or away from the guide team. The learner extends her arm, moves behind the guide, and grasps the guide's arm with the free hand to switch hands before placing her now free hand in a modified upper-body protective technique position with the palm facing outward, keeping her fingers relaxed and together in preparation to receive the opening door.
3	The learner receives the opened door, pushing it further open or holding it open long enough for the guide team to pass through before releasing it.
4	The learner may return to the original guide-team position once the door is closed.

METHOD

STEP 1 The guide approaches the door squarely and describes the door in the following manner: "We are approaching a door that is opening toward us (or away from us) to the right (or to the left)."

Rationale It is important to approach the door directly so that the learner is not at an angle to the door opening. The verbal cue gives the learner a quick frame of reference for preparing to receive the door as it is opened. Guides often tend to describe doors as opening in or out, but describing doors as opening toward or away from the learner is more accurate and better prepares the learner to receive the door.

Variations Some O&M specialists describe the door based on the side of the hinge, such as the door is a push right, push left, pull right, or pull left, with right and left referring to the side of the hinge.

Learners can also determine the direction that the door is opening by interpreting the body movements of the guide. A guide will assume a slight forward lean and continuous motion for push doors that open away and a forward lean and rock backwards for pull doors that open toward the guide team. With practice, especially with an experienced guide, the learner will be able to quickly distinguish these movements in preparation for the opening door.

STEP 2A For doors that **open on the same side as the learner,** the guide opens the door with a push or pull motion, depending on if it is opening toward or away from the guide team. The learner places her free hand in a modified upper-body protective technique position (see Chapter 4) with the palm facing outward (knuckles facing her nose), keeping her fingers relaxed and together in preparation to receive the opening door. This position works regardless of whether the door is opening toward or away from the learner. When the door opens on the same side as the learner, if the guide opens the door with the grip arm, the learner will feel the push or pull movement to a greater extent than if the door is opened by the guide with his free arm.

Rationale The learner does not have to switch hands when the door opens on the same side as she is walking, so her free hand will serve to receive the opening door. The palm faces outward so that the fleshy part of the hand contacts the door, reducing the chance of injury.

Variation with the Long Cane The learner transfers the cane to the hand that is grasping the guide's arm, placing it between the thumb and the guide's arm, before starting Step 2a.

STEP 2B For doors that **open on the opposite side of the learner**, the guide opens the door with a push or pull motion, depending on if it is opening toward or away from the guide team. The learner extends her arm, moves behind the guide, and grasps the guide's arm with the free hand in order to switch hands before placing her now free hand in a modified upper-body protective technique position (see Chapter 4) with the palm facing outward, keeping her fingers relaxed and together in preparation to receive the opening door. This position works regardless of whether the door is opening toward or away from the learner. For doors that open on the opposite side

of the learner, the guide opens the door with the free arm to avoid reaching across his body in an awkward manner. The learner will still be able to feel the push or pull movement. If the learner is not detecting the push or pull movement for doors opening on the opposite side, the O&M specialist can slow down the technique and point out the shift in body movements for each instance until the learner is able to notice the difference.

Rationale The learner moves behind the guide and switches hands when the door opens on the opposite side of where she is walking, so that she can reach with a free hand to receive the opening door. She extends her arm to avoid stepping on the guide's heels. The palm faces outward so that the fleshy part of the hand contacts the door. Maintaining the upper position of the hand for protection in relation to the guide's body reduces the chance of injury and makes it easier for the guide to pass the door to the learner.

Variation with the Long Cane The learner completes the partial switch by grasping the guide's arm with her cane hand and holding the cane vertical and stable between her fingers and the guide's arm prior to starting Step 2b.

STEP 3 The learner receives the opened door, pushing it further open (for doors opening away from the learner) or holding it open (for doors opening toward the learner) long enough for the guide team to pass through before releasing it. Self-closing doors can be released to close automatically once the team has passed through. **The guide may need to pause or slow down slightly when the learner needs to manually close a door behind them.**

Rationale The guide team shares the responsibility for the door, with the guide opening the door and the learner pushing or holding the door open until the team has cleared the door. Self-closing doors can be released to close and other doors manually pulled shut. If a guide tries to open and hold the door open for a learner, both the guide and the learner may end up being turned and facing the wrong direction once through the door, which may result in disorientation or a collision as the guide has his back to the new environment.

STEP 4 **The learner may return to the original guide-team position once the door is closed.**

Rationale Resuming the original guide position enables the team to direct their attention forward to upcoming environmental features.

CONSIDERATIONS FOR NEGOTIATING DOORS WITH A GUIDE

- The narrow-passageway position may be required for doorways that are narrow or heavily congested with people.
- In order to be active participants in traveling through doors, learners should be aware of their surroundings and the movements of the guide in order to anticipate how they will assist with the door. Learners should be prepared to manage doors with both experienced and inexperienced guides.
- When the learner is carrying something, she will need to make a judgment as to whether or not she can continue holding the object in the hand that will contact and manage the door or whether the object needs to be switched to the other hand. If the learner cannot grasp both the object and the guide's arm simultaneously, then she can release the guide's arm and maintain contact with the door until they move through and then switch the object back to her free hand and resume the grasp of the guide.
- While the rule may not always be consistent and may vary for certain locations, generally doors in homes and individual rooms open inward to rooms, while external building doors usually open toward the outside.
- Expose learners to a wide variety of doors so that they are comfortable using handles, knobs, and push bars and become accustomed to weight discrepancies that may be found. Guide teams can practice with a variety of door sets to develop precision and confidence.

ASCENDING AND DESCENDING STAIRS WITH A GUIDE

Purpose: To enable the guide team to safely ascend and descend stairs.

	PROCEDURE AT A GLANCE
1	The guide approaches the edge of the stairs and aligns perpendicularly.
2	The guide pauses at the stairs, allowing the learner to align herself to the stairs alongside the guide.
3	The guide takes the first step and continues to ascend or descend with the learner one step behind.
4	When the guide's first foot approaches the *landing* with one step to go, the guide provides a verbal or nonverbal cue to the learner so that she knows there is only one step remaining.

METHOD

STEP 1 The guide approaches the edge of the stairs and aligns perpendicularly.

Rationale This positioning ensures that the learner does not reach the stairs at an angle, reducing any missteps.

STEP 2 The guide pauses at the stairs, allowing the learner to position and align herself to the stairs alongside the guide. If the learner chooses to use the handrail, the guide positions himself closer to the right side of the stairs so that the learner may extend her hand further to the right to locate the handrail. The guide waits for the learner to locate and grasp the handrail before starting the ascent or descent.

Rationale The slight pause allows the learner time to step alongside the guide. Most learners will feel more comfortable initially if they are given time to contact the stair riser or stair edge with their toes before starting. When the guide positions himself near the side of the stairs, it enables the learner to grasp the handrail as desired, without impeding the flow of others on the stairs. In the United States, a position near the right side of the stairs ensures movement in the same direction as the flow of pedestrians. In other countries, the directional flow of pedestrian traffic may be on the left side of the stairs.

Variation with the Long Cane The learner uses the tip of the cane to contact the stair riser or stair edge to verify her position and then holds the cane in a vertical position with her free hand, ensuring that the shaft or tip of the cane does not impede the guide as he ascends or descends the stairs. When the learner chooses to hold the handrail, the cane can be transferred to the same hand that is grasping the guide's arm. When holding the cane against the guide's arm, between the hand and the thumb, the learner holds the cane slightly below the grip to ensure that the cane does not interfere with the guide's steps or gets caught on a stair.

   If the cane is held together with the handrail, the learner may experience challenges with the cane shaft or tip going over the side of the stairs and entangling with individual handrails depending on the spacing. Some learners who are experienced travelers may prefer to ascend or descend stairs independently using appropriate cane techniques rather than coordinate steps with the guide (see Chapter 5 for details).

STEP 3 The guide takes the first step and continues to ascend or descend with the learner one step behind. The team works to ensure that they are walking at the same pace to maintain the same one-step difference throughout.

Rationale If the distance between the guide and learner varies throughout the ascent or descent, then anticipation and management of the landing becomes more difficult. An even rhythm on the stairs also makes it easier for the learner to judge the depth and height of the stairs and maintain consistent foot placement on each step.

Diane L. Fazzi

STEP 4 When the guide's first foot approaches the landing with one step to go, the guide provides a verbal or nonverbal cue to the learner so that she knows there is only one step remaining. The nonverbal cue can simply be a slight forward movement of the guide's arm, naturally prompting the learner to move forward versus taking another step up or down.

Rationale The verbal or nonverbal cue provides the learner with adequate notice that the set of stairs is complete so that the learner does not feel the need to count steps, overthink the process, or make a misstep on the landing.

Variation Some O&M specialists may use a brief pause to signify they have reached the landing, providing learners with a nonverbal cue; however, the pause should be very brief as interruptions to the forward movement can cause some individuals to lose balance.

CONSIDERATIONS FOR ASCENDING AND DESCENDING STAIRS WITH A GUIDE

- The techniques for ascending and descending stairs with a guide are almost identical, but O&M specialists will typically teach ascending first because it is more comfortable for most people.
- Many learners will be familiar with the architecture and layout of staircases and stairways. However, learners who have had limited experience with stairs, such as young children, will need to be introduced to stair concepts and parts such as step depth, riser height, stair edge, landing, and handrail locations. Attention to these various stair parts differs for ascending and descending stairs and should be introduced prior to instruction in these guide techniques to ensure conceptual understanding on the part of the learner and to build confidence in executing the techniques. For orientation purposes, learners need to understand the change in directional facing upon completion of single and multiple flights of stairs to ensure good orientation at landings and for continuation along a travel route.
- The majority of stair sets encountered by the guide team will include handrails. The O&M specialist may rely on a variety of factors to determine if the handrail should be used, and if so, whether it would be better for the guide or the learner to hold the handrail. Factors for consideration include, but are not limited to, regularity or irregularity of the stairway design, balance and physical abilities of the guide and learner, and congestion on the stairway.
  - □ Guide teams with good balance when ascending or descending evenly spaced stairs may choose to not use a handrail. Being able to manage stairs without a handrail makes it easier when the team's

hands are full, when traveling in crowded areas where the handrail may be less accessible, or in situations in which the cleanliness of the handrail makes it undesirable to hold.

☐ Some guide teams will feel equally comfortable managing the stairs without the use of a handrail and whoever ends up on the side of the handrail may or may not choose to use it.

☐ Some O&M specialists prefer to hold the handrail themselves in order to provide a predictable source of support for the guide team in the event that either makes a misstep.

☐ Some O&M specialists may feel that it is best for the learner to hold the handrail to provide an additional source of orientation or balance on the stairs. In the event of any missteps, the guide will reach across the learner to the handrail in order to provide a brace from falling, if judged to be effective and needed.

☐ Some learners will feel most comfortable holding onto the handrail themselves for a source of orientation or balance on the stairs.

■ The guide and learner should maintain an upright and relaxed posture with evenly distributed body weight. A slight lean "up" the stairs, whether that is an ever so slight forward lean while ascending the stairs or a slight backward lean while descending, is recommended to avoid stumbles down the stairs. Due to momentum and slope, a "fall" upward on a staircase is less likely to lead to injury.

SEATING

General Seating

Purpose: **To enable the learner to easily locate and examine a desired seat.**

	PROCEDURE AT A GLANCE
1	The guide team approaches a desired seat.
2	The guide describes the type of seat and its position in relation to the learner.
3	The guide places his hand on the back of the seat and the learner releases her grasp, following the guide's arm to locate the chair.
4	The learner repositions herself to face the seat and uses a modified upper-hand-and-forearm protective technique to be in position to clear the seat.
5	While bending at the waist, the learner quickly clears the seat by moving the back of her hand in a circular motion.
6	The learner places the back of her legs against the front of the seat and sits down. Maintaining a hold on the seat while sitting provides additional stability.
7	For exiting a seat, the guide initiates contact with the learner at the upper arm.
8	While rising from the seat, the learner moves her hand up to above the guide's elbow without losing contact. When appropriate, the learner may use her free hand to push out of the chair.

METHOD

STEP 1 The guide team approaches a desired seat until the learner is in close proximity.

Rationale Contact with the seat is made easier when the learner is close to it.

STEP 2 The guide describes the type of seat and its position in relation to the learner.

Rationale Understanding the type of chair, for example a chair without arms or a chair with wheels, prepares the learner for the appropriate approach and direction for seating.

STEP 3 The guide places his hand on the back of the seat and the learner releases her grasp, following the guide's arm to locate the chair.

Rationale The guide's hand placed on the back of the seat gives the learner an easy reference point to quickly locate the chair.

Variation If the guide does not contact the back of the seat, the learner, who is in close proximity to the seat, can discretely move her foot to locate the chair.

Variation with the Long Cane The learner can use the long cane to locate the chair. Anchoring the long cane against the chair provides a stationary reference point.

Diane L. Fazzi

STEP 4 The learner repositions herself to face the seat and uses a modified upper-hand-and-forearm protective technique to be in position to clear the seat (see Chapter 4).

Rationale Learners will want to become accustomed to checking that seats are clear before sitting.

STEP 5 While bending at the waist, the learner quickly clears the seat by moving the back of her hand in a circular motion.

Rationale Using a light touch with the back of the hand, fingers, or fingertips reduces the likelihood of disturbing objects that may be found on the seat, such as a purse or sunglasses.

Variation In familiar environments in which the learner is certain that the seat is empty or based on the trusted information from the guide that the seat is clear, the learner can simply clear the seat while being seated. The seamless motion might look or feel similar to the manner in which a person might smooth out a skirt before taking a seat.

Variation with the Long Cane The learner may choose to quickly fold the cane and use the folded cane as a tool to clear the vacant seat.

STEP 6 The learner places the back of her legs against the front of the seat and sits down. Maintaining a hold on the seat while sitting provides additional stability.

Rationale Placing the back of the legs against the front of the seat ensures proper alignment to the chair for sitting.

Variation with the Long Cane Once seated, the learner folds or stores the cane for easy access and makes sure that it is not in the way of others who are seated or walking nearby.

STEP 7 For exiting a seat, the guide initiates contact with the learner. If the guide is already standing, then initial contact may be on the upper arm of the learner with the learner's initial grasp being on the forearm.

Rationale When the guide is standing and the learner is sitting, the initial contact will typically be at the learner's upper arm and can be adjusted as the learner begins to stand.

Variation with the Long Cane The learner retrieves or unfolds the cane in preparation for traveling with the guide.

STEP 8 While rising from the seat, the learner moves her hand to above the guide's elbow without losing contact. When appropriate, the learner may use her free hand to push out of the chair.

Rationale The simultaneous rising and repositioning of the arm provides for a smooth transition from sitting to travel with a guide.

Auditorium Seating

Purpose: To enable the learner to easily locate and examine a desired seat in an auditorium setting.

PROCEDURE AT A GLANCE

1. The guide pauses at the appropriate row and indicates to the learner to position herself alongside him in preparation for entering the row in a sideways manner.

2. The guide starts into the row, sidestepping as needed if there is limited clearance for walking.

3. The learner may use the back of her free hand to trail the back of the seats of the row in front.

4. The guide stops at the appropriate seats, providing a verbal cue that they have arrived.

5. The learner uses the back of her legs to contact the seat and with a continuous movement clears or pushes the seat down in order to sit.

6. To exit, the guide and learner reestablish contact and repeat the process to exit the row.

METHOD

STEP 1 The guide pauses at the appropriate row and verbally or nonverbally indicates to the learner to position herself alongside him in preparation for entering the row in a sideways manner.

Rationale Stopping at the row and positioning the learner alongside the guide prior to entering the row allows for smooth movement into the row of seats.

STEP 2 The guide starts into the row of seats, sidestepping as needed if there is limited clearance for walking. When sidestepping, the guide team is facing the front of the auditorium.

Rationale It is preferable to have the guide lead the way into the row of seats to locate the appropriate seats and to be able to pause if other members of the audience need to adjust their knees or are standing up to make room to pass through. The use of sidestepping is recommended when the space is narrow.

Both the guide and learner face the front of the auditorium while sidestepping rather than facing those already seated in the row.

Variation with the Long Cane The learner holds the cane in a vertical position due to the limited space available. If there is adequate time and the learner has a folding cane, the learner may wish to fold the cane prior to entering the row. The folded cane can be used to lightly trail the back of the seats or to clear the seat when reached.

STEP 3 The learner may use the back of her free hand to trail the back of the seats of the row in front.

Rationale Keeping contact with the back of the seats immediately in front helps the learner to keep track of her position in the row, including her sideways movement, and informs her of the relative distance between the rows.

STEP 4 The guide stops at the appropriate seats, providing a verbal cue that they have arrived.

Rationale A verbal cue helps the learner differentiate between arrival at the seats and other pauses taken while moving through the row.

STEP 5 The learner uses the back of her legs to contact the seat and with a continuous movement clears the seat. Some auditorium and stadium seats automatically fold up. The learner will need to use her hand to also push the seat down in preparation for seating.

Rationale Using the back of the legs is an inconspicuous means of ensuring that the learner is aligned with the seat and allows for a continuous clearing motion and pushing the seat down for seating in a quick and relaxed manner.

Variation with the Long Cane The cane is folded or stored accordingly after seating.

STEP 6 To exit the auditorium, the guide and learner reestablish contact and repeat the process to exit the row.

Rationale The same techniques for entering row seating are effective for exiting row seating.

Variation with the Long Cane The learner retrieves the cane and resumes the previous positioning of the cane to continue travel with the guide.

CONSIDERATIONS FOR SEATING

- Guide teams may approach sofas from the front.
- Seating at tables requires that learners pull out their chairs before seating and push chairs back in when leaving.
- Some individuals may wish to arrive early to events held in auditoriums or stadiums in order to make seating easier before the seats are full. Similarly, they may prefer to wait until the auditorium or stadium clears before exiting the row.
- Learners can use social niceties such as "Excuse me" and "Thank you" when navigating congested rows.
- When carrying food and drinks into auditorium seating, learners must take care to keep the tray level and to avoid bumping people who are seated in the row in front while moving across the row to their seats. Some learners will choose to fold their canes and store them in a purse, back pocket, or along with the food on the carrying tray.

ACCEPTING OR REFUSING ASSISTANCE: HINES BREAK

Purpose: To enable the learner to accept or refuse assistance from a potential guide, as desired.

PROCEDURE AT A GLANCE

1 The learner relaxes the arm that is grasped and raises it toward her opposite shoulder, keeping her feet stationary.

2 With her free hand, the learner grasps the person's wrist while stating her intentions to accept and correct or refuse the assistance.

3 The learner pulls the person's wrist forward until the person loses contact with her arm.

4 To accept while correcting the way the assistance was offered, the learner uses her free hand to assume the proper grasp above the elbow, saying, "Yes, but I will take your arm, thank you."

5 To refuse assistance, the learner simply releases the person's wrist, saying, "No, thank you."

METHOD

STEP 1 The learner relaxes the arm that is grasped and raises it toward her opposite shoulder, keeping her feet stationary.

Rationale When surprised by an offer of assistance in which a stranger comes from behind and grasps the learners arm to push her ahead in what the person assumes to be the desired direction of travel, a natural reaction can be to tense the muscles. The tension may result in the learner being easily pushed forward and losing balance. When the learner learns to react with a relaxed arm paired with a quick verbal response, the person will promptly know that the grasp was inappropriate. As the learner raises her relaxed arm to her opposite shoulder, the person will not be able to push the learner forward and the person's unwanted grip can be more easily dislodged. Keeping the feet stationary will help the learner maintain balance, alignment, and direction of travel for orientation.

STEP 2 With her free hand, the learner grasps the person's wrist to assert control in the situation, while stating her intentions to accept and correct the positioning of the guide or to refuse the assistance offered.

Rationale The grasp of the person's wrist gives the learner control over the situation. The learner will need to make her intentions clear verbally.

STEP 3 The learner pulls the person's wrist forward until the person loses grasp of her arm. If the learner wishes to accept the assistance, then she should maintain her grasp on the wrist and anticipate Step 4 below, bringing the person's arm into place for easy reach of the elbow, and be prepared to grasp the person's arm above the elbow once her arm is free. If the learner does not plan to travel with the person, then she should anticipate Step 5 below.

Rationale This step enables the learner to break the unwanted grasp and also places the potential guide's arm in a position that makes it easy for the learner to correctly grasp above the elbow.

STEP 4 To accept while correcting the way that the assistance was offered, the learner uses her now free hand to assume the proper grasp above the elbow, saying, "Yes, but I will take your arm, thank you," or "Yes, but may I please take your arm?" The guide's elbow is easily located because the learner has directed the guide's arm in Step 3 above.

Rationale The learner is able to assert her intent to travel with the guide while also giving instructions in the appropriate technique to be used.

Variations

Long Cane

If the potential guide grasps the learner on the arm in which the cane is being held, the learner switches the cane into her free hand, holding it firmly between the thumb and index finger. The cane is held firmly to keep it stable during the maneuver. Simultaneously, the learner grasps the person's wrist to release the hold, stating her intention to accept the assistance. The learner places the newly freed hand to assume the proper grasp above the elbow. When traveling with an inexperienced guide, the learner should use a cane technique for travel with an inexperienced and uninformed guide.

When Learner Declines Assistance

If the cane arm is grasped by the potential guide and the learner wishes to decline assistance, she can leave the cane in her preferred hand and reach across with her free hand to release the grasp as needed.

Diane L. Fazzi

STEP 5 To refuse the assistance, the learner simply releases the person's wrist, saying, "No, thank you."

Rationale The learner indicates her intent to not travel with the individual in an assertive yet polite manner.

CONSIDERATIONS FOR ACCEPTING OR REFUSING ASSISTANCE: HINES BREAK

- The learner should calmly indicate her intentions to travel or not travel with the individual while simultaneously using the *Hines break*. Whenever possible, the technique should be used graciously so as not to offend an uninformed person who is receptive to the learner's request.

- Having the cane means that the learner has one more step to consider for the complete technique, depending on whether or not the cane arm is grasped by the potential guide.

- Managing the cane through the procedures for the Hines break requires some practice to ensure that it can be done quickly and somewhat automatically since the technique is typically needed without much anticipation.

- Some individuals may be persistent about attempting to provide assistance and may require a more aggressive verbal response.

- Learners may also experience interactions with individuals who push from behind or grab the long cane to pull the learner in an uninformed attempt to assist the learner. In either case, the learner should firmly plant her feet but relax her upper body to absorb the impact of the push or pull without losing her position. Since there is no grasp to reposition, the learner would provide verbal information to the uninformed individual by either refusing assistance or requesting assistance to be provided in the proper manner by saying something like, "No, I don't want assistance" or "Don't push (or pull) me. Please ask first in the future. For assistance, I would like to take your arm."

Tips for Teaching Guide Techniques

Integrating Orientation

In order for learners to be active participants in travel while walking with a guide, they should be encouraged to maintain full awareness of their travel environment and social surroundings. During instruction, O&M specialists can introduce the use of cardinal directions for orientation purposes as well as route shapes. For learners who have some initial orientation skills, O&M specialists can ask them to serve as the navigator to direct the travel along the route as an opportunity to practice orientation for solo travel.

Sequencing

Sequencing of instruction must take into account each learner's individual circumstances. In a traditional training sequence, guide techniques may be introduced early on as a convenient means for getting to various lesson locations or as a means to refine guide techniques already in practice. Some O&M specialists may choose to teach guide techniques simultaneously with the issuance of the long cane. The logic for this approach is that the guide technique will ultimately be adapted for use with a cane, and starting with both could be more efficient for learners who can learn them together.

As learners become familiar with various guide techniques, they may initially focus on the mechanics of the skill, but as they become more confident with the skills, they can focus more on the information that may be gleaned from paying attention to the guide's movements. As travel with a guide becomes more automatic, learners can then focus on the dynamic environmental information available and optimize their active participation in the process.

For learners who have limited experience with doors, stairs, and unusual seating such as folding seats in an auditorium or bench seating commonly found in cafeterias, O&M specialists will want to provide as much exposure and opportunity for exploration to the variations of these environmental features as possible. Finding unique doors, stairs, or seating arrangements can provide novel opportunities for practicing guide techniques with learners. Full orientation to unique environments, such as auditoriums, prior to an event can make it more comfortable for some learners.

O&M Specialist Positioning

The *O&M specialist's positioning* is fairly consistent during the introduction of guide techniques as the position is dictated by the actual technique, which most often is one step in front of the learner with shoulders aligned. In order to observe the learner's technique from various angles, the O&M specialist would need to observe the learner traveling with a different guide.

Strategies for Different Populations

General

Providing learners with clear verbal instructions will help them to learn the components and rationales of the various guide techniques. Learners who would benefit from practice in describing guide techniques to potential guides can record their instructions and play them back to determine how they can be improved.

Learners can be encouraged to practice auditory skills while traveling with a guide. Skills such as sound localization, identifying *sound shadows* (areas of diminished sound created by the blockage of background noise by an object positioned between the listener and the sound), and using *echolocation* (use of reflected sound to detect the presence of objects) to keep track of parallel wall surfaces can be applied while traveling with a guide.

Learners Who Have Low Vision

The use of visual modeling or demonstration of guide techniques may be used in conjunction with verbal instruction for some learners with low vision. When using visual modeling, O&M specialists should be sure to select an environment that is well lit and free from *glare* and visual clutter. They should also provide contrast as needed to ensure that the key aspects of the techniques are easily seen. Instructors should be careful, however, not to rely solely on the use of demonstration for teaching mobility techniques, as learners with low vision may miss important aspects of positioning and rationale if demonstrations are missing a clear explanation with verbal instructions. Opportunities for practice in natural environments is also key to learning the skills.

A learner who has low vision can be encouraged to practice visual skills while traveling with a guide. Skills such as *scanning* (using eye movements to search for targets or layouts of open areas), *eccentric viewing* (using peripheral vision to look around a blind spot), or distance estimation can be applied while traveling with a guide. Learners who have low vision and are able to successfully track the movements of the guide may simply ask to follow along.

A learner with low vision may not recognize the need to learn guide techniques. In providing instruction, the O&M specialist may wish to highlight specific situations that may apply to that person, such as entering a dark restaurant or movie theater or traveling through a crowd, to assist the learner in recognizing the value of learning guide techniques.

Age Differences

As noted in the description of the guide techniques, the grasp can be adjusted to accommodate very young children who cannot reach the guide's arm above the elbow. The grasp can also be adjusted for older adults who need a bit more support while traveling with a guide. For example, an older adult may need to use an interlocking finger grasp for minor balance support when changing levels, such as when stepping down from a curb.

Learners with Additional Disabilities

Learners with intellectual disabilities may benefit from a combination of verbal and *physical prompts* to maintain good positioning while traveling with a guide. The steps of the techniques described in this chapter can be broken down into even smaller components as part of a *task analysis* to use for planning instruction for learners who have learning challenges. Some learners may need additional support to maintain the grasp of a guide. The guide may need to hold his arm slightly closer to his body in order to provide a sense of light pressure to remind the learner to maintain her grasp. In the event that a learner is inclined to pinch or bite the guide, consistent and positive behavioral supports should be employed and a thick jacket or slide-on pad can be worn to avoid any unnecessary injury to the guide or learner.

Learners who use a wheelchair or other support device for mobility may also benefit from travel with a guide under certain circumstances. Adaptations in the techniques can be made for individuals based on their needs and the configuration of the given environment. For example, a learner who uses a *walker* may ask the guide to hold on to the front corner edge of the walker without actively pulling it to simply provide guidance about stops, starts, and turns to be made. A learner who uses a wheelchair may invite a guide to push a manual wheelchair, but she the learner can still be actively engaged in travel decisions along a route. If a learner is able to operate a power chair with one hand and grasp a guide's arm with the other hand, she can modify techniques in that manner. However, learners must be able to fully control their power chairs to ensure that they travel at the same pace as the guide and do not inadvertently run over the guide's toe. In many instances, guides may simply provide auditory information along a route to learners using wheelchairs or power chairs (see Griffin-Shirley & Bozeman, 2016, for additional information on guide techniques with support devices).

Self-Advocacy

O&M specialists teach their learners guide techniques and their relative utility for eventual travel with familiar and unfamiliar guides who may or may not be informed as to the correct procedures and techniques to follow. Traveling with a guide should be at the discretion of the learner and some learners may need practice making it known that they do not need or want to travel with a guide in a particular instance. It is equally important that learners develop the confidence to be able to instruct others, as needed, in the correct guide techniques and be able to clearly communicate their desire to travel with or without guides. The Hines break technique described earlier in this chapter provides one method for accepting or refusing guidance when it is initiated by a potential guide. In addition, learners need to be able to identify potential guides and initiate requests to travel with other persons when they wish to do so. O&M specialists can incorporate opportunities for learners to practice enlisting the assistance of familiar and unfamiliar guides, as well as direct practice in teaching the techniques to others to boost confidence. The end goal is to ensure that learners have the tools they need for self-determination in a variety of situations they may encounter while traveling in home, school, work, or community environments.

Hand Trailing and Protective Techniques

Hand trailing and *protective techniques* have limited utility for independent travel when used alone, but the selective use of these techniques can provide learners with a means for locating objects that cannot be detected with a cane or referencing landmarks found along a wall. Use of these techniques can help to establish a line of travel that follows a given surface and to find objects that may be encountered in the environment at head, chest, or waist level. When used appropriately, these techniques can supplement key sources of information provided to learners through use of the senses, the long cane, or other orientation and mobility tools. Hand trailing and protective techniques, when used in conjunction with a long cane or other *mobility device*, can provide adequate information for a learner who is blind to travel independently.

Although hand trailing and protective techniques are provided ahead of cane techniques in the following chapter it does not signify that these techniques should be taught prior to, or exist as prerequisites to, travel with a long cane. The long cane, when needed as a mobility tool, should be introduced as early as possible.

In this text (and in the field of orientation and mobility [O&M]), the terms parallel and perpendicular are used to describe the relationship between two objects or between an individual and an object. They also refer to a learner's direction of travel in relation to features or sounds in the environment. The parallel surface is alongside the learner when the learner is aligning with it; the perpendicular surface is the one the learner is walking directly toward or walking away from.

PROTECTIVE TECHNIQUES

Upper-Hand-and-Forearm (Upper-Body) Protective Technique

Purpose: To provide the learner with protection from head- and chest-level obstacles. The technique should be used in conjunction with the long cane, as needed for surface-level preview.

	PROCEDURE AT A GLANCE
1	The arm is positioned in front of the learner, parallel to the floor and at shoulder level.
2	The forearm is bent at the elbow, forming an angle of approximately 120 degrees.
3	The palm is facing forward with fingers and thumb held together and relaxed, and fingertips extended approximately one inch beyond the opposite shoulder.

METHOD

STEP 1 The arm is positioned in front of the learner, parallel to the floor at shoulder level, with the shoulder relaxed and squared.

Rationale The position helps the learner to consistently detect objects at head and chest level that are located directly in front of her. Relaxing the shoulder helps prevent physical fatigue while using the technique and allows for even body alignment and more comfortable movement through the environment.

STEP 2 The forearm is bent at the elbow, forming an angle of approximately 120 degrees.

Rationale This angle positions the hand and loosely cupped fingertips to make initial contact with objects. When an object is located to the side of the hand, the forearm may also act as a bumper, absorbing impact and avoiding contact with the face.

Variation In the event of a known obstacle at head or face level, the learner may angle the forearm upward so that the palm extends across her face and head, keeping the arm from shoulder to elbow parallel to the floor. The learner with low vision should ensure that this alternative forearm position does not impede her use of vision.

STEP 3 The palm is facing forward with fingers and thumb held together and relaxed, and fingertips extended approximately one inch beyond the opposite shoulder.

Rationale Keeping the fingers relaxed and together, with the palm rotated and facing forward, will help to minimize potential injury to the hand and forearm as objects are contacted by the fleshy side of the hand. Extending the fingers one inch beyond the shoulder provides maximum protection to the opposite side of the upper body.

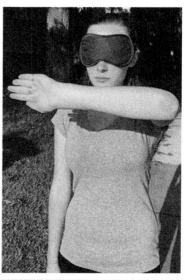

Diane L. Fazzi

CONSIDERATIONS FOR UPPER-HAND-AND-FOREARM PROTECTIVE TECHNIQUE

- Upper-hand-and-forearm protective technique, also referred to as upper-body protective technique, is more effective for providing protection from vertical obstacles at the head and chest level, such as a vertical coat rack, than obstacles that are horizontal, such as a fireplace mantle. This is because when the learner encounters a horizontal obstacle, her arm may go under or over the object.
- Upper-body protective technique may be used with either arm. It is most effective when used in conjunction with a long cane or other mobility device.
- Common errors include the elbow dropping, the arm not being held parallel to the floor, the shoulder being pulled forward, the wrist flexing outward, the hand resting too close to the face, and the palm and fingers drifting to the middle of the body instead of across to the opposite shoulder. These errors,

if not corrected, may negatively impact the learner's line of travel, advanced detection of obstacles, and overall comfort. Incorrect execution may also cause fatigue or reduce the consistency and effectiveness of the technique.

Lower-Hand-and-Forearm (Lower-Body) Protective Technique

Purpose: To provide the learner with protection from waist-level obstacles or the means with which to locate objects found at waist level. The same protection and information can also be obtained through use of the long cane. When the cane is not being used, this technique should only be utilized in familiar areas without drop-offs, surface-level changes, or obstacles.

PROCEDURE AT A GLANCE

1 The learner's upper arm, forearm, wrist, and fingers are held in a straight yet relaxed manner in front of the body, with the hand pointing downward.

2 The palm is facing the body at midline, with the fingers remaining close together, relaxed, and pointing downward.

3 The hand is extended approximately 8 to 12 inches away from the body.

METHOD

STEP 1 The learner's upper arm, forearm, wrist, and fingers are held in a straight yet relaxed manner in front of the body, with the hand pointing downward.

Rationale This position places the hand approximately waist-high and provides maximum waist-level protection when all steps are combined. The actual position of the hand varies according to the ratio of the learner's height to her arm length.

STEP 2 The palm is facing the body at midline, with the fingers remaining close together, relaxed, and pointing downward.

Rationale The midline position is intended to protect the most sensitive lower-body area. Facing the palm toward the body is a natural and comfortable position and is less likely to cause contact with others in an awkward or inappropriate manner.

Variations The learner may position her arm diagonally across the body so that the hand is placed in front of the opposite thigh. This position provides additional coverage on the opposite side of the body. Depending on the arm length and body height of the learner, the position of the lower hand and forearm will vary. Adjustments can be made accordingly. A learner may also wish to wear a waist pouch, position a shoulder bag in the front of her body, or extend an item that is already being carried, such as a notebook for a school-age learner, to provide extra coverage in this area.

STEP 3 The hand is extended approximately 8 to 12 inches away from the body.

Rationale The distance of the hand away from the body allows for bumper protection and adequate reaction time when contacting objects.

CONSIDERATIONS FOR LOWER-HAND-AND-FOREARM PROTECTIVE TECHNIQUE

- Lower-body protective technique should be used selectively, in indoor and familiar environments where waist-level obstacles are more likely to be encountered. Lower-body protective technique may be used together with upper-body protective technique.
- Lower-body protective technique can be used to locate known objects, such as chairs, table edges, doorknobs, and other items at or just below waist-level. For example, a learner may contact a table with the long cane, and then with her free hand positioned in the lower-body protective technique, extend her arm forward to locate a chair.
- Lower-body protective technique is not effective for detecting obstacles or hazards below waist-level. Use of a long cane or other mobility device is required in areas that are unfamiliar or have known drop-offs or low-lying obstacles.
- Common errors include pulling the shoulder forward, resting the hand too close to the waist, and allowing the hand to drift off to the side of the body. These errors, if not corrected, may negatively impact the learner's line of travel, advanced detection of obstacles, and overall comfort, and can reduce the technique's effectiveness.

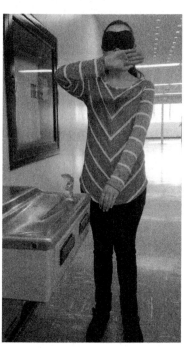

Diane L. Fazzi

Tips for Teaching Protective Techniques

Integrating Orientation

Protective techniques have limited scope for use in travel because they do not provide adequate coverage or comprehensive information to the learner during travel. The upper-body protective technique is best used in combination with the long cane or another mobility device. The lower-body protective technique is not a substitute for the long cane or alternative mobility device. These techniques, whether taught alone or in conjunction with a mobility device, can be integrated with orientation concepts and awareness. O&M specialists can reinforce orientation concepts such as the relation of objects to learners, objects to objects, and cardinal directions. When these techniques are introduced to less experienced learners, they provide a good opportunity to teach and reinforce body concepts (e.g., face, elbow, palm), laterality (e.g., right hand, left shoulder), and basic spatial concepts (e.g., in front of, parallel to, across). Each of these basic body and spatial concepts is an important foundation for understanding the relationship of the body to other people and objects in the environment, and ultimately to route travel and planning.

Sequencing

Sequencing of instruction must take into account learners' individual circumstances. Protective techniques are typically introduced after guide techniques. However, learners' immediate needs may dictate that instruction in the use of the long cane take place prior to or simultaneously with protective techniques. For example, an adult learner who has moved to a residential vision-rehabilitation center may have an immediate need to travel independently within her residence, and as a result, protective techniques combined with instruction in use of the long cane may become the first priority. There are limitations on the amount of protection afforded by using the upper- and lower-body protective techniques alone. A mobility device such as a long cane should be introduced as soon as possible for learners who will benefit from use of such a device.

Protective techniques are commonly introduced and practiced in indoor environments. Since they are used selectively by learners, it is important for O&M specialists to integrate environmental concepts into lessons to reinforce appropriate use of the techniques. For example, familiarization with the location of overhead cupboards in a classroom where they may be left open may help learners to selectively employ upper-body protective technique to avoid open cupboard doors. Ultimately, these techniques should also be used in outdoor environments; for example, locating head-level branches in neighborhoods that have overgrown hedges, avoiding collisions in stores with mid-height displays, and locating bus-stop benches along a city sidewalk.

O&M Specialist Positioning

O&M specialists should observe learners from different angles to check various aspects of hand, arm, and shoulder positions for upper- and lower-body protective techniques. While a learner is moving, the O&M specialist should be in an optimal position to view the learner's technique and monitor the upcoming environment to provide protection from potential hazards (e.g., doors swinging open into a learner's path). O&M specialists may choose to walk backward in some instances as they observe the learner's technique from the front; however, caution must be taken to avoid falls or injury from unexpected obstacles or drop-offs. O&M specialists must assume responsibility for their own safety when teaching and monitoring learner technique and travel.

Strategies for Different Populations

General Strategies

Many learners may be confused by the verbal descriptions of the protective-technique methodology. Once the general introduction and rationale for a technique are established, the O&M specialist should consider ways of providing simplified verbal directions that will aid the learner in finding correct positioning. For example, when teaching upper-body protective technique, the first verbal instruction could be: "Place the back of one hand against your opposite shoulder." This will address Steps 1 and 3 for many learners, resulting in the need for a simple *verbal prompt* to raise the elbow to shoulder height. The following instruction could be: "Now slowly bring your palm forward until I say 'Stop.'" The instructor can then describe the various aspects of correct technique positioning to the learner.

Learners Who Have Low Vision

Modeling or demonstrating upper- and lower-body protective technique may be used in conjunction with verbal instructions for learners who have low vision. O&M specialists should be careful, however, not to be overly reliant on the use of demonstration for teaching mobility techniques, which may result in learners with low vision missing important aspects of positioning and rationale provided through verbal instruction.

Age Differences

Young children may need help with isolating the movements of the shoulder, arm, and elbow to maintain a good position for the technique. For example, some children will raise the shoulder and arm simultaneously when trying to find the correct position. It may be helpful to work with physical education teachers and occupational and physical therapists to develop and practice appropriate physical exercises to help strengthen the learner's range of movements. Young children may also have difficulty finding and maintaining the proper hand position for a technique. When children have poor *proprioceptive* (perception of relative positions and movements received through the bones, joints, and skeletal system) and *kinesthetic* (awareness of movement that results from tactile, proprioceptive, and vestibular inputs) awareness, it can make refinement of a position difficult. They may initially benefit from physical supports from the instructor or fun activities like wearing a "magic glove" as a reminder to keep the hand in position during O&M lesson time.

Older adults may experience joint pain and stiffness from arthritis, making it difficult to maintain the technique for extended periods of time. Older adults who have osteoporosis and are prone to bone fractures may run the risk of injury to the hand or forearm when using these techniques, but they may also avoid injuries by achieving early detection of items found at the head, chest, and waist level. It is important to make individualized recommendations for each technique and modifications to the home to ensure that head-level obstacles are minimized.

Learners with Additional Disabilities

Learners with intellectual or learning disabilities may benefit from having the skills for protective techniques broken down into small instructional elements. Simple instructions and a combination of physical and verbal prompts will help these individuals master the skills of each technique. Some learners struggle with identifying which technique to use in specific situations and may need reminders or prompts.

Learners with physical disabilities sometimes may not benefit from the use of upper- and lower-body protective technique. Some learners may not have a free hand to use for protective techniques because they use a walker or manual wheelchair. Decisions regarding the utility of these techniques can be made on an individual basis.

Self-Advocacy

Once mature learners are familiar with protective techniques, they can determine when to use them for their benefit. They can also assert their ability to manage situations involving these techniques accordingly, explaining to others the challenges and limitations of the techniques.

HAND TRAILING

Trailing along a Wall

Purpose: To enable the learner to establish or maintain a line of travel or locate a specific landmark or destination by contacting and following a wall or other trailed surface. The technique is best used in conjunction with the long cane or other mobility device.

	PROCEDURE AT A GLANCE
1	The learner is positioned parallel to the surface to be trailed and faces the desired line of travel.
2	The arm nearest to the trailing surface is extended forward and down, with the hand at waist height.
3	The palm is slightly cupped, with the fingers and thumb relaxed and close together and the fingers pointing downward.
4	The learner moves forward, with the side of the little finger (pinkie finger) maintaining light contact with the trailing surface.
5	The learner trails the surface until a line of travel is established or a landmark or destination is located.

METHOD

STEP 1 The learner is positioned parallel to the surface to be trailed and faces the desired line of travel.

Rationale This position helps the learner to maintain orientation for the desired line of travel.

STEP 2 The arm nearest to the trailing surface is extended forward and down, with the hand at approximately waist height.

Rationale This position allows for reaction time when objects are contacted along the trailing surface. Keeping the arm extended reduces the chance of contacting a protruding object, such as a drinking fountain, with the hip or lower body.

STEP 3 The palm is slightly cupped, with the fingers and thumb relaxed and close together and the fingers pointing downward.

Rationale This hand position and light tension reduces the likelihood of jamming a finger into an object located along the wall. Positioning the hand and fingers pointing downward aligns the arm and body along the wall; otherwise, rotating the hand often results in rotation of the body toward or away from the trailing surface and results in difficulty maintaining travel parallel to the surface.

STEP 4 The learner moves forward, with the side of the little finger (pinkie finger) maintaining light contact with the trailing surface.

Rationale Light contact and positioning with the side of the little finger reduces the tendency to scrape the skin of the hand or knuckles. It also enables the learner to more easily move around objects encountered at waist height along the surface.

Variations Young children may have a tendency to use the palm of the hand with fingers facing upward to trail a continuous surface. Using the palm provides the child with maximum tactile information about the trailed surface, but has the disadvantage of leading the child to turn and face the wall rather than the desired line of travel. This variation can cause the child to become preoccupied with the wall and detract from overall orientation and interaction with others along the way. This hand position also does not promote keeping the hand extended in front, thereby increasing the likelihood of the child's body making contact with people and objects found along the way. The O&M specialist will need to make adjustments accordingly.

An alternate method is to cup the fingers, with the knuckles facing toward midline, allowing the learner to maintain contact with the surface being trailed with the fingernails. This technique should be avoided for learners who are particular about their fingernails. It also may result in the learner turning her body somewhat away from the surface being trailed.

STEP 5 The learner trails the surface until a line of travel is established or a landmark or destination is located.

Rationale This technique is intended for selective purposes and when overused can create an overreliance on maintaining contact with surfaces for travel. Traveling through open space is a more efficient form of travel. Hand trailing along a wall creates disadvantages in that the learner must travel around permanent and temporary fixtures and items found along the wall such as drinking fountains, lockers, backpacks, doors, and various displays.

Diane L. Fazzi

Crossing Open Doorways and Spaces

Purpose: To enable the learner to cross an open doorway or space using hand trailing while maintaining the desired line of travel.

PROCEDURE AT A GLANCE

1 The learner detects the opening and maintains the forward *extension* of the trailing hand.

2 When crossing the open space, the learner brings the opposite arm into upper-body protective technique to reach across the open space to assist in locating the opposing wall or doorframe and to protect her head and shoulder area from inadvertent contact with the doorframe or other object.

3 Once the opposite side of the doorway or open space is located, the learner may resume hand trailing and the line of travel.

METHOD

STEP 1 The learner detects the opening while maintaining the forward extension of the trailing hand.

Rationale Maintaining forward extension of the trailing hand while preparing to cross the opening helps the learner to keep the intended line of travel.

STEP 2 When crossing the open space, the learner brings the opposite (non-trailing) arm into upper-body protective technique to reach across the open space to locate and contact the opposing wall or doorframe and to protect her head and shoulder area from inadvertent contact with the doorframe or other object. The learner will need to extend the upper forearm fully across the body or turn slightly inward to ensure contact with the opposite side.

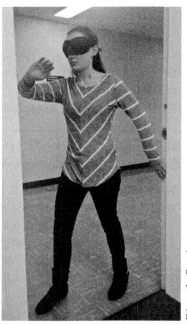

Rationale The upper-hand-and-forearm protective technique, in its extended position, increases the likelihood of making contact with the opposite side of the open space, such as a doorframe, and provides protection for the learner's head and shoulders.

Variation In narrow doorways and openings, the learner can maintain contact with the doorframe with the trailing hand until the opposite side is reached (Jacobson, 2013).

Diane L. Fazzi

STEP 3 Once the opposite side of the doorway or open space is located, the learner may resume hand trailing and the line of travel.

Rationale The learner can continue with the hand-trailing technique to maintain the line of travel or until the desired landmark or location is reached.

DIRECTION TAKING
(FROM WALLS OR SURFACES)

Squaring Off (Perpendicular Surface Alignment)

Purpose: To enable the learner to use a perpendicular surface to establish a straight line of travel for crossing a hallway or other open space. This

PROCEDURE AT A GLANCE

1 The learner aligns her back, shoulders, or heels against a straight surface or object.

2 Using the perpendicular surface as a point of reference, the learner projects a straight line of travel from the midline into the open space and walks forward using the upper- or lower-body protective technique, in conjunction with a long cane whenever possible.

approach can be used while traveling with the long cane or while using upper- and lower-body protective techniques in a familiar indoor environment.

METHOD

STEP 1 The learner positions two symmetrical body parts, typically the back, shoulders, or heels, against a straight perpendicular surface or object.

Rationale This position helps the learner to make sure that she is properly aligned before moving forward. Two points of the body should be used against the surface to ensure correct alignment. Curved or irregular surfaces are not recommended for the squaring-off technique.

Variation The learner may also align herself perpendicular to an underfoot cue such as a curb or the edge of a carpet using her toes or the balls of the feet.

STEP 2 Using the perpendicular surface as a point of reference, the learner projects a straight line of travel from the midline into the open space and walks forward using the upper- or lower-body protective technique, in conjunction with the long cane whenever possible.

Rationale The combination of tactile information and the learner's cognitive projection of a straight line extending from the midline promotes a straight line of travel and helps to reduce veering.

Parallel Alignment

Purpose: To enable the learner to use a parallel surface to establish a straight line of travel. This approach can be used in conjunction with a long cane or upper- or lower-body protective technique in a familiar indoor environment.

> **PROCEDURE AT A GLANCE**
> 1 The learner uses one arm or shoulder to position herself parallel to a straight surface or object.
> 2 Using the parallel surface as a point of reference, the learner projects a straight line of travel from the midline into the open space and walks forward using the upper- or lower-body protective technique, in conjunction with a long cane whenever possible.

METHOD

STEP 1 The learner positions herself parallel to a straight surface or object. The arm or shoulder, and extension of the cane, closest to the surface can be used to establish alignment.

Rationale This position helps the learner to make sure that she is aligned before moving forward. Curved or irregular surfaces are not recommended for this alignment technique.

STEP 2 Using the parallel surface as a point of reference, the learner projects a straight line of travel from the midline, running parallel to the surface, into the open space and walks forward using the upper- or lower-body protective technique, in conjunction with a long cane whenever possible.

Rationale The combination of tactile information and the learner's cognitive projection of a straight line extending from the midline promotes a straight line of travel and helps to reduce veering.

Variations The learner can also establish parallel alignment with a surface while trailing and move slightly away from the surface while maintaining the travel line. Some learners may need to make a very small angle back toward the trailed surface to make sure that they do not drift too far into the hallway. O&M specialists should gauge the need to do so on an individualized basis.

CONSIDERATIONS FOR DIRECTION TAKING

- *Direction taking* from a wall or other travel surface is a technique learners can incorporate into their travel skill set. This technique should be used in conjunction with an appropriate mobility device.
- Learners will use sound sources to assist with alignment, such as the sound of other people walking, sound shadows, or echolocation to obtain auditory feedback to trail a wall or surface in indoor and outdoor environments.
- Learners who have low vision will use visual skills and cues for direction taking in indoor and outdoor environments.

Tips for Teaching Hand Trailing and Direction-Taking Techniques

Integrating Orientation

One of the basic purposes of hand trailing is to enable learners to establish and maintain a line of travel to a desired location. When learners analyze a new environment in which they expect to travel frequently, hand trailing can help build concepts about the relationship of one object to another along a hallway. Hand trailing can be used to discover the sequence of various landmarks along a hallway, which the O&M specialist can reinforce by asking the learner to list the order of the landmarks along the wall in reverse order. Perpendicular and parallel direction taking can support the development and understanding of route shapes, such as I-shape, L-Shape, and U-shaped routes. Route shapes can be introduced along with these skills to help keep learners focused on their orientation while moving.

Sequencing

While hand-trailing and direction-taking skills are often introduced at the beginning of an O&M training program, spending too much time on these skills, which keep learners in frequent contact with travel surfaces, can contribute to overreliance on such contact in the future. The long cane or alternative mobility device, as needed, should be introduced as early as possible to offer learners a tool that provides greater information about the travel environment and allows them to travel with comfort in open spaces.

O&M Specialist Positioning

The O&M specialist can be positioned in a variety of locations when teaching and monitoring these basic skills, depending on the learner and the environment. From different angles (e.g., in front of, behind, or alongside the learner) the O&M specialist can monitor the learner's hand and arm position while anticipating any upcoming obstacles that may present challenges.

Strategies for Different Populations

General Strategies

While hand trailing and direction taking using a wall or surface can be helpful to learners in certain situations, wherever possible, learners should be taught to use auditory skills and information to enhance their travel. Auditory skills, such as echolocation, can be used to follow a wall or consistent surface. When O&M specialists develop and encourage the use of these skills, learners are better able to maintain a straight line of travel, detect openings such as doorways and hallways, and improve environmental orientation without dependence on contacting walls and other surfaces. O&M specialists can build this training into the program early on so that learners can practice in simple environments while building skills for later travel in more complex environments.

Learners Who Have Low Vision

The decision to teach these techniques to learners who have low vision should be based on an individualized O&M assessment. Some learners who require more tactile input in dim lighting conditions may benefit from these techniques. For example, a learner may benefit from using hand trailing to locate the bathroom in the middle of the night. If there is a need for these techniques for learners who have low vision, they can be taught quickly through visual modeling in good lighting conditions and practiced under the same lighting conditions. Once the techniques are developed, they can be practiced and then applied with confidence in dim lighting situations.

Age Differences

Some older adults may have thinner skin that bruises and scrapes more easily due to various medications, such as blood thinners. For these learners, hand-trailing techniques may only be warranted in familiar environments that are known to be free of rough surfaces or unexpected obstacles.

Young children trailing a wall may not be visible to others looking down from higher-positioned windows on doors, and may be at greater risk from fast-opening doors. Also, as noted previously, when children turn toward a trailing surface, it slows down their rate of travel.

Learners with Additional Disabilities

Learners with intellectual or learning disabilities may learn to use hand-trailing or direction-taking techniques best when the skills are broken down into small instructional elements. O&M specialists should use simple instructions and a combination of physical and verbal prompts until the skills are mastered. Some learners may struggle with identifying when to use these techniques and may need reminders or prompts in appropriate situations.

Learners who use wheelchairs, scooters, or walkers for mobility purposes may find it cumbersome to reach the wall for purposes of hand trailing and are likely to need both hands to fully operate or manage their mobility devices. O&M specialists can work with physical therapists to design functional modifications such as *curb feelers* (attachments to wheelchairs that enable individuals to maintain tactile contact with a wall or other surface while moving) to provide alternative means for trailing walls or surfaces. Decisions regarding the utility of these techniques can be made on an individualized basis.

Self-Advocacy

Once experienced learners are familiar with the hand-trailing and direction-taking techniques, they can determine when to use the techniques to their benefit. They can also assert their own ability to manage situations involving these techniques accordingly, explaining to others the purposes of their use.

CHAPTER

5

Cane Techniques

The long cane continues to be the primary mobility device used by individuals with visual impairments for travel across a wide range of home, school, work, and community environments. The long cane provides the individual with *object* and *surface preview* with advanced tactile and reflective auditory information about the environment, including changes in texture, density, slope, and level of walking surfaces, and the presence or absence of obstacles, protrusions, and openings in the pathway. Objects at waist height or lower directly in front of or to the side of the traveler can be detected by the long cane in advance of reaching the object.

Changes in the walking surface can be detected through the friction or force generated between the cane tip and the surface as the cane makes contact with or slides continuously across the surface. This information is transmitted through the cane shaft to the learner's hand for interpretation based on her perceptual abilities and understanding of the travel environment. For example, while traveling on a sidewalk in a residential community in which many driveways are formed with hard-packed soil, the learner may interpret a change in tactile information received through the cane when it taps on her right side as meaning that she is positioned very close to a driveway while her feet remain on the sidewalk. When the long cane is positioned and used in a consistent manner, changes in slope or level of the walking surface may be detected by the learner as a slight lowering of the wrist or hand position.

The long cane also provides reflective auditory details about surroundings, such as height of ceilings, density of wall surfaces, presence or absence of hedges, fences, and other environmental features in close proximity to the individual. Sounds emitted either from the tapping or sliding of the cane tip across surfaces are reflected differently in closed versus open areas (e.g., a narrow hallway with low ceilings versus an open lobby area in a multi-floor building), or against dense versus less dense surfaces (e.g., cement wall versus a hedge).

Different cane techniques, which will be described in detail in this chapter, result in different amounts and types of sensory information for the learner. (See Long & Giudice, 2010, and Guth, Rieser, & Ashmead, 2010, for a thorough review of perception, movement, and travel for individuals with visual impairments.)

Cane Basics

Variations in Long Canes

A variety of materials have been incorporated into the construction of long canes for use by individuals who are blind or who have low vision. The goal is to provide a tool that conducts vibratory, tactile, and auditory information to the traveler in advance, providing the learner with an opportunity to react and determine next steps in the environment. Long canes are also designed to increase visibility for the traveler during both day and night travel.

Rigid canes and a wide variety of folding and collapsing versions of the long cane are available. Folding canes vary according to how many pieces the cane folds into, resulting in different sizes for storage. The joints between the pieces of the shaft also vary and can be made of metal, plastic, or rubber materials. While long canes typically incorporate white reflective tape, with red tape near the bottom of the shaft, additional colors have been used in some countries to signify that an individual has low vision but is not considered legally blind. The reflective tape used on many long canes is illuminated by headlights at night. Some canes, which are typically thinner and lighter weight, are referred to as identification canes. These are generally used by individuals who have low vision to identify themselves as having a visual impairment.

Parts of the Long Cane

Despite the unique designs of various long canes, all styles have three common elements: a *grip* to grasp the cane, a long *shaft* comprising the main body, and the *tip* at the end of the cane, which typically remains in regular contact with the walking surface. Some canes also have an elastic strap for hanging on a hook or for holding the joints of a folding cane together when folded and not in use. Perhaps less common are canes with a crook, which is either a curved or square extension found just above the grip. Learners may use a crook to hang a rigid cane from a hook. Some canes also come equipped with various electronic devices for enhanced obstacle detection or orientation, but such devices are not covered in this book. (See Smith & Penrod, 2010, for additional resources related to long canes and electronic travel and orientation devices.)

Cane Grip

The most common cane grip is similar to the grip found on a golf club. The grip is made of rubber and has a flat edge on one side. The rubber material reduces slippage. The grip is typically black, but other colors, such as blue, orange, green, or pink, are also available. (These colorful models are usually marketed to teens and young adults.) Other types of grips are made from synthetic leather-like material, nylon, or plastic, and may be cylindrical in shape to allow the grip to easily roll back and forth in the palm of the hand. Some canes are built without a defined grip.

Cane Shaft

The length of the cane shaft is carefully selected and recommended based on an individual's height, stride length, walking pace, reaction time, and coverage needs. Generally, the length of the cane runs from a minimum height of about 2 inches above the sternum to a maximum height at the individual's eyebrow.

There are varied opinions in the field of orientation and mobility (O&M) as to the utility of varied cane lengths. Rodgers and Wall Emerson (2005) found that individuals using a cane length slightly taller than the height of the sternum were significantly more reliable in detecting drop-offs than those that used shorter or longer canes. More research in this area is needed and continues to be conducted. O&M specialists who remain up-to-date on the most current research will be able to assist learners with cane selection based on evidence-based practices well into the future.

The selection of cane length is typically made by the O&M specialist and learner together as they examine the pros and cons of various heights and make a selection based on sound rationale. The rationale for recommending a cane that is about 2 inches above the sternum (also sized by easily fitting under the armpit) is that the path preview provided by the cane will be approximately one step in front of the learner as she walks. While the cane is not previewing the exact next step of the learner, it provides immediate, ongoing information about pathway obstacles and terrain changes with adequate time for most learners to adjust their direction or speed of travel, so they may stop as needed. The rationale for a longer cane length is that it provides advanced preview that may be two steps or more in front of the learner and increased reaction time to upcoming environmental features. It can also reinforce a faster walking pace—which may increase with confidence and experience—exhibited by some learners (Willoughby & Monthei, 1998). A longer cane length may require more finesse in crowded areas. Ultimately, it is important that the learner not step beyond the area previewed and that the cane provide the learner with ample advance notice to perceive and interpret the information previewed so she can safely navigate the environment with consistency and confidence. Once a cane length is selected, it may be adjusted according to changes in the individual's travel needs.

The hollow shaft is commonly made of aluminum alloy, composites, fiberglass, or graphite. Graphite is slightly more expensive and slightly lighter in weight than aluminum or composites, but heavier than fiberglass. These different materials vary in flexibility and have different conductive and sound qualities. The shaft is commonly covered with white reflective tape and red tape at the bottom. While the white shaft with red tape at the bottom is most commonly used in North America, some canes designed as identification tools for individuals who have low vision may come in other colors, such as green (Argentina). Reflective tape can also be found in black, yellow, and other colors. Identification canes are typically shorter and about one-third lighter in weight. In Great Britain, two red strips at the bottom indicate that the individual is deafblind.

Long canes come in both rigid one-piece models and folding or telescoping models. Folding canes typically come in four, five, or six sections. The increased number of folding sections results in a smaller folding size, but may lead to decreased durability and conductivity. The sections are held together by a double elastic cord inside the shaft and the individual sections have joints that may be made of plastic, aluminum with rubber finger guards, or O-rings that fit firmly together for use. Other canes collapse in a telescoping manner, similar to a large spyglass commonly depicted in pirate movies, where each section fits and slides within another as the cane is collapsed.

Cane Tip

A variety of shapes, sizes, and materials have been used for the tip of the long cane. The tip selection is made by the instructor and the learner, based on preference, ability, and the types of environments the learner is most likely to encounter. A metal glider (disc-type) tip is commonly used with some rigid canes and may provide auditory input regarding the travel surface. For example, in quiet, indoor areas, the learner can distinguish the difference in sound of linoleum laid on a concrete base versus a wooden floor installed on a plywood subfloor. Metal glider tips are very durable.

Long-wearing nylon tips in the shape of an elongated cylinder with a half-inch diameter (sometimes referred to as a pencil or chalk tip) or a wider "marshmallow" shape (a cylinder with a 1.25-inch diameter and a beveled end) come in models that connect to the internal elastic cord with an internal hook, or

slip on over the shaft. The nylon tips will wear down after consistent use and need to be replaced periodically. Some cane tips combine the nylon cylinder with a metal glide to take advantage of the benefits of both materials for the traveler, using the feel of the nylon tip and the smooth glide of the metal tip.

Rubber ball and nylon roller tips—2 to 3 inches in diameter and sometimes designed with a flat bottom—have become very popular with learners and instructors to ease the movement of the cane from side to side and eliminate the cane tip from getting stuck in uneven surfaces such as broken sidewalks or seams between concrete slabs. However, it can be more difficult to maintain a defined and consistent arc with these rolling tips because the rolling motion makes it more difficult to stop at a specific spot. The roller-tip gliding motion can also cause the learner to miss some of the subtleties on the walking surface, such as differences in pavement or minor changes in elevation.

Long canes designed for travel in areas with tall grass, or unpaved, wooded, or rugged terrain may have a curved shaft—with or without a nylon tip at the end of the cane—which helps the cane move more easily across uneven surfaces. The original design for this type of cane was the Bundu Basher, which had a U-shaped half-inch nylon tip (Smith & Penrod, 2010, p. 245).

With further research and the creation of new materials, the long cane will undoubtedly continue to evolve, with improved conductivity, durability, ergonomics, style, and fashion. Ambrose-Zaken (2005) found that many adults who traveled with a cane saw the purpose of having a variety of canes depending on the travel environment or social situation. Regardless of the design, the long cane should be responsive to the abilities of the individual traveler and the demands of the travel environment.

Proper Care of the Long Cane

In general, the long cane is a low-maintenance tool. It can be wiped clean with a soft damp cloth after traveling in a wet or muddy area. Learners may need to be reminded that the long cane is not constructed to support weight or balance and should be encouraged not to lean on the cane with their full body weight. Other learners may need reminders to avoid using the long cane for pointing, as swinging the cane in the air may result in injury to other pedestrians or run the risk of getting it stuck in a door or gate. Younger learners and their class-mates may need to be taught that the long cane is not to be used as a simulated sword or stick for play. Even with the best care, long canes can break and it is advisable to have a spare one available.

Learners may need to replace elastic straps when they break or nylon tips when they wear down. Roller tips may need regular cleaning, as hair and other debris can catch in the ball-bearing section. Aluminum joints may incur small dents with heavy use, making it harder to fold and unfold the cane. The reflective tape may also begin to wear down and peel over time. Learners can be taught to do simple repairs on the long cane, but with an average cost of less than forty dollars, they may simply prefer to replace worn canes. On junior-high or high-school campuses, metal-shop classes may be enlisted to repair broken or worn canes.

Cane Storage

Whether the learner uses a folding or rigid long cane, she will need to plan for *cane storage* in a variety of situations. For the most part, individuals who use a folding cane will opt to fold the cane while not in use and store it in a briefcase, purse, or personal travel bag, or in a cane holder worn attached to a belt much like a cell-phone case attaches to a belt. The folded cane can also be placed on a table or counter surface immediately in front of its owner or next to or under a seat for quick access; however, storing a cane on a table surface where food may be served is not advisable because the cane tip has come in contact with a variety of walking surfaces.

A rigid cane may be placed vertically against the wall in an office space, or securely propped against a bookshelf, cabinet, or corner of a room if the individual does not wish to use the cane to navigate the familiar room. For seating, the long cane can be tucked against the parallel edge of a couch, auditorium seat, or a restaurant booth, perpendicular to the individual's feet. Lightly resting a foot on the cane may help to keep track of it while people are moving through the seating area. The best location for placement of the cane depends on the size and layout of the seating arrangement and the furniture present.

For school-age learners, the folding or rigid cane may be stored in the same place as other personal items in the classroom, such as in a personal cubby space, hung by the loop on a coat rack, or placed vertically against a bookshelf, cabinet, or corner near the door. In classrooms in which there are two or more cane users, some learners enjoy decorating their canes by attaching distinctive key chains or charms to the loop or by using paint or stickers to distinguish one cane from another. When learners have assigned seating in the classroom, the folding cane can be stored in or on top of the desk depending on space availability. A rigid cane can be placed underneath the seat either parallel or perpendicular to the learner's feet depending on the size, shape, and layout of the desks and rows in the classroom. Some learners will opt to place the cane underfoot to ensure constant contact with the cane. Easy access to the cane is an important factor to consider, as is keeping the cane out of high-traffic areas. In other seating arrangements, such as those for a limited amount of time like public transportation, the learner may choose to hold the cane vertically between or beside her legs so that it is ready for use when the bus or train approaches her stop or station.

Cane Techniques

There are a number and variety of cane techniques. Some are the result of regional differences, university of preparation, evidence-based practices, or anecdotal experience. Several authors have described the various techniques for using the cane to travel in a variety of environments and formats (see Hill & Ponder, 1976; Jacobson, 1993, 2013; LaGrow, 2010; LaGrow & Long, 2011; LaGrow & Weessies, 1994; Pogrund et al., 2012).

Travel with a long cane is both a motor and a cognitive process. The motor aspects include the physical execution of the technique through proper manipulation of the cane and coordination for walking, negotiating doors, climbing stairs, and other motor tasks. Building stamina will help the learner maintain good position and technique in a variety of environments. The cognitive aspects of travel with a long cane include interpreting auditory and tactile feedback obtained from the cane while moving through the environment, maintaining awareness of surroundings and general orientation, and knowing when to use which technique based on that awareness. Mastery of the motor aspects of cane techniques will help learners to focus on the cognitive aspects of travel.

O&M specialists may notice that some learners' cane techniques will deteriorate (e.g., uneven arc width or hand drifting away from center) once they begin to apply the technique in a new or more complex environment, especially in environments with uneven or rough surfaces. It may be beneficial to plan for skill practice and review sessions in new environments prior to adding on new travel elements in order to refine the technique or make adjustments.

DIAGONAL CANE TECHNIQUE

Grasps and Positioning for the Diagonal Cane Technique

Purpose: To enable the learner to travel independently in a familiar indoor environment using the long cane to gather sensory information and provide some degree of lower-body protection, but without reliable drop-off detection.

PROCEDURE AT A GLANCE

1 The hand is positioned on the grip so that the index finger is extended along the flat edge of the grip, the thumb is up, and the remaining fingers are *flexed* around the grip so that the grip rests comfortably against the palm of the hand (index finger grasp).

2 The upper arm and forearm are slightly extended, with the grip hand positioned 10 to 12 inches in front of the hip and the hand positioned waist high.

3 The forearm and wrist are rotated together so that the back of the hand is facing upward and the palm of the hand is facing the ground.

4 With a slight bend in the elbow, the cane shaft is angled diagonally across the front of the body.

5 The cane tip lightly rests on the ground and across the body so that it is 1 to 2 inches beyond the width of the opposite shoulder and about 2.5 feet in front of the learner.

METHOD

STEP 1 The hand is positioned on the grip so that the index finger is extended along the flat edge of the grip, the thumb is up, and the remaining fingers are flexed around the grip so that the grip rests comfortably against the palm of the hand (index finger grasp). Many learners are able to grasp the cane in this position with either the dominant or nondominant hand as necessary for the learner or travel environment.

Rationale While a variety of grasps can be effectively used for the diagonal cane technique, an advantage of the index finger grasp is that the same grasp can be used for multiple cane techniques and makes switching from one technique to another a smooth transition for learners.

Variations A variety of grasps for use with the diagonal cane technique have been successfully used, including the thumb and pencil grasps described here. O&M specialists and learners can select the grasp to use with the technique that best meets the learner's ability and travel environments.

Thumb Grasp

- The thumb is positioned on the flat edge of the grip and the fingers are flexed around the grip. The thumb is extended so that it points down the shaft.
- The upper arm and forearm are extended, with the grip hand positioned 10 to 12 inches in front of the hip, making sure that the same side shoulder does not shift forward and cause the learner to

veer, or divert from the intended line of travel, while walking forward. (Some instructors may choose to have the learner position the upper arm and forearm in a more relaxed position at or near the hip. In doing so, the cane will not provide as much protection from waist-level obstacles and the cane may need to be a longer length to provide greater reaction time to changes detected by the cane tip.)

- The forearm and wrist are rotated inward so that the back of the hand is facing upward and is angled toward the learner.

Rationale One advantage of using the thumb grasp is that positioning the thumb on the flat edge gives learners firm control of the cane while walking in open spaces. The thumb placement allows the learner to apply pressure to keep the cane tip out in front, while keeping the position of the cane shaft stable.

Pencil Grasp

- The pencil grasp can also be used with the diagonal cane technique. The learner holds the cane in a manner similar to that of a pencil, with the cane grip resting between the middle and index fingers and the thumb applying light pressure to keep the grasp firm and the cane steady.
- The wrist is maintained in a relaxed manner with the back of the hand facing away from the body.

Rationale An advantage of the pencil grasp is that the positioning is more relaxed and comfortable for some learners. Since there is less pressure exerted on the cane, the tip will tend to move more easily around obstacles, which works very well in congested areas as the tip is less likely to be entangled in other people's feet or stuck against obstacles or floor-surface changes. (For these same reasons, this grasp can be effective when traveling with a guide.) Learners can adjust the grasp further down the cane shaft as needed.

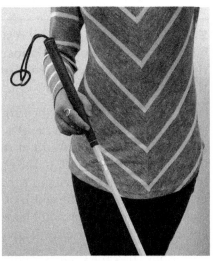

Diane L. Fazzi

STEP 2 The upper arm and forearm are slightly extended, with the grip hand positioned 10 to 12 inches in front of the hip, making sure that the same side shoulder does not shift forward and cause the learner to veer while walking forward. The hand is positioned waist high.

Rationale The position of the arm extends the cane to a further point that provides the learner with advanced information and reaction time. The hand is held waist high so that once the cane is positioned diagonally it will provide contact with objects in front of the learner that are at waist height or lower.

Variations In some variations of the diagonal cane technique the arm may be positioned more comfortably at the learner's side. In this position, the cane will provide less detection of waist-level objects in the travel path and, because it is not extended, will reduce reaction time when the travel path changes. A longer length can increase the advanced preview and reaction time. In congested areas, the learner may bring the cane tip in, closer to midline, and the length of the cane can be further shortened by "choking up" (grasping the cane lower along the grip or even the shaft as needed).

STEP 3 The forearm and wrist are rotated together so that the back of the hand is facing upward and the palm of the hand is facing the ground. (The pencil-grasp variation does not require the same rotation of the forearm and wrist for the diagonal cane technique.)

Rationale The forearm and wrist rotate in unison, which many learners find more comfortable for extended use of the diagonal cane technique because it does not require the learner to maintain a flexed position of the wrist throughout the use of the technique.

STEP 4 With a slight bend in the elbow, the cane shaft is angled diagonally across the front of the body. When viewed from the front, the diagonal line is formed from the point at which the learner grasps the cane to the point at which the cane tip rests on the floor.

Rationale The slight bend in the elbow enables the learner to maintain the diagonal position across the body without resting the arm on the side of the body. The position of the cane across the learner's body provides information about objects at waist level or lower that are located directly in the travel path, so that the learner may make contact and navigate around them as needed.

Variation Some learners may wish to rest the arm on the side of the body during use of the diagonal cane technique. The diagonal position of the cane across the learner's body, while helpful in locating obstructions, may cause difficulty in maneuvering the cane when the cane tip sticks in uneven surfaces because the arm is less free to move.

STEP 5 The cane tip lightly rests on the ground and across the body so that it is 1 to 2 inches beyond the width of the opposite shoulder and about 2.5 feet in front of the learner. The cane tip should be further in front of the body than the already extended hand that is grasping the cane.

Rationale Lightly resting the cane tip on the ground provides the learner with constant information about lower obstacles and travel surfaces while reducing potential for the tip sticking in uneven surfaces. The tip is positioned forward of the grip hand to provide maximum advanced preview and 1 to 2 inches beyond the width of the opposite shoulder to provide a good diagonal line that can serve as a bumper for lower obstacles in the learner's path of travel. However, because the tip of the cane remains in a position beyond the width of the learner's travel path, it does not provide adequate information about drop-offs or slope and texture changes and should therefore be used only in familiar indoor environments that are free from drop-offs.

Variation The cane tip may be lifted about an inch off the floor, with the learner touching it down every few steps. This approach may decrease the risk of getting the tip stuck in uneven surfaces. However, this variation is most appropriate for individuals who have low vision because it does not provide constant information about the travel surface. A more defined technique is the *verification cane technique*, which is described later in this chapter. This technique is used only by individuals who have low vision as it is used in conjunction with systematic use of visual skills for travel in the environment.

Changing Hands and Grasps with the Diagonal Cane Technique

Purpose: To enable the learner to shift the cane from one hand to the other or from one grasp to another while traveling. (It can also be used with other cane techniques described later in this chapter.)

PROCEDURE AT A GLANCE

1 The learner moves the palms of both hands toward the center of the body, facing each other, in order to switch the cane from one hand to the other.

2 The learner grasps the cane with the opposite hand, resuming the grasp of choice.

3 To change grasps in the same hand, the learner may rotate her wrist, change finger positions, or use the free hand to help reposition from one grasp to another.

4 The cane tip remains on the ground during the switch from one hand to the other and moves to the front of the opposite shoulder as the angle of the cane shaft shifts from one side to the other.

METHOD

STEP 1 The learner moves the palms of both hands toward the center of the body, facing each other, in order to switch the cane from one hand to the other.

Rationale Moving the hands toward one another near the center of the body provides a smooth and natural movement for many learners and may not require much instruction.

STEP 2 The learner grasps the cane with the opposite hand, resuming the grasp of choice and rotating the wrist appropriately if using the index finger or thumb grasp, and extending the arm into the proper position for the diagonal cane technique.

Rationale The rotation of the wrist is determined by the learner's preferred grasp. Rotation of the wrist is required for the index finger or thumb grasp, but not for the pencil grasp.

STEP 3 To change grasps in the same hand, the learner may rotate her wrist, change finger positions, or use the free hand to help reposition the cane from one grasp to another. Depending on the manual dexterity of the learner, the free hand can be used to assist in repositioning the cane into the new grasp.

Rationale Using the free hand to reposition the grasp ensures that the cane is not dropped during the switch from one grasp to another.

STEP 4 The cane tip remains on the ground during the switch from one hand to the other and moves to the front of the opposite shoulder as the angle of the cane shaft shifts from one side to the other.

Rationale Keeping the cane tip out in front during the switch provides continuous information about the ground surface and makes it easier to assume the diagonal position desired once the switch of hands or grasps has been completed.

Detecting and Moving around Obstacles

Purpose: To enable the learner to maneuver around obstacles detected by the cane without losing the line of direction.

PROCEDURE AT A GLANCE

1 After contacting the object, the cane tip is anchored against the object.

2 The learner stops and determines the intended next steps to either explore the object or move around it.

3 To explore the object, the learner rotates her hand (outward or inward) until the cane is positioned more vertically, allowing the learner to walk closer to the object that is directly in front of her.

4 To move around the object the learner notes its location, selects and clears a space to the right or left of the object, and then continues to travel, reestablishing the desired line of travel as soon as possible.

METHOD

STEP 1 After contacting the object, the cane tip is anchored against the object. To anchor the cane, slight pressure is applied to the cane to keep it stationary against the contacted surface. Initially, the learner may also need to make sure that she does not move her feet upon contact with the object until she has determined its relative location and her next planned steps.

Rationale The cane tip is anchored or held firmly against the object to serve as a reference point as the learner approaches the obstacle. The learner should stand still until the relative location of the object is determined. The location of the object relative to her position changes when the learner continues to move forward or around the object. If the learner is still working on developing orientation skills, it will be beneficial to maintain a stationary position until the desired path of travel is determined.

STEP 2 The learner stops and determines the intended next steps to either explore the object or move around it.

Rationale While an experienced traveler may not need to come to a full stop, a moment of pause allows the learner to process the information before making the decision to explore or move around the object. Not taking the time to think about the environment may result in unnecessary movements and steps that may interfere with efficient travel and orientation.

STEP 3 To explore the object, the learner rotates her hand (outward or inward) until the cane is positioned more vertically, allowing the learner to walk forward along the same line to approach the object that is directly in front of her. The vertically positioned cane is then pressed up against the object to measure its height and then moved in a horizontal fashion from left to right to measure the width of the object. The learner determines whether further exploration of the object by hand is desired. If so, the learner may use a modified upper-hand-and-forearm protective technique (see Chapter 4) to locate the object. The learner may also use her foot to quickly explore the bottom portion of the object.

Rationale The rotation of the learner's hand enables the learner to maintain a straight line of travel and move directly toward the obstacle without having to reposition the cane. The vertical position of the cane against the object gives the learner information about the relative height of the obstacle in her path. If further exploration of the object is desired, the cane provides a reference point for the location, surface material, and relative height of the object. The modified upper-hand-and-forearm protective technique provides the learner with an approach that will help to detect face-level protrusions and prepares her for contact with the obstacle, whether at or below her face.

Variation Switching to the pencil grasp may make it easier to explore the object because the cane is more flexible in that position.

STEP 4 To move around the object the learner notes its location, selects and clears a space to the right or left of the object, and then continues to travel, reestablishing the desired line of travel as soon as possible. The learner applies her understanding of the environment to select the side that is most likely to be clear for continued travel. For example, when traveling on the right side of the hallway a learner may encounter an object in her path and assume that there will be more clear space to the left of the object. If the space is not clear, then the learner would check the space on the right to see if there is enough room to pass between the object and the wall on the right side of the hallway.

Rationale Most of the time the learner will simply want to maneuver around objects in her path unless she is looking for a landmark or is disoriented and needs information about her current location. The learner remains stationary until a clear path is found, otherwise the learner may walk into the object while attempting to locate the clear area and the relative location of the object will change as a reference point for orientation.

Trailing with Diagonal Cane Technique

Purpose: To enable the learner to verify a location, establish a straight line of travel, or locate a desired destination or landmark along a wall or solid indoor surface.

PROCEDURE AT A GLANCE

1	The learner faces the desired line of travel and aligns herself parallel and close to the surface to be trailed.
2	The cane is held using the diagonal cane technique in the hand opposite the surface being trailed.
3	The cane tip lightly contacts the point where the floor and the wall (or trailed surface) meet.
4	The learner moves forward while maintaining a body position parallel and close to the trailed surface, negotiating obstacles and open spaces as needed.

METHOD

STEP 1 The learner faces the desired line of travel and aligns herself parallel and close to the surface to be trailed. The shoulder and hip can be used as a reference point for parallel alignment. While physical contact with the wall during trailing while using a cane is not recommended, when starting out, a learner may choose to contact the wall with her arm to establish and visualize the initial alignment.

Rationale By using parallel alignment and positioning herself somewhat close to the surface to be trailed, the learner can establish a straight line of travel and make sure that the diagonal position of the cane remains across and in front of her body.

STEP 2 The cane is held using the diagonal cane technique in the hand opposite the surface being trailed (e.g., in the left hand when walking on the right side of the hallway or travel area).

Rationale The cane should be positioned across and in front of the body to detect obstacles and maintain a consistent diagonal position. Learners should plan to travel on the side of the hallway that is typical for the region or nation so that they are going with the flow of pedestrian traffic. While traveling on the right side of the hallway, the learner must be able to manage the cane in the left hand so that the tip can be placed against the surface to be trailed on the right side. If it is common to travel on the left side, then the positioning should be reversed.

Variation When searching for a doorway or object on the opposite side of a hallway, the learner may need to travel for a short distance on the "wrong" side of the hallway.

STEP 3 The cane tip lightly contacts the point where the floor and the wall (or trailed surface) meet, which is approximately 2.5 feet in front of the learner's body.

Rationale The light touch of the cane tip enables the learner to keep the tip moving forward and keep it free to easily adjust to small changes in the surface area. If the learner applies too much pressure, then the tip may get stuck against a floorboard, causing the learner to walk next to or overstep the tip of the cane.

Variation Keeping the cane tip about 1 inch off the ground while trailing a wall surface can help the learner to avoid missing the detection of openings such as doorways. When the cane tip is maintained on the floor it will contact threshold plates—protrusions commonly installed under door sills to delineate adjacent floor surfaces—which may confuse the learner about the continuation of the wall surface in the absence of other clues.

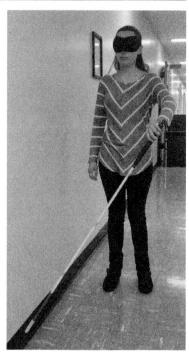

Diane L. Fazzi

STEP 4 The learner moves forward while maintaining the cane position in front of the body and positioning the body parallel and close to the trailed surface, negotiating obstacles and open spaces as needed (see the previous section on Detecting and Moving around Obstacles).

Rationale Using parallel alignment and positioning the body close to the surface to be trailed, the learner can establish a straight line of travel and make sure that the diagonal position of the cane remains across and in front of her body.

CONSIDERATIONS FOR THE DIAGONAL CANE TECHNIQUE

■ The diagonal cane technique is an effective bumper in some, but not all, circumstances. For example, if the learner is holding the cane in the right hand and the tip is aligned in front of the left shoulder area, it would likely provide a bumper for a small trash can 12 inches in height if encountered on the left side, but not for a similar trash can found directly in front of or on the right side of the learner. No protection for objects above waist level is provided by this technique. Some learners may selectively combine the use of upper-body protective techniques in anticipation of cabinet areas or other known protrusions from the upper wall.

■ Similar to the bumper function, the diagonal cane technique does provide a probe into the environment and can help the learner to recognize some changes in terrain, such as a change in walking surface, but it is limited to probing only to the side of the learner where the tip is positioned, not where the learner is stepping.

■ The diagonal cane technique **cannot** be relied on for detection of drop-offs such as stairs or curbs because the tip is positioned in a manner in which detection is provided only at the position of the actual tip. For this reason, the diagonal cane technique has limited utility for learners who are blind. Some O&M specialists may not teach the technique at all or may teach this technique after cane techniques that provide greater area coverage, such as touch technique (see the Two-Point-Touch Cane Technique later in this chapter). The diagonal cane technique should only be used in familiar indoor environments that do not have drop-offs.

■ Diagonal cane technique and other cane techniques have been adapted by some O&M specialists for use with learners who have low vision (see the Verification Cane Technique later in this chapter).

■ When using the diagonal cane technique, learners may experience a *cane tip drift* in which the learner either over- or under-extends the reach of the cane. Cane tip drift can be caused by changes in the position of the opposite shoulder. For example, if a learner is holding the cane in the right hand and drops the right shoulder, the entire arm position will change and the tip will likely move further to the left than intended. If the learner moves the right arm away from her body to the right, then the cane tip will also move right and closer to the midline. If the cane tip moves frequently or significantly, then the learner will have to work harder to perceive and interpret the information provided from the cane in relation to her body and location.

■ Cane tip drift and veering are commonly associated with each other.

■ Keeping the tip consistently positioned out in front may be challenging for some learners and they may not perceive the tip position moving closer to their body. This can be caused by the learner not applying firm pressure to the cane grip to maintain the proper position and will result in less advanced information being available to the learner.

■ The movement of the arm and shoulder should absorb the impact of contact with objects or features in the environment. Absorbing the impact in a relaxed manner helps the learner to maintain arm, hand, and cane position and line of travel.

■ For learners who will be making frequent use of the diagonal cane technique, the ability to switch hands will be useful and O&M specialists may wish to have learners practice this skill first while stationary and then while moving. Switching the cane to the opposite hand is a skill that will also be needed when using other cane techniques.

■ When making 90-degree turns while using diagonal cane technique, the cane should be in the hand opposite the direction of the turn. For right turns the cane should be in the left hand and for left turns the cane should be in the right hand. Mastering the art of switching cane hands becomes useful for making 90-degree turns.

■ O&M specialists will want to monitor *cane coverage* and cane tip drift by observing the learner from multiple angles.

■ In congested areas where learners may contact pedestrians with the cane, learners should bring the cane in closer to their body.

TWO-POINT-TOUCH CANE TECHNIQUE (TOUCH TECHNIQUE)

Purpose: To enable the learner to travel independently in a variety of indoor and outdoor environments, using the long cane to gather sensory information, provide a degree of lower-body protection, and detect drop-offs.

PROCEDURE AT A GLANCE

1 The hand is positioned so that the cane grip rests in the middle of the palm with the back of the hand facing to the side, away from the learner's midline, in the same position as a handshake.

2 The index finger is extended downward along the flat side of the grip.

3 The thumb is positioned over and around the grip, with the remaining fingers flexed around the bottom of the grip.

4 The cane is centered at the midline of the learner's body with the arm extended forward and the hand at waist height.

5 The wrist is flexed, extended out, and *hyperextended* to move the cane in an arc from side to side, with the cane tip contacting a point just beyond the widest point of the learner's body (shoulder or hips) on each side.

6 As the learner moves forward, the cane tip lifts just slightly off the ground, no more than 1 inch above the ground at the highest point of the arc.

7 The learner moves forward so that the cane tip and the heel of the opposite foot (*in step*) contact the ground simultaneously (*in rhythm*).

8 If the learner gets out of step, she can tap the cane tip twice on one side in order to regain the in-step position.

METHOD

STEP 1 The hand is positioned so that the cane grip rests in the middle of the palm with the back of the hand facing to the side, away from the learner's midline, in the same position as a handshake.

Rationale The cane is held in this position to support a firm grasp and provide maximum tactile information to the hand. The technique is typically taught for use with the dominant hand, but many learners can learn to use the technique with both hands, providing flexibility that can be helpful in various travel situations.

Variation The pencil grasp, as used for the diagonal cane technique, can also be used for touch technique. The grasp is especially effective for use in congested travel areas because it is easier to hold at a vertical angle, allowing the learner to pull it in closer while continuing to provide arc coverage.

STEP 2 The index finger is extended downward along the flat side of the grip.

Rationale The index finger positioned along the flat side of the grip provides good tactile information as well as control of the cane.

Variation Not all cane styles incorporate the common golf-club grip and may not have a flat edge on the grip. Some grips are cylindrical. In such cases the cane grip can still be grasped in the middle of the palm with the thumb on one side and the fingers wrapped around the other side.

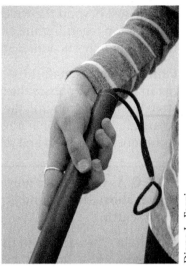

Diane L. Fazzi

STEP 3 The thumb is positioned over and around the grip, with the remaining fingers flexed around the bottom of the grip.

Rationale The thumb is positioned to provide balance, stability, and control of the cane.

STEP 4 The cane is centered at the midline of the learner's body with the arm extended forward but not locked. The hand is held at waist height.

Rationale Centering the cane at the midline of the learner's body makes it easier to create and maintain an arc width that provides even coverage for both sides of the body and facilitates a straighter line of travel for some learners. The forward extension of the arm provides a buffer, minimizing the impact of the cane being pushed into the learner's midsection when the cane makes sudden contact with an object.

Variation Not all learners—due to body shape, physical ability, or ability to concentrate—can maintain a hand-centered position with an extended arm for the long cane. In some cases, learners may be able to maintain hand-centered positioning with an arm position that is slightly bent at the elbow to help angle the forearm toward the center of the body. The slightly bent elbow can help absorb any impact of the cane hitting an object. A longer cane can be selected to make up for any loss of cane length. However, LaGrow, Blasch, and De l'Aune (1997) found that the hand-centered position was most effective in detecting obstacles at foot level (below the ankle).

STEP 5 The wrist is flexed, extended out, and hyperextended to move the cane in an arc from side to side, with the cane tip contacting a point just beyond the widest point of the learner's body (shoulder or hips) on each side.

Rationale The continuous movement of the wrist from a flexed, through an extended, and finally to a hyperextended position helps to move the cane in an arc from side to side in a consistent manner. It is common for many learners to have a wider arc width on the opposite side of the dominant hand due to the ease of flexing the wrist toward the nondominant side as opposed to hyperextension of the wrist toward the dominant side. It is also common to see a learner roll the wrist and entire hand over to move the cane back and forth in a slapping motion or to move the entire arm back and forth to try and get the same effect. While both approaches may result in functional coverage of the body with the cane, the extra movements of the hand or arm seem to reduce the consistency of *arc height* (distance the cane lifts up from the walking surface at the apex), arc width, and tactile information available for interpretation for the purposes of mobility and orientation. Wall and Ashmead (2002) found that moving the cane with just the wrist results in better arc coverage than using the whole arm. The arc width—just beyond the widest part of the learner's body—is intended to provide the learner with information regarding the path to be traveled, without including unnecessary information beyond what the learner may encounter and without posing a tripping hazard for others.

Variation Jacobson (2013) describes an alternative "fingertip method," in which the learner bends her index finger, presses the fingertip against the flat edge of the grip, and then pushes her finger to straighten it out, moving the cane in the direction she is pointing, to the nondominant side, and then returning to the original finger position with the cane returning to the dominant side. With this technique, the thumb and remaining fingers act as pivots as the cane swings back and forth.

STEP 6 As the learner moves forward, the cane tip lifts just slightly off the ground, no more than 1 inch above the ground at the highest point of the arc, which is near the center of the learner's body width.

Rationale The natural lift in a learner's step is typically enough to allow the tip to lift off the ground (Jacobson, 2013). When the cane is lifted more than 1 inch off the ground, important information may be missed and the cane tip may bounce when it reaches the endpoint of the arc.

Variations Some learners, who exert very firm pressure on the cane or who use a cane with a marshmallow or roller tip, may not experience this natural lift. In such cases, the O&M specialist can suggest that the learner should feel the cane tip lift as she walks to see if it prompts the desired arc height. The O&M specialist may wish to have the learner practice lifting the cane tip off the ground. Many learners benefit from the constant contact of the cane tip along the travel path, and those learners can be taught constant-contact cane technique as their primary travel technique (see section on Constant-Contact Cane Technique later in this chapter).

STEP 7 The learner moves forward so that the cane tip and the heel of the opposite foot (in step) contact the ground simultaneously (in rhythm).

Rationale The in-step strike of the cane tip on the opposite side of the *heel strike* provides the learner with continuous coverage and clears the travel path in advance of the next step of the opposite foot. Maintaining a rhythm supports the in-step coverage and consistency in information gathering.

Diane L. Fazzi

STEP 8 If the learner gets out of step, she can tap the cane tip twice on one side while taking the next step in order to regain the in-step position.

Rationale By tapping the cane twice on one side, the learner can regain the in-step position without having to stop or interrupt the flow of travel.

Variations A *skip step*, commonly referred to as the military change step, is an alternative method for getting back in step. With this approach, the cane movement remains unchanged while the learner inserts a skip into her step pattern to regain the in-step position.

Congested-Area Technique with Touch Technique
In crowded areas, the learner may narrow the arc of the cane slightly, slow the pace, choke up on the cane shaft, and flex the elbow to bring the cane in closer at a vertical angle so that the cane shaft and tip are not protruding as far ahead and to limit unnecessary contact of the cane with other people's feet or legs or closely placed furniture. Once in a clear area, the learner should resume regular touch technique to provide full advance coverage for walking at a typical walking speed.

Trailing with Touch Technique
When a learner wishes to follow a raised surface for a period of time, she can use trailing with the touch technique by walking parallel to and near the surface to be followed. The learner taps the cane tip to the opposite side of the surface to be followed and swings the arc back until the tip reaches the surface to be trailed, maintaining the same rhythm and step. The learner uses a low, flat arc, returning the cane tip to just beyond the opposite shoulder, and repeats the process until it is no longer needed.

CONSTANT-CONTACT CANE TECHNIQUE

Purpose: To enable the learner to travel independently in a variety of indoor and outdoor environments, using the long cane to gather sensory information, provide a degree of lower-body protection, and detect drop-offs with the tip of the cane, which remains in constant contact with the walking surface.

PROCEDURE AT A GLANCE

1	The hand is positioned so that the cane grip rests in the middle of the palm with the back of the hand facing to the side, away from the learner's midline, in the same position as a handshake.
2	The index finger is extended downward along the flat side of the grip.
3	The thumb is positioned over and around the grip, with the remaining fingers flexed around the bottom of the grip.
4	The cane is centered at the midline of the learner's body with the arm extended forward.
5	The wrist is flexed, extended out, and hyperextended to move the cane in an arc from side to side, with the cane tip stopping at a point just beyond the widest point of the learner's body (shoulder or hips) on each side.
6	As the learner moves forward, she exerts light pressure on the cane to keep the tip continuously on the ground.
7	The learner moves forward so that the cane tip and the heel of the opposite foot (in step) reach the end of the arc simultaneously (in rhythm).

METHOD

STEP 1 The hand is positioned so that the cane grip rests in the middle of the palm with the back of the hand facing to the side, away from the learner's midline, in the same position as a handshake.

Rationale The cane is held in this position to support a firm grasp and provide maximum tactile information to the hand. The technique is typically taught for use with the dominant hand, but many learners can learn to use the technique with both hands, providing flexibility that can be helpful in various travel situations.

Variation The pencil grasp, as used for the diagonal cane technique, can also be used for constant-contact cane technique. The grasp is especially effective for use in congested travel areas because it is easier to hold at a vertical angle, allowing the learner to pull it in closer while continuing to provide arc coverage.

STEP 2 The index finger is extended downward along the flat side of the grip.

Rationale Positioning the index finger along the flat side of the grip provides good tactile information as well as control of the cane.

Variation Not all cane styles incorporate the common golf-club grip and may not have a flat edge on the grip. Some grips are cylindrical. In such cases the cane grip can still be grasped in the middle of the palm with the thumb on one side and the fingers wrapped around the other side.

STEP 3 The thumb is positioned over and around the grip, with the remaining fingers flexed around the bottom of the grip.

Rationale The thumb is positioned to provide balance, stability, and control of the cane.

STEP 4 The cane is centered at the midline of the learner's body with the arm extended forward but not locked.

Rationale Centering the cane at the midline of the learner's body makes it easier to create and maintain an arc width that provides even coverage for both sides of the body and facilitates a straighter line of travel for some learners. The forward extension of the arm provides a buffer, minimizing the impact of the cane being pushed into the learner's midsection when the cane makes sudden contact with an object.

Variation Not all learners—due to body shape, physical ability, or ability to concentrate—can maintain a hand-centered position with and extended arm for the long cane. In some cases, learners may be able to maintain hand-centered positioning with an arm position that is slightly bent at the elbow to wrap around or rest against the stomach area. The slightly bent elbow can help absorb any impact of the cane hitting an object. A longer cane can be selected to make up for any loss of cane length.

STEP 5 The wrist is flexed, extended out, and hyperextended to move the cane in an arc from side to side, with the cane tip stopping at a point just beyond the widest point of the learner's body (shoulder or hips) on each side.

Rationale The continuous movement of the wrist from a flexed, through an extended, and finally to a hyperextended position helps to move the cane in an arc from side to side in a consistent manner. It is common for many learners to have a wider arc width on the opposite side of the dominant hand due to the ease of flexing the wrist toward the nondominant side as opposed to hyperextension of the wrist toward the dominant side. It is also common to see a learner roll the wrist and entire hand over to move the cane back and forth. While both approaches may result in the functional coverage of the body with the cane, the extra movements of the hand or arm seem to reduce the consistency of tactile information available for interpretation for the purposes of mobility and orientation. The arc width—just beyond the widest part of the learner's body—is intended to provide the learner with information regarding the path to be traveled, without including unnecessary information beyond what the learner may encounter.

Variation Jacobson (2013) describes an alternative "fingertip method" in which the learner bends her index finger, presses the fingertip against the flat edge of the grip, and then pushes her finger to straighten it out, moving the cane in the direction she is pointing, to the nondominant side, and then returning to the original finger position with the cane returning to the dominant side. With this technique, the thumb and remaining fingers act as pivots as the cane swings back and forth.

STEP 6 As the learner moves forward, she exerts light pressure on the cane to keep the tip continuously on the ground.

Rationale The cane tip may naturally lift off the ground as the learner walks, so light pressure may be needed to maintain constant contact with the walking surface.

STEP 7 The learner moves forward so that the cane tip and the heel of the opposite foot (in step) reach the end of the arc simultaneously (in rhythm).

Rationale The in-rhythm synchronization of the cane tip stopping at the edge of the arc at the same time that the learner steps with the opposite foot (in step) provides the learner with continuous coverage and clears the travel path in advance of the next step.

Variation

Congested-Area Technique with Constant-Contact Cane Technique
In crowded areas, the learner may use congested-area technique to narrow the arc of the cane slightly, slow the pace, choke up on the cane shaft, and flex the elbow to bring the cane in closer at a vertical angle so that the cane shaft and tip are not protruding as far ahead and to limit unnecessary contact of the cane with other people's feet or legs or closely placed furniture. Once in a clear area, the learner should resume regular constant-contact technique to provide full advance coverage for walking at a typical walking speed.

CONSIDERATIONS FOR TWO-POINT-TOUCH AND CONSTANT-CONTACT CANE TECHNIQUES

- Rather than using a wrist motion, some learners may rotate the hand so that the back of the hand is facing up. In this scenario, the learner may end up rolling her hand to move the cane back and forth, which may result in a hard landing for touch technique and cause the tip to bounce up higher than intended, possibly missing some terrain changes or objects found at lower levels. This approach makes it more difficult to remain in rhythm because the timing of the cane arc can become uneven.

- When the arc height for touch technique is more than 1 inch off the ground or touches down with an exaggerated bouncing motion, drop-offs become more difficult to detect.

- O&M specialists may need to spend some time walking backward to observe the learner from the front to determine whether she is maintaining a hand-centered position. However, significant deviations from this hand-centered position can also be observed from behind the learner.

- For constant-contact technique, a rounder cane-tip shape such as a marshmallow tip, roller tip, or ball tip, will make it easier for the learner to move the cane from side to side, and the additional weight of the tip will make it easier to maintain constant contact with the walking surface without the need to exert any pressure. Roller or ball tips may present some challenges in stopping the movement of the cane tip at the edge of the arc and in maintaining a consistent arc width and in-step and in-rhythm technique. However, Kim, Wall Emerson, and Curtiss (2010) found that a marshmallow roller tip was effective in locating drop-offs. Together, the learner and O&M specialist will assess the most appropriate tip to use. Tip choices may change depending on the learner's health (e.g., a more pronounced neuropathy may indicate the need for a slightly heavier tip that may provide more tactile information) or environmental demands (e.g., moving from an area with smooth sidewalks to an area with pronounced cracks and juts).

- Since the tip of the cane lands just beyond the widest part of the body, the arc in the touch technique does not clear the place where the next footstep will be taken. Constant-contact cane technique has been found to provide more reliable drop-off detection than touch technique (Kim & Wall Emerson, 2012; Kim et al., 2009, 2010). Learners may choose to use both techniques and switch as they consider which will work best in the environment in which they are traveling. Some learners who prefer touch technique and have good anticipation of drop-offs may wish to combine the two techniques by using touch technique as the primary cane technique and switching to constant contact upon anticipation of drop-offs.

- Constant-contact cane technique is the same as two-point-touch technique without the height of the arc. Remaining in rhythm and in step is still important for consistent surface preview and information gathering.

- Some learners may find that the constant-contact cane technique causes their walking pace to slow as a result of the drag created by maintaining the tip on the ground on a variety of surfaces and because the end point of the arc can become less defined and cause the learner to slow down in between steps.

- A learner may struggle to keep her hand in a centered position for the constant-contact cane technique and may benefit from using her free hand ("helper hand") to monitor the center position initially to help establish a kinesthetic sense of the desired position.

- Initially the O&M specialist can use his legs, positioned just beyond the correct width, to provide the learner with a reference point to ensure that the arc is not too wide. While stationary, the learner simply moves the cane from side to side and if the cane contacts the specialist's legs, ankles, or feet, she will know she has gone too far. Similarly, cones or a PVC pipe fashioned as an "arc definer" can be used for the same purpose. It is important that the learner focus on the kinesthetic sense of the arc width rather than simply moving the cane until it hits the O&M specialist.

- Long canes should be of adequate length to ensure that learners are not overstepping the path that has been cleared by movement of the cane tip. Learners have their own individual reaction times that must also be taken into consideration. The cane tip must reach obstacles, terrain changes, and drop-offs with sufficient advanced warning so that learners have adequate time to stop, slow down, or change direction as needed. O&M specialists should observe learners from all angles to ensure that they are not overstepping the arc created by their cane tip. Observation methods include using a tile line as a marker to judge the step in relation to the arc of the cane tip. For example, the O&M specialist selects a tile line in front of the learner, and while observing the learner, mentally marks the timing at which the cane tip passes the tile line in comparison to the learner's foot. If the foot reaches the line prior to the cane tip, then the learner is overstepping. Similarly, walking a learner through a wet spot on the pavement and creating footprints is another approach to marking the arc of the cane tip in comparison to the learner's footstep. Finally, measuring the angle at which the cane strikes a wall or obstacle in front of the learner is another method the O&M specialist can use.

- In addition to learning the mechanics of touch and constant-contact techniques, learners will need to refine their ability to walk in a straight line in a smooth manner. Learners may veer from their desired line of travel until they develop confidence in the technique and speed up their walking pace. When learners contact a walking surface, wall, or object that indicates they may have veered, they can turn back to their desired line of travel and readjust the line by straightening out. One common problem is that learners may overcorrect and veer across a hallway or walkway to the opposite side and back again, resulting in what is referred to as pinballing. O&M specialists can emphasize the use of microcorrections (very small adjustments in line of direction) and practice them as needed. O&M specialists may also choose to safely walk backward in front of their learners to provide auditory cues for a straight line of travel until learners gain confidence. Likewise, O&M specialists can encourage learners to listen to the reflected sounds in the environment to aid in maintaining a straight line of travel.

TOUCH-TRAILING CANE TECHNIQUE (SHORELINING)

Purpose: To enable the learner to establish or maintain a line of travel parallel to a wall or surface area, locate a landmark along the wall or trailed surface, or locate an opening or intersecting sidewalk or hallway. The application of *touch trailing* to outdoor environments, in which a learner follows a line between a sidewalk and grass line (*shoreline*), is also commonly referred to as *shorelining* by O&M specialists (see next section on Touch-and-Drag Cane Technique for other approaches).

> **PROCEDURE AT A GLANCE**
>
> **1** The learner is aligned parallel to and near the surface to be followed or trailed.
>
> **2** The learner taps the cane tip to the opposite side and then back to contact the surface to be trailed, maintaining the same rhythm and step.
>
> **3** The learner uses a low, flat arc, returning the cane tip to just beyond the opposite shoulder, and repeats the process until the objective is located.

METHOD

STEP 1 The learner is aligned parallel to and near the surface to be followed or trailed.

Rationale The parallel position near the surface to be followed helps the learner to maintain contact with the surface while using a consistent arc on both sides and maintaining a relatively straight line of travel.

STEP 2 With a slowed pace, the learner uses the same hand position, height, rhythm, and in-step used for touch technique to create a full arc by tapping the cane tip to the opposite side, then back to contact the base of the wall or flat, trailed surface, and back again to the opposite side. The arc may need to be slightly wider on the side that is being trailed.

Rationale In order to maintain rhythm and step, the learner slows her walking pace. The cane tip is brought from the point of the arc to the trailed surface to ensure that the learner maintains contact with the surface, which may have a raised or other subtle difference. Learners may wish to widen the arc slightly on the side of the trailed surface to eliminate the need to walk too close to the trailed surface and reduce the chance of tripping on uneven or low, raised surfaces such as a threshold or doorsill.

Variation For locating a less prominent intersecting edge (such as two different flooring surfaces meeting between a room and a hallway), the learner may further slow her pace and choke up on the cane. In this situation, constant-contact technique may be preferred by some learners. When using constant contact, the learner needs to ensure she is staying in touch with the actual edge line and not a crack or other irregularity in the floor or sidewalk.

STEP 3 The learner uses a low, flat arc, returning the cane tip to just beyond the opposite shoulder, and repeats the process until the objective is located.

Rationale The continuation of the regular arc width provides optimum coverage for the learner and keeps the returning arc low and flat, which makes the tip less likely to bounce on contact and makes it easier to bring the tip back across to the trailed surface.

CONSIDERATIONS FOR TOUCH-TRAILING CANE TECHNIQUE

- Touch trailing should not be used over long distances or as a default technique because it is more tiring, requires a slower pace, and may encourage reliance on tactile information at the cane tip, leading to decreased awareness of auditory information.
- Learners should understand that touch trailing should not be used in all situations. In order to use this technique in outdoor travel, there must be a detectable change in the surface texture beside the sidewalk, such as grass or gravel.
- For beginning outdoor instruction, a straight sidewalk with a defined regular grass edge should be utilized.
- Common errors may include the following:
  - Failure to be positioned parallel to the edge line, which may cause the learner to continually veer away from the edge
  - Inadequate coverage on the side away from the wall or grass line being trailed
  - Dragging the cane tip across the walking surface, thereby misinterpreting seams and cracks in the edge being trailed
  - Overstepping the cane tip when it snags in the surface area being followed
  - Failure to maintain the proper hand position, especially when the surface being trailed is on the same side as the grip hand
  - Failure to maintain forward projection into the environment
- To reestablish a straight line of travel, the learner positions one foot lengthwise along the edge, with the foot on the same side as the hand holding the cane. With the cane extended forward on the edge, she mentally projects a straight line.

TOUCH-AND-DRAG CANE TECHNIQUE (SHORELINING)

Purpose: To enable the learner to maintain a desired line of travel or locate a landmark, opening, or change along a surface of slightly different elevation; for example, curbs, grass lines, sidewalk expansion joints (areas between slabs of concrete that allow for expansion and contraction of the concrete slabs), retaining walls and fences, and train platforms located to the learner's side.

PROCEDURE AT A GLANCE

1 The learner is aligned parallel to and near the surface to be followed.

2 The learner taps the cane tip to the opposite side of the surface to be followed and drags the tip until it reaches the surface to be trailed, maintaining the same rhythm and step.

3 The learner uses a low, flat arc, returning the cane tip to just beyond the opposite shoulder, and repeats the process until it is no longer needed.

METHOD

STEP 1 The learner is aligned parallel to and near the surface to be followed.

Rationale The parallel position near the surface to be followed helps the learner maintain constant contact with the surface while using a consistent arc on both sides and maintaining a relatively straight line of travel.

STEP 2 Slowing her pace, the learner taps the cane tip to the opposite side of the surface to be followed and drags the tip until it reaches the surface to be trailed, maintaining the same rhythm and step. Learners may wish to widen the arc slightly on the side of the trailed surface to eliminate the need to walk close to the dropped or raised surface.

Rationale In order to maintain rhythm and step, the learner may need to slow the pace of walking. The cane tip is dragged from the endpoint of the arc to the trailed surface to ensure that the learner maintains contact with the surface, which may only differ slightly. During the dragging motion, a bit more pressure is placed on the cane, which provides the learner with more surface information and the exact location of the surface being followed. If using touch technique, the learner's cane tip may swing past the surface that the learner wishes to follow. When used with drop-offs such as a down curb, learners will feel the cane tip drop off the edge as opposed to contact with a slightly raised surface. Learners may wish to widen the arc slightly on the side of the trailed surface to eliminate the need to walk close to the raised surface and reduce the chance of stepping off dropped surfaces or tripping over low, raised surfaces.

Variation For pronounced raised surfaces such as walls, fences, or storefronts, the learner may choose to simply use trailing with touch technique (see Variations for Touch Technique) to follow the surface, ensuring an even arc width and that the cane tip reaches the trailed surface to her side.

STEP 3 The learner uses a low, flat arc, returning the cane tip to just beyond the opposite shoulder, and repeats the process until it is no longer needed.

Rationale The continuation of the regular arc width provides optimum coverage for the learner. Keeping the returning arc low and flat makes it less likely that the tip will bounce on contact and easier to drag the tip back across to the trailed surface.

CONSIDERATIONS FOR TOUCH-AND-DRAG CANE TECHNIQUE

- When using touch-and-drag cane technique, as with touch trailing, a common error for learners is to drift away from the trailed surface, which can result in an uneven arc as the learner is forced to reach further to contact the trailed surface. While it is desirable to have a slightly wider arc on the side that is being trailed, learners who sense that the arc is increasing in width on that side may sense that they are drifting away from the parallel trailed surface.

- Some learners find it challenging to maintain rhythm and step when using touch and drag because the technique may lead to a slower walking pace. Whenever a cane technique influences the pace of walking, rhythm may be affected.

- In addition to the potential uses of touch-trailing and touch-and-drag techniques already described, these techniques can be used for street-crossing alignment and locating landmarks near the curb or edge of a sidewalk.

TOUCH-AND-SLIDE CANE TECHNIQUE

Purpose: To enable the learner to detect surface changes such as changes in texture, expansion joints in sidewalks, blended curbs, or subtle drop-offs. The technique can also be used to probe below wet leaves or small amounts of snow found along the path in order to contact the sidewalk.

> **PROCEDURE AT A GLANCE**
>
> **1** The learner slows her pace.
>
> **2** The learner narrows the arc width so that the cane tip touches at a point in front of the instep or toe of each foot.
>
> **3** At the point of each cane tip contact, the learner slides the tip further forward to the point beyond the opposite shoulder, continuing the technique until it is no longer needed.

METHOD

STEP 1 The learner slows her pace to accommodate the additional slide of the cane tip for the technique. The learner starts to slow down as soon as she anticipates she is in close proximity to the desired objective.

Rationale Slowing the pace helps the learner to maintain rhythm and step with the cane technique, as well as greater reaction time if the learner is looking for an anticipated subtle drop-off or blended curb. The slower pace will also allow the learner to quickly free the cane from any obstructions.

STEP 2 The learner narrows the arc width so that the cane tip touches at a point in front of the instep or toe of each foot.

Rationale The arc width is slightly narrowed so that the remaining body-width area is covered by sliding the tip forward to complete the arc.

Variation The cane tip can be slid forward from the normal point of contact from the two-point-touch technique. In doing so the learner gleans surface information from points slightly ahead of her and slightly beyond her body frame width.

STEP 3 At the point of each cane tip contact, the learner slides the tip further forward to the point beyond the opposite shoulder, continuing the technique until it is no longer needed.

Rationale The learner slides the cane tip forward to gather additional surface information when there is an anticipated need, such as a drop-off or escalator plate. The cane tip is slid to the point beyond the opposite shoulder to ensure full body-width coverage.

CONSIDERATIONS FOR TOUCH-AND-SLIDE CANE TECHNIQUE

- When using touch-and-slide cane technique, learners may experience increased sticking of the cane tip in irregularities in the walking surface due to the additional pressure exerted to push the tip forward with each movement.
- The technique is included here because some O&M specialists and learners feel it is beneficial in certain circumstances, even though constant-contact technique is used more predominantly.
- Using touch-and-slide cane technique changes the rhythm of the cane arc and may slow the pace of walking, making it difficult for some learners to maintain in step and rhythm.
- The touch-and-slide cane technique can be helpful for learners who have difficulty detecting drop-offs tactilely, as long as they can anticipate those drop-offs in advance, especially for blended curbs for which there is little to no depth difference between sidewalk and street.

THREE-POINT-TOUCH CANE TECHNIQUE

Purpose: To enable the learner to follow a raised surface and detect a desired location on a level higher than the current walking surface.

METHOD

STEP 1 While standing on the lower surface (e.g., a street), the learner positions herself parallel to the vertical raised surface (e.g., a curb).

Rationale The parallel alignment with the vertical raised surface enables the learner to use a consistent cane motion while traveling.

STEP 2 The learner slows her pace so that three taps of the cane fit into one complete two-step stride sequence.

Rationale The slower pace helps the learner to remain in step, fitting three taps of the cane within two steps. The slower pace also reduces the chance of overstepping the desired location because the cane will ultimately touch the higher-level surface with less spacing between contacts.

STEP 3 Maintaining the hand-centered position, the learner moves the cane tip from just beyond the shoulder opposite the vertical surface over to the vertical surface, similar to the arc coverage in touch technique.

Diane L. Fazzi

Rationale Step 3 is very similar to trailing with the touch technique in that the initial arc is the same and contact is made with a desired raised surface on one side. This technique ensures full coverage for the walking surface while preparing for a preview of the upper-level surface. If the learner is able to tap the upper half of the vertical surface, Step 4 will be easier.

STEP 4 The tip is brought up and over the vertical surface to contact the level above. If the cane tip taps the upper half of the vertical surface in Step 3, then the cane can be easily slid up and over the vertical surface in a quick and fluid motion. If the cane tip taps the lower portion of the vertical surface, the learner may need to further slow her pace while sliding the cane tip up and over the vertical surface until the higher-level surface is contacted. This technique continues until the desired location is found.

Rationale The cane tip is brought to the upper surface by sliding it lightly up the vertical surface to reduce the possibility of the cane tip ricocheting back toward midline and disrupting the rhythm and step of the technique.

Variation A variation of *three-point-touch cane technique* can be used on level surfaces to locate landmarks and objects that the learner anticipates to be found beyond the typical arc width, or outside the sidewalk area. For three-point touch on level surfaces, the learner repeats the process described above except that the third touch of the cane is directed to the landscape strip or grass line and toward the desired object beyond the path of travel.

Diane L. Fazzi

CONSIDERATIONS FOR THE THREE-POINT-TOUCH CANE TECHNIQUE

- The three-point-touch cane technique is primarily used to locate the intersecting sidewalk in recovery from an errant street crossing.
- Maintaining close proximity to the curb is important during temporary travel in the street, to keep the learner at a distance from moving vehicles. Parked cars make this technique nearly impossible to

use, and with heavy traffic it is more advisable to step up onto a grassy area. Learners should take caution to avoid diagonally placed guy-wires or tree branches that may be located on the grassy area. Use of upper-body protective technique when stepping up provides additional information about the possible presence of overhanging obstacles in an unfamiliar area.

- The three-point-touch cane technique can be used on sidewalks with low retaining walls to locate steps for a desired walkway on a higher level.

VERIFICATION CANE TECHNIQUE (V-TECH)

Purpose: To enable the learner who has low vision and who can relate visually with the environment to integrate systematic use of visual and auditory skills in combination with adapted use of the long cane for independent travel and increased-distance visual awareness (Ludt & Goodrich, 2002).

PROCEDURE AT A GLANCE

1	The hand is positioned so that the cane grip rests in the middle of the palm with the back of the hand facing to the side, away from the learner's midline, in the same position as a handshake.
2	The index finger is extended downward along the flat side of the grip.
3	The thumb is positioned over and around the grip, with the remaining fingers flexed around the bottom of the grip.
4	The cane, typically held in the left hand, is positioned at the learner's hip with a relaxed arm.
5	The cane is extended diagonally across the learner's body, with the tip resting on the walking surface just beyond the learner's opposite shoulder.
6	As the learner moves forward, she uses dynamic scanning techniques to visually navigate the environment, with the cane providing verification as needed.
7	Upon visual recognition or anticipation of changes in terrain (e.g., a drop-off), the learner sweeps the cane in a side-to-side arc for the constant-contact cane technique, with her arm remaining relaxed at her side.

METHOD

STEP 1 The hand is positioned so that the cane grip rests in the middle of the palm with the back of the hand facing to the side, away from the learner's midline, in the same position as a handshake.

Rationale The cane is held in this position to support a firm but light grasp and provide maximum tactile information to the hand. In the United States and many other nations, pedestrians typically walk to the right of center along hallways and sidewalks. For verification cane technique, the learner is typically taught to hold the cane in the left hand so that the tip verifies obstacles more commonly found on the right side of the travel path, such as trash cans placed along a wall or open front-yard gates along a sidewalk. Learners can master the technique with both hands, providing them with flexibility depending on the circumstances.

STEP 2 The index finger is extended downward along the flat side of the grip. The grasp is the same as for the index finger grasp for the diagonal or two-point-touch technique.

Rationale   The index finger positioned along the flat side of the grip provides good tactile information as well as control of the cane.

STEP 3 The thumb is positioned over and around the grip, with the remaining fingers flexed around the bottom of the grip. The grasp should be light so that the weight of the cane rests lightly on the fingers that are flexed around the bottom of the grip.

Rationale   The thumb is positioned to provide stability and control of the cane.

STEP 4 The cane, typically held in the left hand, is positioned at the learner's hip with a relaxed arm. The learner's pant seam can be used as a reference point for correct positioning. The cane should be a few inches longer than typically recommended for touch technique to accommodate for the off-center positioning.

Rationale   Positioning the cane in a relaxed fashion provides the learner with a more comfortable technique. The longer length of the cane compensates for the positioning of the cane off to the side of the leg and ensures adequate extension in front of the learner to verify visually identified objects and drop-offs in the travel path.

STEP 5 The cane is extended diagonally across the learner's body, with the tip lightly resting on the walking surface 2 inches beyond the learner's opposite shoulder. Using a clock face for reference, the tip is kept at two o'clock.

Rationale   Lightly resting the cane tip on the ground provides the learner with information about lower obstacles and travel surfaces while reducing the potential of the tip sticking in uneven surfaces. With the tip positioned 1 to 2 inches beyond the width of the opposite shoulder, the cane provides a good diagonal line that can serve to verify lower obstacles in the learner's path of travel.

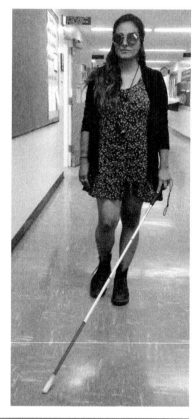

Diane L. Fazzi

STEP 6 As the learner moves forward, she uses dynamic scanning techniques to visually navigate the environment, with the cane providing verification as needed.

Rationale   Since this technique is recommended only for learners who visually relate to the travel environment and benefit from cane verification, the verification cane technique must be integrated with the use of visual *dynamic scanning* (systematic use of visual scanning while moving). The dynamic scanning and attention to visual cues helps the learner to recognize obstacles and changes in terrain from greater distances and with sufficient time to react.

STEP 7 Upon visual recognition or anticipation of changes in terrain (e.g., a drop-off), the learner sweeps the cane in a side-to-side arc for the constant-contact cane technique, with her arm remaining relaxed at her side. Upper-body protective technique can be used when overhangs are visually detected.

Rationale The diagonal positioning of the cane means that it will not provide verification of drop-offs consistently, so the learner will need to switch to the modified constant-contact cane technique once she visually anticipates the approach to the drop-off.

CONSIDERATIONS FOR THE VERIFICATION CANE TECHNIQUE

- O&M specialists will need to determine, through a comprehensive assessment process, whether individual learners who have low vision would be best suited for traditional touch technique, constant-contact technique, or verification technique.

- Learners with stable vision and the potential to improve their visual ability to detect obstacles and hazards along the travel path may be good candidates for this technique (Ludt & Goodrich, 2002).

- Additional considerations for selecting learners who may be good candidates for verification cane technique may include:

  □ Can the learner visually establish and maintain a straight line of travel?

  □ Can the learner visually identify obstacles beyond the distance of the extended long cane, use visual cues, and detect surface changes while traveling, allowing for adequate reaction time to adjust course or technique?

  □ Can the learner visually adjust the line of travel to determine clear paths and navigate around obstacles?

  □ Does the learner have consistent visual functioning in varied lighting (e.g., for day or night travel)?

- Verification cane technique must be combined with the use of systematic scanning patterns, eccentric viewing (as appropriate), interpretation of visual cues in the travel environment, and *glare remediation* (reducing the damaging impact of glare on the learner's ability to function visually and travel in the environment).

- Verification cane technique, combined with systematic visual scanning, is intended to assist learners in directing their vision forward to preview the environment.

- Learners can use their vision to recognize environmental cues at a distance that will assist in their visual planning, such as noticing that people who they are walking behind are "getting shorter," signaling an impending drop-off.

- The combination of verification cane technique and a modified position for constant-contact cane technique provides the learner with verification of obstacles, terrain changes, and drop-offs that are detected visually.

NEGOTIATING DOORS WITH A CANE

Purpose: To ensure that the learner manages her cane safely and efficiently while negotiating doors and doorways.

PROCEDURE AT A GLANCE

1 After contacting the door, the cane tip is anchored against the door or metal plate of the doorway.

2 The learner rotates her hand (outward or inward) until the cane is positioned vertically, allowing the learner to walk forward toward the door.

3 The learner moves the cane vertically to the right and then to the left across the door until she contacts the door handle.

4 The learner slides her free hand down the cane shaft to contact the door handle, transferring the cane, if necessary, to the hand nearest the door opening.

5 The learner uses her free hand to open the door by either pushing forward or pulling toward her and crosses the threshold using constant-contact cane technique to ensure full clearance.

6 The learner closes the door behind her by either releasing a self-closing door or returning the door to its original position.

METHOD

STEP 1 After contacting the door, the cane tip is anchored against the door or metal plate (threshold) of the doorway.

Rationale The cane tip is anchored against the door to serve as a reference point as the learner approaches the door.

STEP 2 The learner rotates her hand (outward or inward) until the cane is positioned vertically, allowing the learner to walk forward toward the door.

Rationale The rotation of the learner's hand enables the learner to maintain a straight line of travel while moving directly toward the door without having to reposition the cane.

STEP 3 The learner moves the cane vertically to the right and then to the left across the door until she contacts the door handle.

Rationale Using the cane to search to the right and left provides systematic and maximum coverage to quickly locate the door handle. This approach helps the learner determine the type of handle and is most useful for smaller doorknobs and handles that may be located at different locations on a door, or for double doors, when the learner is not certain whether she has reached the door to her left or her right.

Variation Threshold plates are often placed on the floor as part of a doorframe. The learner may wish to raise the cane tip slightly off the ground while searching for the doorknob to avoid getting her cane stuck in the threshold plate.

STEP 4 The learner slides her free hand down the cane shaft to contact the door handle, transferring the cane, if necessary, to the hand nearest the door opening (e.g., left hand if the door opens to the right and vice versa).

Rationale Using the cane shaft to locate the door handle, knob, or push bar provides a solid reference point to quickly locate the handle. Some learners may slide their hands down the shaft to a specific location while others find the general reference point adequate for grabbing the handle. Transferring the cane to the hand nearest the opening, if necessary, helps position the cane to extend out the doorway without tangling with the hand pulling or pushing the door.

Diane L. Fazzi

STEP 5 The learner uses her free hand to open the door by either pushing forward or pulling toward her and crosses the threshold using constant-contact cane technique to ensure full clearance.

Rationale Using the free hand to open the door enables the learner to fully use the cane to clear the path while crossing the threshold.

STEP 6 The learner closes the door behind her by either releasing a self-closing door or returning the door to its original position, and transfers the cane back to the preferred hand if necessary.

Rationale The pressure of a self-closing door, whether push or pull, is evident when opened by the learner.

CONSIDERATIONS FOR NEGOTIATING DOORS WITH A CANE

- Expose learners to a wide variety of doors so that they are comfortable managing their canes while using handles, knobs, and push bars.
- Learners may need practice managing the cane while handling doors to ensure that the cane does not get stuck in the doorjamb or in a self-closing door.
- Some doors are heavily trafficked by pedestrians and it can be difficult to determine their exact location as groups of people move through the door. Learners will need to be prepared to have self-closing doors close on them unexpectedly from the person in front of them, while other individuals will hold the door open for learners as they go through.
- See Negotiating Doors with a Guide section in Chapter 3 for procedures for negotiating doors with a guide and Negotiating Revolving Doors and Negotiating Elevators sections in Chapter 9 for procedures for negotiating revolving doors and elevators.

ASCENDING AND DESCENDING STAIRS

Ascending Stairs

Purpose: To enable the learner to safely ascend stairs using the long cane.

PROCEDURE AT A GLANCE

1 Upon initial contact with the base of the stairs, the learner anchors the cane tip against the base of the first stair.

2 The learner rotates her hand (outward or inward) until the cane is positioned vertically, allowing the learner to walk forward toward the stairs.

3 Keeping the cane in a vertical position against the base of the step, the learner lowers her grasp onto the shaft of the cane and moves the cane left and right along the base of the stairs, repositioning herself near the desired side of the stairs. If use of the handrail is desired, she transfers the cane to the opposite hand and grasps the handrail.

4 The learner lifts the cane until the tip moves over the top edge of the first step and pushes the cane forward so that the cane tip moves across the tread of the first step and rests against the next riser at the step edge.

5 With her arm extended, using either the thumb or pencil grasp, the learner lifts the cane slightly so that the tip rests lightly on the riser of the second step, about 1 to 2 inches below the step edge.

6 The learner begins the ascent, keeping her arm extended, leaning slightly forward, and exerting enough pressure on the cane to keep the tip moving from one riser to the next, one to two steps ahead of the learner's steps on the stairs.

7 When the tip no longer contacts a riser and swings clear, the learner prepares for the landing by clearing the landing with the cane prior to taking the last step.

8 The learner resumes proper cane technique in preparation for moving forward or approaching another set of stairs.

METHOD

STEP 1 Upon initial contact with the base of the stairs, the learner anchors the cane tip against the base of the first stair.

Rationale Anchoring the cane tip provides a reference point as the learner approaches the stairs.

STEP 2 The learner rotates her hand (outward or inward) until the cane is positioned vertically, allowing the learner to walk forward toward the base of the stairs.

Rationale The hand rotation allows the learner to comfortably change the cane to a vertical position.

Variation Some learners may be able to combine steps 1 and 2. With practice, this should become one fluid motion.

STEP 3 Keeping the cane in a vertical position against the base of the step, the learner lowers her grasp onto the shaft of the cane and moves the cane along the base of the stairs from midline to the left and back to midline (with the cane in the left hand) and from midline to the right and back to midline (with the cane in the right hand). If needed, the learner can position herself closer to the desired side of the stairs or within reach of the handrail. (The desired side of the staircase is typically determined by the flow of pedestrians or the region or country of travel. For example, traveling on the right-hand side of the stairs is typical in the United States, but in Australia travel is typical on the left-hand side. Stairs in an office building may conform to typical pedestrian flow patterns for the region, while in a high school the flow may change from one side to the other because of the sheer volume of use and number of people.) For travel on the right side of the stairs when use of the handrail is desired, the learner transfers the cane to the left hand and grasps the handrail with her right.

Rationale Moving the cane along the base of the stairs helps the learner to confirm or correct her body alignment perpendicular to the stairs, gauge the relative width of the staircase, and locate the right-hand side of the stairs, as well as the possible location of the handrail, while clearing the area. At this point, the learner can move closer to the desired side of the stairs and ascend with the flow of pedestrian traffic. This check is also an opportunity for the learner to locate and use the handrail during ascent. If a handrail is being used, the cane is transferred to the free hand. The lower grasp on the cane makes it easier to move the cane from one side to the other, keeping the forearms parallel to the floor and the cane in the vertical position. Switching the grasp of the cane makes the horizontal movement of the cane easy to maintain while keeping the body parallel to the stairs. (The width of the area checked is adjusted based on the flow of pedestrian traffic so that the learner does not extend her arm in front of oncoming pedestrians.)

STEP 4 The learner lifts the cane until the tip moves over the top edge of the first step and pushes the cane forward so that the cane tip moves across the tread of the first step and rests against the next riser at the step edge.

Rationale The movement of the cane provides the learner with information about the height and depth of the stairs and positions the cane for the beginning of the ascent.

STEP 5 With her arm extended, using either the thumb or pencil grasp, the learner lifts the cane slightly so that the tip rests lightly on the riser of the second step, about 1 to 2 inches below the step edge.

Rationale The cane is positioned high on the riser so that by applying firm pressure as the learner and cane ascend, the tip contacts each subsequent riser.

Variation Depending on the learner's arm reach and depth of the stairs, the cane tip can be placed on the third riser, providing a two-step warning of the approach to the landing.

STEP 6 The learner keeps her arm extended and begins the ascent, leaning slightly forward and exerting enough pressure on the cane to keep the tip moving from one riser to the next, one to two steps ahead of the learner's steps on the stairs.

Rationale Keeping the arm extended and exerting light pressure helps the learner retain control over the cane placement and maintain a consistent distance between her and the cane tip, preventing the learner from catching up to or overstepping the cane while on the stairs. Consistent contact with each riser ensures that the cane will provide timely information when the landing is reached.

Diane L. Fazzi

STEP 7 When the tip no longer contacts a riser and swings clear, the learner prepares for the landing by clearing the landing with the cane prior to taking the last step.

Rationale Using the cane to detect the landing eliminates the need for trying to anticipate the landing or overstepping it, and provides a natural transition to constant-contact cane technique as the learner completes the stairs.

STEP 8 The learner resumes constant-contact cane technique in preparation for moving forward or approaching another set of stairs.

Rationale On unfamiliar staircases, beginning constant contact at the landing provides the best clearance and possible detection of additional stairs in the vicinity.

Variation If the learner is continuing to ascend the stairs and is looking for the next flight of stairs, she continues her constant-contact arc to the right to locate the base of the next set of stairs and to avoid running into the stream of pedestrians descending the stairs on the opposite side. The sides will be reversed in some countries (e.g., Australia).

Descending Stairs

Purpose: To enable the learner to safely descend stairs using the long cane.

	PROCEDURE AT A GLANCE
1	Upon initial contact with the stair edge, the learner anchors the cane tip against the edge of the stair.
2	The learner rotates her hand (outward or inward) until the cane is positioned vertically against the stair, allowing the learner to walk forward toward the stairs.
3	Keeping the cane anchored against the stair in a vertical position, the learner moves the cane to locate the desired side of the stairs, transferring the cane to the free hand and grasping the handrail if desired.
4	The learner lowers the cane to the tread of the first step, and then slides it forward to the edge of the step.
5	The learner lifts the cane until the tip moves over the top edge of the step and extends it downward to hover slightly below the next step, without contacting the riser.
6	The learner begins the descent, leaning slightly backward and extending the arm enough to keep the cane tip hovering just below the step edges ahead of the learner's steps on the stairs.
7	When the cane tip contacts the landing, the learner anticipates the last step and prepares for forward travel by clearing the landing with the cane prior to stepping onto the landing.
8	The learner resumes constant-contact cane technique in preparation for travel or approaching another set of stairs.

METHOD

STEP 1 Upon initial contact with the stair edge, the learner anchors the cane tip against the edge of the stair.

Rationale This positioning ensures that the learner knows the location of the edge of the stairs, reducing any possible missteps.

STEP 2 The learner rotates her hand (outward or inward) until the cane is positioned vertically against the stair, allowing the learner to walk forward toward the stairs.

Rationale The hand rotation allows the learner to comfortably change the cane to a vertical position.

Variation Some learners may be able to combine Steps 1 and 2. With practice, this should become one fluid motion.

STEP 3 Keeping the cane anchored against the stair in a vertical position, the learner moves the cane to locate the desired side of the stairs, transferring the cane to the free hand and grasping the handrail if desired.

Rationale Anchoring the cane provides the learner with a reference point for the stair edge while determining the width of the stairs and locating the handrail if desired. If use of the handrail is desired, the cane is transferred to the free hand to be used during the descent.

STEP 4 The learner lowers the cane to the tread of the first step, and then slides it forward to the edge of the step.

Rationale This lowering of the cane provides information about the depth and width of the steps.

STEP 5 The learner lifts the cane until the tip moves over the top edge of the step and extends it downward in the diagonal cane technique position to hover slightly below the next step, without contacting the riser.

Rationale It is not necessary for the learner to contact each riser while descending stairs. Extending the cane downward helps to ensure that the cane tip does not protrude and get stuck in stair rails or collide with other people on the stairs. The downward extension also ensures that the cane tip will reach the landing with advanced notice for the learner.

Variation Some learners feel the need to contact each step with the tip of the cane during the descent and adapt this technique to include a tap of each step edge or riser (depending on whether the step edge protrudes over the riser), with the cane tip synchronized with the descending steps. The learner will need to use a slight pull motion to ensure contact with each step. The cane tip will still reach the landing in advance of the learner.

STEP 6 The learner begins the descent, leaning slightly backward and extending the arm enough to keep the cane tip hovering just below the step edges ahead of the learner's steps on the stairs.

Rationale Because the learner is extending the cane downward, a slight lean backward helps to provide balance for the learner during the descent.

Diane L. Fazzi

STEP 7 When the cane tip contacts the landing, the learner anticipates the last step and prepares for forward travel by clearing the landing with the cane prior to stepping onto the landing.

Rationale Since the cane is extended downward, the tip will reach the landing before the learner and provide a cue that the learner is about to reach the landing. Clearing the landing is important because another set of stairs or other obstacles may be present and should be detected as quickly as possible.

STEP 8 The learner resumes constant-contact cane technique in preparation for travel or approaching another set of stairs.

Rationale On unfamiliar staircases, using constant-contact cane technique on the landing provides the best clearance and possible detection of additional stairs in the vicinity.

Variation If the learner is continuing to descend the stairs and is seeking the next flight of stairs, she continues her constant-contact arc to the right to follow the stairwell to locate the top of the next set of stairs and to avoid running into the stream of pedestrians ascending the stairs on the opposite side. The sides will be reversed in some countries (e.g., Australia).

CONSIDERATIONS FOR ASCENDING AND DESCENDING STAIRS

■ The majority of stair sets encountered by the learner will include handrails. The learner and O&M specialist may rely on a variety of factors to determine if the handrail should be used. Factors for consideration include, but are not limited to, regularity or irregularity of the stairway design, balance and physical abilities of the learner, and congestion in the stairway.

□ Learners with good balance when ascending or descending evenly spaced stairs may choose to not use a handrail. Being able to manage stairs without a handrail makes it easier when the learner's hands are full, the learner is traveling in crowded areas in which the handrail is less accessible, or in situations in which the cleanliness of the handrail makes it undesirable to hold.

□ Some O&M specialists may feel that it is better for the learner to hold the handrail to provide an additional source of orientation or balance on the stairs.

■ O&M specialist positioning for monitoring stair travel for ascending and descending stairs should be slightly below and to the side of the learner to fully view the technique and to provide stability to the learner in the event of a misstep.

■ During instruction, O&M specialists should try to build in practice with a variety of stair sets, and using the cane in both the right and left hand.

■ In crowded situations such as rail stations, it is essential for the learner to execute these techniques quickly and fluidly.

■ See the section on Negotiating Escalators in Chapter 9 for procedures on how to negotiate moving stairs.

Diane L. Fazzi

ENTERING AND EXITING VEHICLES

Entering Vehicles

Purpose: To enable the learner to easily locate and enter a vehicle.

PROCEDURE AT A GLANCE

1 The learner contacts the vehicle.

2 The learner locates the doorjamb between the front and back windows, and moves her hand to find the door handle.

3 The learner uses the cane to quickly clear the step into the vehicle.

4 The learner opens the vehicle door while transferring the cane to the same hand, maintaining contact with the door.

5 With her free hand, the learner contacts the edge of the roof.

6 The learner then contacts the back of the seat, quickly clears the seat, and sits down.

7 The learner brings the cane into the vehicle with the tip on the floor, announces that she is closing the door, and closes the vehicle door.

8 The learner either folds the cane or stores the cane with the tip on the floor and cane over the shoulder or along the floor between the door and the seat.

METHOD

STEP 1 The learner contacts the vehicle. At the point of contact, the learner can confirm the height of the vehicle and its position relative to the street, other parked cars, and the immediate surroundings.

Rationale Contact with the vehicle and determination of the position and height of the vehicle enables the learner to quickly locate the door.

STEP 2 With her hand, the learner trails along the vehicle, locates the doorjamb between the front and back windows, and moves her hand to find the door handle.

Rationale The area between the front and back windows is an easy area to locate and identify and it provides the learner with a good reference point for locating the door and door handle. In four-door vehicles, the handle closest to the doorjamb should be for the front passenger seat and the one further from the doorjamb should be for the backseat. In two-door vehicles, there will still be a seam between the door and the back section of the vehicle to use as a reference.

STEP 3 The learner uses the cane to quickly clear the step into the vehicle. Since the cane is likely to be in a somewhat vertical position by this point, it can be lightly moved in a circular fashion, with the tip on the ground to check the next step. If the vehicle is parked curbside, the cane can be used to quickly measure the height of the curb and the distance between the vehicle and the curb. Based on this information, the learner determines whether she will step directly into the vehicle or will need to make an additional step into the street before entering the vehicle.

Rationale Vehicles may be parked in driveways, parking lots, or curbside. Generally, it is a good idea to clear the next step to ensure the pavement is even and clear of debris. It is most important to clear the step when a vehicle is parked curbside to determine the height of the step down as well as whether the area might contain a drainage grate or be full of water, mud, or debris.

STEP 4 The learner opens the vehicle door while transferring the cane to the same hand, maintaining contact with the door.

Rationale The learner transfers the cane to the hand opening the door to free the other hand to check for the position of the roof and to clear the seat in preparation for seating. Contact is maintained with the door to ensure that it does not open further than intended, does not bump adjacent parked cars, and provides clear information as to the width of the opening before getting into the vehicle.

STEP 5 With her free hand, the learner contacts the edge of the roof.

Rationale The learner contacts the edge of the vehicle roof in order to judge the space for head clearance and to determine how much of a bend is needed prior to getting into the vehicle. Learners who are tall may have to bend down more when entering small cars such as sedans.

Variations Some learners find it easier to use the cane, while still in a vertical position, to locate the roof edge of the vehicle. In addition, when using a folding cane, some learners will be more comfortable folding the cane quickly before entering the vehicle and can then use the folded cane to clear the seat.

Diane L. Fazzi

STEP 6 The learner then contacts the back of the seat, quickly clears the seat, and sits down.

Rationale Contacting the seat gives the learner information about how far down the seat is positioned. Learners should always check that seats are clear before sitting since drivers frequently leave personal items, such as sunglasses, in the passenger seat.

Variation In familiar vehicles in which the learner is certain that the seat is empty, or based on information from the driver that the seat is clear, the learner can quickly check the area while being seated.

STEP 7 The learner brings the cane into the vehicle with the tip on the floor, announces that she is closing the door, and closes the vehicle door. As a precaution, the learner announces that she is closing the door to avoid any potential finger-slamming accidents. The learner may simply ask, "Is everybody in?" or "All clear?" as a cue to others.

Rationale The learner needs to bring the cane fully into the vehicle prior to closing the door to avoid breaking the cane. There are circumstances in which it is important to announce that the door is being closed. For example, when young children may have inadvertently placed their hands where they could be caught in the door. Developing the habit of announcing the door is closing will help to avoid these types of potential problems.

STEP 8 The learner either folds the cane or stores the cane with the tip on the floor and cane over the shoulder or along the floor between the door and the seat.

Rationale Although it may depend on the length of the trip, most learners will prefer to fold their canes for easier storage in the car. While the cane can be leaned over the learner's shoulder, it does not afford the learner with as much hands-free movement to access technology or written or brailled materials that the learner may wish to use during the trip.

Exiting Vehicles

Purpose: To enable the learner to easily exit a vehicle.

	PROCEDURE AT A GLANCE
1	The learner opens the door while maintaining a firm grip, ensuring the door does not open further than intended.
2	The learner uses the cane to clear the area about to be stepped onto.
3	The learner transfers the cane into the same hand that is holding the door ajar.
4	The learner checks the roofline with her free hand and exits the vehicle, clearing the door area.
5	The learner transfers the cane back to the free hand and closes the door.

METHOD

STEP 1 The learner opens the door while maintaining a firm grip, ensuring the door does not open further than intended.

Rationale The learner should open the door with caution due to the possibility that the vehicle may be parked next to another vehicle in a parking lot, parked next to a curb that may catch the door depending on the proximity and relative height, parked next to a retaining wall or gate in a driveway, or parked close to a wall, tool shelf, or other vehicle in a home garage. It is generally not recommended for passengers to exit vehicles on the street side when it can be avoided. Some parking areas allow very limited space between vehicles; in such cases the door should only be opened as far as necessary to exit the vehicle.

STEP 2 The learner uses the cane to clear the area about to be stepped onto. Since the cane is likely to be in a somewhat vertical position at this point, it can be lightly moved in a circular fashion, with the tip on the ground to check the next step. If the vehicle is parked curbside, the cane can be used to quickly measure the height of the curb and the distance the vehicle is parked from the curb. Based on this information, the learner determines whether she will step directly onto the curb or will need to make an additional step into the street before stepping up.

Rationale Vehicles may be parked in driveways, parking lots, or curbside. Generally, it is a good idea to clear the next step to ensure that the pavement is even and clear of debris. It is most important to clear the step when a vehicle is parked curbside to determine the height of the step up as well as whether the area might contain a drainage grate or be full of water, mud, or debris.

STEP 3 The learner transfers the cane into the same hand that is holding the door ajar.

Rationale The learner transfers the cane to the hand that is holding the door open to free the other hand to check for the position of the roof in preparation for exiting the vehicle. Contact is maintained with the door to ensure that it does not open further than intended, does not bump adjacent parked vehicles, and provides clear information about the width of the opening before getting out of the vehicle.

STEP 4 With her free hand, the learner contacts the edge of the roof. The hand can remain in this position as the learner gets out of the seat or returns to the seat to help support herself as she gets up to exit the vehicle and clear the door area.

Rationale The learner contacts the edge of the vehicle roof to judge the room for head clearance and to determine how much room is available prior to getting out of the vehicle. Some learners may not need this step because they remember the height of the roofline from entering the vehicle.

STEP 5 The learner transfers the cane back to the free hand and closes the door. As a precaution, the learner may announce that she is closing the door to avoid any potential finger-slamming accidents.

Rationale There are circumstances in which it is important to announce that the door is being closed. For example, when young children may have inadvertently placed their hands where they could be caught in the door. Developing the habit of announcing the door is closing will help to avoid these type of potential problems.

CONSIDERATIONS FOR ENTERING AND EXITING VEHICLES

■ While the learner may be a vehicle passenger, it should not be assumed that they will be guided to the passenger side of the vehicle and have the door opened for them prior to entering. Many learners will want to manage this task independently, which is why the guidance of these techniques is offered here. Learners, particularly younger learners, may ride in rear seats of vehicles as well as the front passenger seat. Learners should have experience with entering vehicles from both sides and being seated in rear seats, including van seating.

■ Vehicles come in a wide variety of shapes, heights, and sizes. Learners who have limited exposure to different types of vehicles should be provided with various experiences to increase their skill level.

■ Longer, rigid canes may be difficult to position within a vehicle. The learner may need practice bringing the grip end in first and positioning it over her shoulder, bringing the tip end in the door, and resting it on the floor of the vehicle.

■ There are many types of door handles, door openings, and locking systems. Some door handles are completely flush with the vehicle and may be more difficult to locate. Some vehicle doors slide open—such as in many styles of minivans—and may open with the use of a remote key system. Some front and back doors open in opposite directions from the doorjamb. Some doors, trunks, and hatchbacks open overhead, and extra care needs to be taken when placing or removing items, such as luggage or groceries, from the vehicle.

■ Some learners may need a review of safety procedures, including the use of safety restraints such as seatbelts.

LOCATING DROPPED OBJECTS

Purpose: To enable the learner to easily locate and retrieve a desired item, using the cane shaft to search the environment as needed.

PROCEDURE AT A GLANCE

1. The learner estimates the location of the dropped object.
2. The learner turns toward the estimated location of the dropped object.
3. Using upper-body protective technique as needed, the learner squats closer to the floor surface to reach for the object.
4. The learner places the shaft of the cane flat on the floor surface close to where the object is suspected to have landed.
5. Keeping the grip of the cane on the floor aligned with the center of her body, the learner moves the cane shaft from left to right in an arc shape.
6. The learner stops the cane sweep when the item is contacted, using the cane as a reference point to locate and pick up the dropped object.
7. If the item is not found during the full sweep, the learner may adjust her position and repeat the procedure.

METHOD

STEP 1 The learner estimates the location of the dropped object. For floors or walking surfaces that are not cushioned, the learner can use sound localization to determine the spot where the object hit the surface and possibly even the trajectory of the object if it bounces or rolls upon landing. For cushioned surfaces, such as carpet, the object may not make a noise when dropped. In these instances, the learner can use logic about the size, shape, and weight of the object and height from which it was dropped to estimate the location.

Rationale Learners will be more successful in locating dropped objects when they take the time to think about the likely location of the object prior to starting the search. During this moment, the learner may also determine the congestion of the area and the worth of the object dropped to determine if she wishes to proceed in locating it.

STEP 2 The learner turns toward the estimated location of the dropped object, aligning feet, body, and head in the proper direction to make the search pattern as successful as possible.

Rationale By turning the entire body to face the direction of the estimated location of the dropped object, the learner increases the probability of searching for the item in the correct vicinity.

STEP 3 Using upper-body protective technique as needed, the learner squats closer to the floor surface to reach for the object.

Rationale Using a squat motion along with the upper-body protective technique when reaching toward the floor provides the learner with information about any protruding objects that may be located at mid-level and helps to avoid head collisions.

STEP 4 The learner places the shaft of the cane flat on the floor surface close to where the object is suspected to have landed. Folding canes can be placed in the same manner on the floor, even while folded.

Rationale Placing the shaft of the cane on the floor surface close to where the dropped object is suspected to be provides a good reference point in preparing for the search. Not all floor surfaces are pleasant to touch and may have unexpected dirt and grime that can be avoided using this approach.

Variation Some O&M specialists teach the skill for locating dropped objects prior to issuing a long cane and may teach the learner to place her hand on the floor surface to locate the dropped object. The learner may also choose to ask for assistance in retrieving the object from other individuals that may be in the vicinity.

STEP 5 Keeping the grip of the cane on the floor aligned with the center of her body, the learner moves the cane shaft slowly from left to right in an arc shape. The motion is similar to that of opening and closing a paper fan. The learner must be aware of the congestion (people and furniture) in the area and adjust the size of the arc and extension of the cane accordingly so as not to trip pedestrians while also being able to execute a full arc.

Rationale Using the long cane, whether it is folded or extended, provides the learner with the ability to cover more surface area with one sweep than a hand search would allow. It also reduces the chances of having her hand stepped on during the search. The cane is moved slowly to avoid pushing the dropped object out of reach and to detect the object more easily. The arc shape should be familiar to the learner from the touch technique. Using the folded cane can be effective in avoiding contact with people and furniture.

Variation If the learner intends to search for the dropped object with her hand, she can move the hand in overlapping and increasing concentric circles, beginning in the center and moving out toward the left, and then back to the center moving out toward the right. (The learner may wish to use hand sanitizer after searching the floor.)

STEP 6 The learner stops the cane sweep when the item is contacted, using the cane as a reference point to locate and pick up the dropped object. When using a hand search, the learner picks up the item as soon as she contacts it.

Rationale Being able to trace the length of the cane to locate the dropped object makes the technique more efficient.

STEP 7 If the item is not found during the full sweep, the learner may adjust her position and repeat the procedure if she wishes to continue the search. The learner makes a slight adjustment in the direction she estimates the object to be (typically a step or two forward) before repeating the pattern.

Rationale The learner adjusts her position slightly to make sure that a new area is being searched. The adjustment is slight to ensure that the learner searches in an overlapping pattern, increasing the odds of locating the item. The new area to be searched should have a slight overlap with the initial area searched to reduce the possibility that the object is in an area between the two searches and missed altogether.

CONSIDERATIONS FOR LOCATING DROPPED OBJECTS

■ Traditional O&M training sequences may suggest that developing the skill for locating dropped objects should take place during a basic skills unit and prior to the use of the long cane. While time can readily be spent on the auditory and spatial skills involved in locating dropped objects, the long cane (whether extended or folded) covers a greater area during the search pattern and can help learners avoid the need to sweep the floor with their bare hands. Ultimately, the appropriate time and approach for teaching this skill depends on the needs of the learner.

■ The ability to localize sounds is foundational to locating dropped objects in environments where a given object creates a noise and the learner can hear the sound. Sound localization is a skill that can be developed and reinforced throughout the O&M training program.

■ O&M specialists should review auditory reports and conduct a functional assessment of the learner's ability to localize sounds prior to beginning a unit on locating dropped objects.

Tips for Teaching Cane Techniques

Integrating Orientation

For learners to be actively engaged in travel while using the long cane, they should be encouraged to maintain full awareness of their travel environment and social surroundings. During instruction, O&M specialists can introduce or review the use of cardinal directions and route shapes for orientation purposes. Learners who have some initial orientation skills can serve as navigators, directing travel along the route. This is a good opportunity to practice orientation for solo travel.

Jacobson's (1993, 2013) five-point travel system (see Chapter 2) provides learners with a consistent structure in which to organize orientation information. O&M specialists can review the five points prior to introducing or reviewing a cane skill to stress the importance of knowing where a learner is in the environment. Once cane skills are mastered, the steps can be incorporated into lessons that fully integrate orientation strategies and effective cane use.

Sequencing

Various cane techniques are introduced grouped together in this chapter. Their sequence in the chapter, however, does not mean that all cane techniques should be introduced at the same time or in the order provided. The O&M specialist will choose the proper timing and environment to introduce various techniques. O&M specialists should include all applicable techniques in the course of training to enhance learner use and knowledge.

The instruction sequence must take into account each learner's individual circumstances. Some traditional sequences introduce the use of the long cane after working on guide techniques and upper- and lower-body protective techniques. The logic for this approach is that learners may learn best when taught skills in a perceived order of simple to complex. Some O&M specialists may choose to teach the use of the long cane prior to guide techniques and basic skills. The logic of this approach is to teach independent travel as soon as possible with the technique that will be used most often. To date, research has not been conducted to determine the efficacy of one approach over another. Whichever sequence the O&M specialist chooses for individual learners based on their travel needs and abilities, advancing to cane techniques that provide optimum coverage and information to the learner should be done as soon as it is feasible.

Learners may initially focus on the mechanics of a skill when learning various cane techniques, but as they grow more confident in their skills they can focus more on the information that can be gleaned from paying attention to orientation clues. As travel with the long cane becomes more automatic, learners can focus on the dynamic environmental information available to them and optimize their active participation in the process.

For learners who have limited travel experience, O&M specialists will want to provide as much exposure and opportunities to explore variations in environmental features as possible. Finding unique hallways, lobby areas, doors, stairs, and unusual seating, such as folding seats in an auditorium or bench seating commonly found in cafeterias, in which to apply cane skills will help with generalization of skills in novel environments.

O&M Specialist Positioning

The O&M specialist's position in relation to the learner during these exercises varies considerably during the introduction of cane techniques. The position is dictated by the specific technique and each step of the learning process. The O&M specialist should observe the learner from different angles. Arc width coverage can be observed from behind or in front of the learner. O&M specialists who choose to walk backward in front of their learners must be aware of their own surroundings to avoid injury. O&M specialists may walk alongside learners who have low vision to observe eye movements for eccentric viewing or scanning while using the long cane. Specialists should face forward when ascending and descending stairs, positioned to the side and slightly below the learner to ensure the safety of the learner and the specialist. When instructing on detection of drop-offs, specialists will want to arrive at the drop-off in advance of their learners to ensure that beginning learners do not step off curbs without preparation.

Some learners—due to attention span, cognitive understanding, or physical abilities—may struggle to keep their hands in a centered position for the touch technique and may benefit from using their free hand ("helper hand") to monitor the center position initially to help establish a kinesthetic sense of the desired position. O&M specialists may need to adjust their positioning to monitor learners' ability to maintain a consistent position.

Regardless of the technique being presented or reviewed, O&M specialists must always be positioned so that they are physically and mentally able to react to the environment on behalf of their learners, based on their learners' abilities, ages, and medical and physical capabilities. The goal is to encourage learners to problem solve and react to the travel environment with increasing independence. Ultimately, learners will have independent travel experiences and must learn to deal with unexpected situations in dynamic travel environments. O&M specialists should collaborate with learners and their families to ensure that learners have a full complement of appropriate travel experiences to prepare them for increased levels of independence.

Strategies for Different Populations

General Strategies

O&M specialists may use a variety of strategies to promote cane use and appreciation. Newer learners (regardless of age) can be introduced to experienced learners who practice effective cane use and can serve as role models. Younger learners can color or label the parts of the cane on a life-size diagram or 8.5 by 11-inch worksheet. Involving the family in creating a diary or photo collage of the many places that learners visit using their canes can provide encouragement to younger learners and their families and promote positive associations with cane usage for others. Posters with positive images of older individuals using long canes can help to encourage cane use on a school campus.

Since most cane techniques involve movement and some cadence or rhythm, musical notes and sound patterns can be used to teach various techniques. For example, the two-point-touch technique can be thought of as two half notes for a complete arc from one side to the other (**tap** hold, **tap** hold) and the three-point-touch technique sequence would be half note, quarter note, quarter note (**tap-tap-tap**) for one swing of the cane. Similarly, one can say or sing a tap-tap cadence for two-point-touch and a swish-swish cadence for constant-contact cane technique. Metronomes, songs, chants, and rhythmic instruments have been used to help younger learners keep time when practicing touch technique (see Fazzi & Petersmeyer, 2001, for specific ideas). Another option is to attach a small strip of sandpaper to the floor at the midpoint of the arc when learning constant-contact cane technique so the learner has an auditory cue for the midpoint or apex as well as a sense of the evenness of the arc.

Providing learners with clear verbal instructions will help them to learn the components and rationales of the various cane techniques. Some learners may benefit from describing cane techniques to others, or recording their instructions and playing or reading them back to determine how they might be improved.

Learners can practice using auditory skills while traveling with a cane. Skills such as sound localization, identifying sound shadows, and using echolocation to keep track of parallel wall surfaces or outdoor hedges and building lines can be applied while traveling with a cane.

Learners Who Have Low Vision

Many learners who have low vision will benefit from use of the long cane. Some learners will use touch technique or constant-contact cane technique as a primary technique to provide surface preview. Some learners will use verification cane technique or a similar adaptation of touch technique or diagonal cane technique to supplement the visual information they are already using. And some learners may carry a long cane solely for identification purposes. When conducting a comprehensive O&M assessment that includes an examination of common mobility problems experienced by individuals who have low vision, O&M specialists will work with their learners to determine the most appropriate cane techniques to use given the learner's ability to visually navigate the environment.

For learners who will be using cane techniques, the use of visual modeling or demonstration of cane techniques may be used in conjunction with verbal instruction. When using visual modeling, O&M specialists should select an environment that is well lit and free from glare and visual clutter, and provide contrast as needed to make sure that the key aspects of the techniques are easily seen. For example, the correct position of the cane for diagonal technique can be shown to the learner. The long white cane and its position across the specialist's body will be more visible if the O&M specialist is wearing dark clothing. O&M specialists should be careful, however, not to rely primarily on the use of demonstration for teaching mobility techniques, as learners with low vision may miss important aspects of positioning and rationale if they are not paired with a clear explanation.

Learners who have low vision can be encouraged to practice visual skills while traveling with the long cane. Skills such as scanning, eccentric viewing, visual path preview, distance vision recognition, or distance estimation can be combined with cane techniques so that learners integrate information from multiple senses to enhance travel experiences. Some of these skills can be taught in an indoor environment and then applied to outdoor environments. For example, if a learner has mastered the touch technique, the O&M specialist can introduce visual path preview and planning using three levels of *vertical scanning*: head level at the greatest distance at which the learner can resolve images, mid level at the greatest distance at which the learner can resolve images, and lower level at

the greatest distance at which the learner can resolve images. (See Chapter 10 for a more detailed description of scanning techniques.) Once the learner has practiced this scanning pattern, she can then use it to plan her path of travel around obstacles that may be present in a hallway or lobby area. These same skills can be applied in outdoor environments and later used to anticipate drop-offs, obstacles, and overhangs in a variety of travel environments. In pairing visual skills with cane techniques, O&M specialists may notice an initial reduction in the quality of cane skills exhibited while the learner is concentrating on something new. However, with practice, both skills can be readily mastered in conjunction with each other.

Similarly, O&M specialists will want to consider the incorporation of optical and nonoptical low vision devices during cane-technique instruction. Nonoptical means for reducing glare, such as wearing a hat or visor with a minimum 3-inch brim or appropriate tints, can be incorporated into cane-technique lessons as needed. Introducing a device such as a monocular *telescope* may need to be done in a separate unit and then paired with the use of the cane in indoor and outdoor environments.

While learning new cane techniques, some learners may need to focus primarily on the cane skill and the tactile and auditory information provided. Some O&M specialists elect to use a sleep shade for initial cane-skill training for learners who have low vision, but the integration of visual and cane skills is the end goal and the two should be worked on in combination as much as possible. When the two skill sets are clearly integrated, learners can develop a good idea of how each will benefit travel in a variety of environments and under changing conditions.

Age Differences

Cane techniques can be introduced and taught to children as young as two years old (or younger if the child has adequate balance for walking) and to adults in their nineties and beyond. For very young children, canes are available in petite sizes with adapted grips to make finger placement on the flat edge of the grip easier to maintain. The National Federation of the Blind (NFB) straight fiberglass cane with metal glider tip, which is relatively lightweight, can also be effective with young children. NFB sponsors a program in which canes can be ordered free of charge online (see the Resources section in the online AFB Learning Center). Early exposure to and

Diane L. Fazzi

use of the long cane by toddlers and preschool-age children helps to establish early concepts of the cane as a tool and the general concept of tool usage.

O&M specialists should use developmentally appropriate approaches, taking into consideration the child's age, to teach young children to use the long cane for purposeful movement. (See Cutter, 2004; Pogrund & Fazzi, 2002; Skellenger & Sapp, 2010, for additional strategies for teaching O&M to young children.)

Adventitiously blind adults may be most interested in getting moving and going to destinations and may become frustrated with practicing techniques without purposeful travel. They may learn basic techniques rapidly as well.

Older adults can also benefit from use of the long cane in their homes or community travel environments. For those with health limitations or problems with stamina, instruction may need to be broken down into meaningful steps, with nonphysical activities planned during rest breaks.

Learners with Additional Disabilities

Learners with intellectual disabilities may benefit from a combination of verbal and physical prompts to maintain good positioning while traveling with a cane. The steps of the techniques described in this chapter can be broken down into even smaller components as part of a task analysis to use for planning instruction for learners who have learning challenges. Some learners may need additional

support to maintain the grasp on the cane, either through a system of behavior supports or with the help of an adapted grip.

Learners who use a wheelchair or other support device for mobility may also benefit from travel with a cane under certain circumstances. Adaptations to techniques can be made for individuals based on their needs and the configuration of the given environment (see Griffin-Shirley & Bozeman, 2016; Rosen & Crawford, 2010). For example, learners who use a walker may have a long cane mounted to the walker on a swivel hitch so that the learner may clear the path in advance of taking the next step. The process can be tiring but the learner can still rely on the walker for support and balance. Adults who have low vision and use four-wheeled walkers can be taught to effectively use their vision to anticipate surface-level changes and safe techniques for braking to use the walker in a variety of environments. Similarly, learners who use a wheelchair may use a long cane for surface preview. Curb feelers can be attached to the wheelchair to trail a wall surface. Drop-off detection is a major concern for adults who have visual impairments and use mobility devices. While the cane and low-vision techniques can help learners develop strategies for independent travel, a complementary approach is to also work to modify the environment to reduce drop-offs by installing ramps or provide advanced warning of impending drop-offs by installing tactile tiles.

O&M specialists may work with physical therapists and orthotic and prosthetic specialists to design long canes that can be used by individuals with physical and health impairments, including those with limb amputations (Smith & Penrod, 2010).

Self-Advocacy

O&M specialists teach their learners cane techniques and their utility for future travel in familiar and unfamiliar areas. It is equally important for learners to develop the confidence to be able to explain to others, as needed, the correct cane techniques or purposes behind them. The end goal is to ensure that learners have the tools they need for self-determination in a variety of situations they may encounter while traveling in home, school, work, or community environments.

Block Travel

Block travel encompasses the skills and techniques used in travel within or around a block, an area typically bounded by four streets. This travel includes walking along a sidewalk, making turns to intersecting sidewalks, utilizing *tactile* and *auditory alignment* techniques (using available auditory or tactile cues, the long cane, or a body part to establish or maintain a straight line for travel), detecting or recognizing the end of the block and the edge of the street, and reviewing street-corner familiarization. Travel within a block provides orientation and mobility (O&M) specialists and learners with great opportunities to practice guide techniques, cane skills, and to apply orientation skills in an outdoor environment. Street-crossing strategies and techniques are covered in Chapter 7.

The techniques presented in this chapter should be applied, practiced, and reintroduced, in both residential and commercial areas. The mobility techniques and orientation strategies used in a residential area and those used in a small business or urban area are basically the same, just applied in different situations with different environmental features.

When selecting the starting environment in which to introduce a technique, the O&M specialist must take into consideration the features of the sidewalk as well as the learner's abilities, comfort, and convenience. At times, the needs of the learner or a motivating destination may influence the choice of teaching area for block travel. For example, learners at a rehabilitation center located in a small business area may be more interested in traveling to small shops or restaurants than practicing walking on the sidewalk in a residential area. Other learners may be more interested in traveling in a residential area to visit friends.

Some O&M specialists may prefer learners begin outdoor travel on a wide commercial sidewalk, rather than a quiet sidewalk in a residential area. While some quiet residential areas may have fewer perceived distractions for practicing cane techniques, a wide sidewalk in a commercial area with steady vehicular traffic and minimal pedestrian traffic can be an ideal location to practice cane techniques and aligning with parallel traffic while walking. Driveways are uncommon and sidewalks are typically well maintained in these areas. Sidewalks in residential areas are generally 4 to 5 feet wide and provide a regular edge or landscape strip that may be beneficial for some learners, but may result in overcorrection from one side of the sidewalk to the other or overreliance on trailing the edge of the sidewalk. Residential sidewalks often have many driveways and irregularities that can interrupt the smooth flow of travel and may not contain enough traffic to provide orientation cues. Both residential and commercial environments should be covered during instruction, but the order may be adjusted by individual O&M specialists to suit their learners' needs.

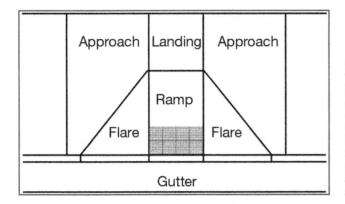

Figure 6.1

Parts of a Curb Ramp

Source: Kirschbaum, J. B., Axelson, P. W., Longmuir, P. E., Mispagel, K. M., Stein, J. A., & Yamada, D. A. (2001). Designing sidewalks and trails for access, Part II of II: Best practices design guide. Washington, DC: US Department of Transportation, Federal Highway Administration. Retrieved from http://www.fhwa.dot.gov /environment/bicycle_pedestrian/publications/sidewalk2 /sidewalks207.cfm

Common Terminology and Concepts in Block Travel

There are many different terms used to describe sidewalks, curb ramps, *crosswalks,* landscaped areas, and the various components of those features. Different terms may be used by different professions or user groups, in different regions of the United States, and in different countries. For example, regional variations in the name for the grass or landscaping that is located between the sidewalk and the street include: landscape strip, collector strip, parking strip, planter strip, planting strip, park strip, idiot strip, hell strip, buffer, boulevard, tree lawn, furnishing zone, furniture zone, landscape area, terrace, greenway, snow zone, grass lawn, parkway, verge, lawn extension, and utility strip (Federal Highway Administration, 2008). O&M specialists may prefer to use the common term for their region, but should provide examples of other terms used in other areas. In this book *landscape strip* will be the term used to describe the area between the street and the sidewalk and *grass line* will be used to describe the area where the sidewalk meets the vegetation, dirt or gravel, lawn, or other yard feature found along the edge of the sidewalk furthest from the street.

Terms used by *traffic engineers* vary from those commonly used by O&M specialists. In this book, some of the common traffic-engineering terminology will be used and some O&M terms that may be misunderstood by engineers will be identified. Aligning the terminology used by O&M specialists, traffic engineers, and urban designers will allow for better communication across disciplines and increased professional collaboration and research.

Both driveways and curb ramps may be referred to as curb cuts. The term *curb ramp* usually refers to the ramp leading to a crosswalk that is intended for use by pedestrians traveling on that route. Figure 6.1 shows the components of a curb ramp. The components of curb ramps, as described by the US Access Board (2011) include the ramp, flares, landing or turning space, grade break or gutter, and *detectable warning surface*. As listed in the *Americans with Disabilities Act (ADA)* regulations, detectable warning surfaces (gray area pictured at the bottom of the ramp in Figure 6.1) are specific surface textures that are detectable underfoot, intended to notify individuals who are blind or who have low vision that their next step will be into a street, train track area, or other hazardous location. The surfaces are not intended to provide information about the alignment of the crosswalk and should not be used as an alignment aid by pedestrians who are blind. A *blended curb,* or blended transition, is a slope to the street from the sidewalk that has a grade less than 5 percent, where the entire corner area may be level with the street. In the United States, detectable warning surfaces are required on all curb ramps or blended transitions constructed since 2001 to provide a cue to the location of the edge of the street.

Curb ramp design will vary from different locations within a city and from city to city. The type of ramp built depends on the space available, whether there is a landscape strip or a slope, and other geographic features. Some types of curb ramps may have curbs along the edges of the ramp, referred to by traffic engineers and public works officials as returned curbs. Learners should be introduced to a variety of curb ramps for travel preparation in a variety of environments, and O&M specialists should be familiar with the proper terminology for discussing curb ramps.

Transition to Outdoor Travel: Cane Technique Practice

While learners may have developed and practiced various cane techniques in an indoor environment, outdoor travel introduces additional challenges in terms of surfaces, obstacles, and textures that can disrupt the use of various techniques. The first lessons should concentrate on refining cane techniques and applying them to outdoor environmental features such as concrete sidewalks with grass or other landscaping along the edges.

Lessons should begin on smooth, relatively wide sidewalk areas with subsequent practice on more challenging blocks. Some O&M specialists prefer to begin practice on the sidewalk of a campus, church, or office facility to further solidify cane techniques before introducing orientation and other activities in block travel. Some of these facilities may include small sets of stairs that can be used to improve sensitivity to drop-offs. The time involved in refining cane techniques in outdoor environments and progressing to block travel will vary from learner to learner. Basic recovery skills, further orientation concepts, travel around the block, and technique modifications may be introduced in subsequent lessons while still reinforcing appropriate cane technique.

When evaluating and practicing cane techniques, important aspects to consider include technique refinement, pace, straight line of travel, and detection of changes in surface and drop-offs.

Technique Refinement

The O&M specialist and learner should critically analyze all components of the constant-contact or two-point-touch technique as applied to sidewalk travel, with special emphasis on

- consistent arc width coverage;
- consistent arc height (if using touch technique), which minimizes the cane's contact with minor undulations in the sidewalk;
- maintaining rhythm and staying in step; and
- the learner's reaction when the cane sticks in the grass line, uneven pavement, or cracks

(a relaxed wrist, elbow, and shoulder should be used to absorb the shock when the cane sticks).

Pace

The learner should maintain a consistent and fluid pace to enhance his straight line of travel.

Straight Line of Travel

Along with a good pace, the ability to maintain a straight line of travel will minimize veering and recovery situations on the part of the learner.

Poor line of travel (veering) can be caused by

- poor posture (check and correct the traveler's body positioning, starting with the head and moving down to feet; check all body parts),
- uneven or lopsided arc width (check that the hand is centered and refine arc width),
- overcorrecting when the learner contacts a landscape strip or grass line (emphasize making microcorrections), and
- slow travel speed, which can result in poor balance.

Detection of Changes in Surface and Drop-Offs

The learner should recognize level changes either in the path of travel or along the edges of the sidewalk, such as slopes, drop-offs, curbs, or stairs, and make minor corrections when contacting the grass line, landscape strip, or drop-off along the edge of the sidewalk. The learner should attempt to keep a consistent pace when the cane tip contacts the landscape strip or grass line, simultaneously correcting toward the desired line of travel.

If the learner is having difficulty detecting curbs, the O&M specialist can consider the following possible causes and remedies:

- The learner may be overstepping his cane and may need to extend his arm further.
- The cane may not be the proper length and a longer cane length may need to be selected.
- The learner's pace may be too fast and he should practice walking at a more controlled pace.
- The learner may have poor distance awareness and need to practice anticipating the length of a typical sidewalk and integrate the use of auditory and other sensory cues for this purpose.

- The learner may be using ineffective cane skills, such as an arc height that is too high, and may need to refine the current technique or switch to a technique that more easily detects drop-offs such as constant-contact.

- The learner may have slow reaction time and may need to focus on auditory and sensory cues to better anticipate curb approach, or work with a longer cane or different cane technique to compensate for the reaction time.

TACTILE ALIGNMENT WITH PHYSICAL BLOCK FEATURES

Purpose: To assist the learner in maintaining a straight line of travel on the sidewalk by using available tactile cues.

PROCEDURE AT A GLANCE

1 The learner establishes initial alignment with a landscape strip, grass line, fence, or wall found along the sidewalk by using his cane tip, and foot if needed, to determine his relative position on the sidewalk.

2 Once aligned, the learner travels forward in a straight line and touches the landscape strip, grass line, or sidewalk edge again only if he has veered or if the sidewalk has a variation in width or direction.

3 If the landscape strip, grass line, or sidewalk edge is contacted, the learner makes a minor correction to move away from it and then straightens slightly.

METHOD

STEP 1 The learner establishes initial alignment with a landscape strip, grass line, fence, or wall found along the sidewalk by using his cane tip extended in front of him to determine his relative position on the sidewalk. If needed, he can also use the side of his foot for alignment with the landscape strip or grass line, but he may need to reposition his foot to make sure he is not walking on the edge between the sidewalk and landscape strip because the vertical height between the two can vary along the sidewalk, leading to missteps. When traveling to the right of center, the grass line, fence, or wall should be approximately 4 to 6 inches beyond the learner's right shoulder.

Diane L. Fazzi

Rationale The learner can use his cane tip to reach slightly to the side to determine if there is a landscape strip or grass line and to establish an initial position that is slightly right of center (for regions in which walking to the right of center is common) and slightly to the left of the landscape strip, grass line, fence, or other feature found along the edge of the sidewalk. A position 4 to 6 inches from the edge ensures that the learner is not overreaching with his cane and provides a general guideline to follow and will vary depending on the width of the sidewalk.

Diane L. Fazzi

STEP 2 Once aligned, the learner travels forward in a straight line and touches the landscape strip, grass line, or sidewalk edge again only if he has veered or if the sidewalk has a variation in width or direction.

Rationale Unplanned contact with the landscape strip or grass line provides the learner with a tactile cue to realign for a desired straight line of travel along the sidewalk.

STEP 3 If the landscape strip, grass line, or sidewalk edge is contacted, the learner makes a minor correction to move slightly away from it and then straightens slightly to regain his straight line of travel (see Recovery from Minor Veer later in this chapter).

Rationale Especially in residential areas where sidewalks may only be 4 to 5 feet wide, the learner should make only minor corrections using *tactile alignment* or he will find himself contacting the grass on the opposite side of the sidewalk. Contact from one side of the sidewalk to the other, sometimes referred to as pinballing, is detrimental to establishing a straight line of travel and can be frustrating and disorienting to some learners. Minor corrections should be practiced as needed to avoid or reduce possible pinballing. It is not necessary for most learners to stop travel to make these microcorrections. As long as the learner has a clear perception of the direction he has veered, he can use auditory or tactile cues to make a microcorrection to regain his position and line of travel.

AUDITORY ALIGNMENT WITH PARALLEL TRAFFIC

Purpose: To assist the learner in maintaining a straight line of travel on the sidewalk or when crossing open areas parallel to traffic using available auditory traffic cues.

PROCEDURE AT A GLANCE

1 The learner stands still on the sidewalk and listens to several cars as they pass on the street beside him.

2 The learner aligns his body to the sound of the parallel traffic by projecting a line of travel toward the furthest point at which vehicles are heard traveling.

3 Continuing to listen, the learner travels parallel to the line heard, further adjusting alignment as needed while walking.

METHOD

STEP 1 The learner stands still on the sidewalk and listens to several cars as they pass on the street beside him.

Rationale Listening for more than one car, if possible, can provide a better sense of vehicle movement to use for alignment cues.

STEP 2 The learner aligns his body to the sound of parallel traffic by projecting a line of travel toward the furthest point where vehicles are heard traveling parallel to his path. The approach to aligning with parallel traffic varies slightly according to the direction of the traffic and the direction that the learner is traveling along the sidewalk. When the learner is walking in the same direction as the nearest parallel traffic, then the learner should listen to traffic passing and make sure it sounds loudest as it passes and has relatively similar alignment when heard approaching from behind and out in front of him. He maintains this body alignment as he travels, listening to and aligning with the parallel traffic path as far ahead as possible. When the learner is walking in the opposite direction of the near-lane-parallel traffic (see Figures 7.4 and 7.5 in Chapter 7), he will align himself using the first point where the traffic is heard and adjust his alignment so the sound is loudest as it passes him and has relatively similar alignment behind him.

Rationale Listening to traffic further out along the street can provide better alignment cues in terms of proximity to the line of travel on the sidewalk.

Variation If the learner must use the far-lane-parallel traffic (see Figures 7.4 and 7.5) for alignment, such as in a situation when there is no near-lane-parallel traffic, the learner needs to recognize and adjust his alignment in relation to the traffic sounds furthest away.

STEP 3 Continuing to listen, the learner travels parallel to the line heard, further adjusting alignment as needed while walking.

Rationale Practicing aligning with the auditory cues of parallel traffic while moving will facilitate efficient travel.

CONSIDERATIONS FOR AUDITORY ALIGNMENT WITH PARALLEL TRAFFIC

- Whether using tactile or auditory approaches to alignment, O&M specialists can practice microcorrections with learners when working to establish a straight line of sidewalk travel.

- As a practice exercise while the learner stands in one place, the O&M specialist may deliberately have the learner misalign himself and correct that alignment solely by listening. The O&M specialist may provide feedback at first to help the learner correctly align with traffic.

- Initial practice with this skill may be static, but it should be practiced while moving as well. Feedback from the O&M specialist may be helpful as the learner first travels and aligns with traffic while moving.

- If the learner has consistent difficulty with auditory alignment on one side or the other, it may indicate a hearing loss or issues with conceptual understanding and may require additional time to develop the concepts of parallel and perpendicular alignment. With practice, learners with hearing loss may be able to compensate for auditory alignment challenges. Results of a functional auditory assessment should be made available to the learner and O&M specialist before this phase of training.

- A one-way street can be a good location to begin working on this auditory skill, standing and walking first in the same direction as the flow of vehicular traffic and then switching to the opposite direction. Practicing on both sides of the street allows the learner to experience traffic on both his left and right side. It is best to begin practice at a mid-block location, rather than at a corner where turning cars may make the task more difficult. Two-way traffic and more intermittent traffic patterns can be introduced after the learner has demonstrated the ability to align with one direction of traffic.

- Various techniques may be used. Some O&M specialists encourage their learners to "aim their noses" in the direction where a car was last heard and walk in that direction, or trace the movement of the car with the arm and hand while standing and listening. A clock face analogy can be used in teaching this skill by asking learners to assign clock reference points to the sounds. For example, when aligned, a vehicle may first be heard at seven o'clock, disappear at eleven o'clock, and be loudest at the nine o'clock position. In areas with substantial traffic, learners may be able to envision the traffic as a wall of sound and a reference point from which to align.

- The auditory alignment skill is used in street crossing and when recovering from a major veer.

AUDITORY ALIGNMENT WITH (SQUARING OFF TO) PERPENDICULAR TRAFFIC

Note: Some O&M specialists prefer to use the term "squaring off to traffic" for perpendicular alignment; others use "squaring off" only in relation to a solid tactile object such as a curb or a wall.

Purpose: To assist the learner in recognizing the distance to the traffic lanes when approaching a street and to develop skills in aligning perpendicularly to traffic sounds (an essential skill in recovery from veering).

PROCEDURE AT A GLANCE

1 The learner listens for vehicles traveling on the street, which is roughly in front of him.

2 The learner turns his body so traffic is passing directly across the front of his body plane.

3 Approaching from various distances and listening to traffic, the learner stops approximately 5 feet from the street edge.

METHOD

STEP 1 The learner listens for vehicles traveling on the street, which is roughly in front of him. Listening for more than one car, if possible, can provide a better sense of the vehicle movement to use for alignment cues.

Rationale Taking time to listen to the cars on the street in front of him enables the learner to localize the sounds and attend to the sounds as the cars move from left-to-right and right-to-left in front of him. The sound of vehicles can be combined with other techniques for alignment, but it is essential for the learner's safety to be aware of the distance and movement of vehicles when approaching a street.

Variation Alignment to perpendicular traffic when it is behind the learner is also an important skill in recovering from a major veer from the sidewalk or during a street crossing and should be practiced as well.

STEP 2 The learner turns his body so traffic is passing directly across the front of his body plane, sounding roughly equal in each ear and loudest when directly in front of him. If the sound of the traffic is loudest in his right ear or his left ear, then he is not aligned perpendicularly to the traffic sounds in front of him. He can conceptualize the flow of traffic in front of him as a wall of sound to square off with. He should be encouraged to listen to traffic from each direction to try and determine how far away the vehicles are (i.e., which lane they are in).

Rationale The sounds of both near-lane-perpendicular and far-lane-perpendicular traffic provide additional cues and listening angles that can help the learner to align with perpendicular traffic.

STEP 3 Approaching from various distances and listening to traffic, the learner stops approximately 5 feet from the street edge.

Rationale Learning to judge the distance of traffic lanes and stopping before reaching the street is a necessary safety measure when approaching a street.

Variation The learner should also practice aligning to traffic with his back to the street. This skill can be important in reorienting from a major veer and in recovering during a street crossing.

CONSIDERATIONS FOR AUDITORY ALIGNMENT WITH (SQUARING OFF TO) PERPENDICULAR TRAFFIC

- As a practice exercise, the O&M specialist may deliberately have the learner misalign himself and correct that alignment solely by listening. The O&M specialist may provide feedback at first to help the learner correctly align with traffic.
- Auditory alignment with perpendicular traffic is a skill that is needed when recovering from a major veer and during street crossing.

RECOGNIZING AND NEGOTIATING A CROSS SLOPE (SLOPE PERPENDICULAR TO THE LINE OF TRAVEL)

Purpose: To enable the learner to detect cross slopes or driveways that intersect the sidewalk.

> **PROCEDURE AT A GLANCE**
>
> **1** The learner detects a cross slope underfoot and under his cane.
>
> **2** While continuing walking, the learner widens his arc slightly on the side away from the street to see if he has veered from the sidewalk. He listens for traffic and adjusts his pace and alignment slightly away from the street to maintain a straight path of travel on the sidewalk through a sloped driveway area.
>
> **3** If a level area is detected underfoot or by the cane, the learner moves toward it to continue on the sidewalk.

METHOD

STEP 1 The learner detects a *cross slope* underfoot and under his cane. The learner may notice that his stance is uneven, with one foot slightly lower than the other, or the learner may perceive that he is being "pulled" toward one side or the other as he walks. Similarly, the arc of the cane may feel as if it is becoming wider on the downslope side.

Rationale Detecting the cross slope is the first step in preventing veering into the street. The cross slope often indicates driveways and the need to modify cane technique and alignment.

Diane L. Fazzi

STEP 2 While continuing walking, the learner widens his arc slightly on the side away from the street to see if he contacts a more level area that is likely to be the sidewalk. He listens for traffic to make sure he is not getting closer to the parallel traffic, and adjusts his pace and alignment slightly away from the street to maintain a straight path of travel on the sidewalk through a sloped driveway area. If the learner is using touch technique, recognition of a cross slope is a good time to switch to constant-contact cane technique in anticipation of potential drop-offs.

Rationale When crossing a driveway, particularly in a commercial area, it is generally better to move out of the driveway area quickly, so it may be best to continue walking while checking for the level area of the sidewalk. Additional awareness of traffic and a modification of pace and alignment may prevent veering down the driveway slope and help to maintain a straight path of travel.

STEP 3 If a level area is detected underfoot or by the cane, the learner moves toward it to continue on the sidewalk.

Rationale Sidewalks are supposed to have a slope of less than 2 percent for wheelchair accessibility, so the sidewalk area should generally be level and without a severe cross slope.

CONSIDERATIONS FOR RECOGNIZING AND NEGOTIATING A CROSS SLOPE

- Some learners may automatically make adjustments to cross slopes without specific instruction or feedback, but others may need practice and help in recognizing the slopes and how to make appropriate adjustments to maintain a straight line of travel.
- In general, steeper cross slopes are more detectable underfoot. In newer sidewalk designs, where the sidewalk is required to be level for wheelchair access, any slope may indicate a veer down a driveway and the need to correct onto the level sidewalk. In older areas, there may still be driveways with significant cross slopes across the sidewalk.

RECOVERY FROM SIDEWALK VEER

Recovery from Minor Veer

Purpose: To enable the learner to relocate the desired sidewalk after a minor veer in a safe, efficient, and systematic manner.

PROCEDURE AT A GLANCE

1 The learner, upon realizing that he has veered away from the intended sidewalk, should stop and remain aware of his intended line of direction.

2 The learner checks the ground on both sides of his body with the full length of his cane.

3 If the learner locates the sidewalk when executing this procedure, he makes the necessary correction to place himself on the sidewalk and continues in his desired direction.

METHOD

STEP 1 The learner, upon realizing that he has veered away from the intended sidewalk, should stop and remain aware of his intended line of direction and the location of the parallel street.

Rationale Stopping allows the learner to maintain his existing line of travel until he has determined the correct direction to regain his position and orientation. Stopping to think about the location of the parallel street also provides a reminder of the intended direction as well as potential clues.

STEP 2 The learner checks the ground on both sides of his body with the full length of his cane and listens for a passing car on the parallel street to confirm his distance from the street and that he has not stepped into the street.

Rationale The learner checks both sides to facilitate efficient and systematic location of the sidewalk if he has veered less than 3 or 4 feet from his intended line of travel. Listening to traffic and confirming the distance from the street can provide orientation and safety information.

Variation The learner may switch the cane from one hand to the other to increase the area he is exploring.

STEP 3 If the learner locates the sidewalk when executing this procedure, he makes the necessary correction to place himself on the sidewalk and continues in his desired direction.

Rationale Locating and repositioning on the sidewalk helps the learner to travel efficiently as he resumes his straight line of travel and ensures continual safety.

CONSIDERATIONS FOR RECOVERY FROM MINOR VEER

- Common clues that can help inform the learner that he has veered include contacting a car, curb, landscape strip, or grass line in his path of travel, or a change in slope or type of terrain.
- The learner must be taught to check ahead of himself and to each side to ensure contact with the proper surface. A common error is for the learner to move his feet or turn his body when following this procedure.
- The learner may initially search on the side where he thinks the sidewalk is located.
- To increase the area to be examined, the learner may wish to move closer to the object or grass line in front of him.

Recovery from Major Veer

Purpose: To enable the learner to relocate the desired sidewalk in a safe, efficient, and systematic manner when he has veered farther than his cane's reach from the sidewalk.

	PROCEDURE AT A GLANCE
1	The learner, upon realizing that he has veered away from the intended sidewalk, should stop and remain aware of his intended line of travel.
2	The learner checks the ground on both sides of his body with the full length of his cane.
3	If the learner does not locate the sidewalk through cane extension, he determines the location of the parallel street through available clues and turns and walks directly toward the parallel street.
4a	If the learner locates the desired sidewalk before reaching the street, he stops and turns in the intended line of travel.
4b	If the learner does not locate the desired sidewalk before reaching the street, he detects the street, then makes a 180-degree turn and walks back away from the street, following the edge of the driveway (if possible) on the side closer to his original travel direction, looking for the sidewalk until the desired sidewalk is located.
5	The learner resumes travel in his original intended line of direction.

METHOD

STEP 1 The learner, upon realizing that he has veered away from the intended sidewalk, should stop and remain aware of his intended line of travel and the location of the parallel street.

Rationale Stopping allows the learner to maintain his existing line of travel until he has determined the correct direction to regain his position and orientation. Stopping to think about the location of the parallel street also provides a reminder of the intended direction as well as potential clues.

Diane L. Fazzi

STEP 2 The learner checks the ground on both sides of his body with the full length of his cane and listens for a passing car on the parallel street to confirm his distance from the street (and that he is not in the street).

Rationale The learner checks both sides to facilitate efficient and systematic location of the sidewalk if he has veered less than 3 or 4 feet from his intended line of travel. Listening to traffic and confirming the distance from the street can provide orientation and safety information.

Variations The learner may switch the cane from one hand to the other to increase the area he is exploring. Other variations for this procedure include sweeping the cane in a 180-degree arc and using the three-point-touch variation for level surfaces—for front and lateral recovery.

Diane L. Fazzi

STEP 3 If the learner does not locate the sidewalk through cane extension, he determines the location of the parallel street through available clues and turns and walks directly toward the parallel street. The learner should be aware of the street location when approaching it and use constant-contact cane technique to locate the slope or drop-off.

Rationale The learner walks to the street to establish a reference point for a systematic search and to maintain orientation. He turns directly toward the street to minimize the amount of time it takes to reach the street.

Variations If no traffic is present, the learner may use other clues (such as the slope of the terrain, the angle at which he has contacted the object, or pedestrian traffic) to determine the location of the street. The learner may utilize constant-contact or touch-and-slide cane technique to detect small changes while negotiating an all-concrete area when approaching the parallel street. Through environmental clues, such as cracks that may border the sidewalk or a leveling of the pavement, the learner may be able to locate the sidewalk without going all the way to the street.

STEP 4A If the learner locates the desired sidewalk before reaching the street, he stops and turns in the intended line of travel.

Rationale There is no need to continue further if the sidewalk has been located.

Diane L. Fazzi

STEP 4B If the learner does not locate the desired sidewalk before reaching the street, he detects the street, then makes a 180-degree turn and walks back away from the street, following the edge of the driveway (if possible) on the side of his original intended line of travel away from the street, looking for the sidewalk until the desired sidewalk is located.

Rationale The learner makes a 180-degree turn and walks toward the sidewalk to maintain orientation and the location of the desired sidewalk. The 180-degree turn is the most direct route back to the desired sidewalk. The learner may wish to square off with the curb to facilitate a straight line of travel back to the desired sidewalk.

STEP 5 **The learner resumes travel in his original intended line of direction.**

Rationale Resuming the original intended line of travel is the ultimate goal of the technique and assists the learner with orientation and reaching the desired destination.

Diane L. Fazzi

CONSIDERATIONS FOR RECOVERY FROM MAJOR VEER

- Common clues that can help inform the learner that he has veered include contacting a car or other large object, a change in slope or type of terrain, or a change in traffic or pedestrian patterns.
- This technique for *recovery from sidewalk veer* is often used when a learner has drifted into a parking lot or driveway. Congenitally blind learners may not understand the nature of the relationship between a driveway, a sidewalk, and a parking lot without proper instruction and concept development using maps and models.
- The learner may utilize the upper-hand-and-forearm protective technique in conjunction with proper cane skills, particularly when contacting vehicles, negotiating construction zones, or walking across grassy areas.
- Traffic sounds are the most important clues available to learners in most recovery situations.
- The learner should be aware of any directional changes he makes during the recovery situation. If small obstacles block the learner's line of travel, the learner should use the normal clearing process and proceed around the obstacle.
- On occasion, a learner may contact an object, such as a car or tree, in the middle of the sidewalk, and mistakenly think he has veered. By walking toward the street, he can determine the nature of the situation, circumvent the object, return to the sidewalk, and continue in his desired direction. However, if the object is a vehicle, it is usually best to travel around the vehicle on the side of the sidewalk away from the street because the vehicle is likely to move toward the street.
- If the learner's path is entirely blocked by a vehicle and the learner can determine that it is not running, he should move away from the parallel street and trail around the vehicle to the opposite side, estimate the approximate distance from his current location and where the contact was made, and resume normal travel. The learner should be aware that the engines in some vehicles—hybrid, electric, and some gasoline-powered cars—may shut off when stopped and can start up very quickly, without notice. The learner should also be aware that some cars blocking the pathway may be parked at an angle. This may cause difficulty for the learner in realignment.
- When the learner encounters a vehicle with the engine running, he should stop, carefully step back, and wait until either he has a clear understanding of the situation or the vehicle has departed. Drivers of trucks and other large vehicles may be unable to see the learner if he stands too close to the vehicle.

- When construction or barriers are blocking the sidewalk, the learner can explore, carefully, to see if there is a path around the blocked location. The learner may also seek assistance or elect to take an alternate route. There are several potential strategies that should be discussed and considered by learners and O&M specialists. In commercial areas, there may be a covered walkway intended as a safe path for pedestrians, slightly offset from the typical sidewalk path. At an active construction site, there may be workers who can be asked to provide assistance in traveling around the area. Although not recommended, another strategy for an experienced adult learner in a familiar area with perceived limited risk can be to walk to the street, use the curb to trail the street (using three-point-touch cane technique as appropriate) until he has cleared the construction area, return to the sidewalk, and resume normal travel. However, the learner should be aware that there may be construction equipment in the street as well. Travel in the street is not generally advisable for learners in most areas due to reduced visibility, the potential for parked cars, and the lack of control over traffic patterns, regardless of the need to circumvent a construction area. Knowing that most construction areas may not have consistent accessible signage, barriers, or clearly marked safe pathways around the construction, learners may need to take a detour by going back to the nearest corner, crossing the street, traveling on the sidewalk on the other side of the street to the next intersection, then crossing back over to continue the route.
- If the learner seldom veers from the sidewalk, the O&M specialist may select a practice environment that contains obstacles and situations that will provide the learner with the opportunity to practice appropriate sidewalk recovery skills.

MAKING TURNS TO INTERSECTING SIDEWALKS

Purpose: To help the learner continue to travel around the block or make an accurate turn to prepare to cross the parallel street.

	PROCEDURE AT A GLANCE
1	Upon detecting the street, the learner stops and makes a 180-degree turn.
2	The learner takes 3 to 5 steps, then makes a 90-degree turn in the desired direction.
3	The learner extends his cane and confirms that there is a sidewalk in front of him. If he is not at a sidewalk, he searches with his cane to the right and left for the sidewalk.
4	If the learner did not reach the intersecting sidewalk on the first attempt, he turns back 90 degrees to the original direction, takes a few more steps, and once again turns 90 degrees in the desired direction to find the intersecting sidewalk.

METHOD

STEP 1 Upon detecting the street, the learner stops and makes a 180-degree turn.

Rationale The learner walks all the way to the street to confirm his location. A 180-degree turn then positions the learner to return in the direction of his approach to the street.

STEP 2 The learner takes 3 to 5 steps, then makes a 90-degree turn in the direction of the intersecting sidewalk.

Rationale On a typical sidewalk setback, 3 to 5 steps, or 6 to 10 feet, is about the correct distance to travel to locate the intersecting sidewalk or curb ramp.

Variations There are many designs and configurations of sidewalks and curb ramps. This technique will be most appropriate in areas with a 6- to 10-foot separation between the sidewalk and curb, or areas with wide sidewalks.

STEP 3 **The learner extends his cane and confirms that there is a sidewalk in front of him. If he is not at a sidewalk, he searches with his cane to the right and left for the sidewalk.**

Rationale The learner needs to confirm that he has reached a location where he should continue with travel. Depending on the design of the sidewalk and curb ramps, the distance from the street may vary.

STEP 4 **If the learner did not reach the intersecting sidewalk on the first attempt, he turns back 90 degrees to the original direction, takes a few more steps, and once again turns 90 degrees in the desired direction to find the intersecting sidewalk.**

Rationale Depending on the learner's stride length or the inset of the intersecting sidewalk, more than five steps may be needed to locate and turn onto the intersecting sidewalk.

CONSIDERATIONS FOR MAKING TURNS TO INTERSECTING SIDEWALKS

- To turn onto an intersecting sidewalk before reaching the street, the learner can begin using touch-trailing technique on the side of the sidewalk furthest from the parallel street when he thinks he is approaching the street.
- If the *corner radius* is large (very rounded), this technique is not appropriate. This technique works best in older residential and commercial areas with smaller radius corners (square corners), perpendicular curb ramps, and some landscape separation between the sidewalk and street.
- Understanding the various designs of curb ramps (e.g., parallel, perpendicular) can be helpful in making a decision about the proper technique and strategy to use. If the sidewalk is right alongside the curb (at the back of the curb), it may be necessary to make the turn when beside the street.

LOCATING LANDMARKS AND DESTINATIONS

Purpose: To enable the learner to identify specific features that can be used as landmarks in future travel, or to find existing landmarks while traveling to a specific destination. (See Chapter 2 for definitions of terms related to landmarks and clues.)

PROCEDURE AT A GLANCE

1 The learner slows his pace and walks close to the desired edge of the sidewalk, using touch-trailing or touch-and-drag technique to locate a potential landmark or destination.

2 When an object is contacted, while maintaining his position on the sidewalk, if possible, the learner uses appropriate techniques to explore and identify the object.

3 The learner determines if it is a good landmark to use, then makes a note (mental or recorded in some manner) about its location in relation to other objects and destinations, or its location within the block.

4 In order to find a known landmark, the learner repeats Steps 1 and 2.

METHOD

STEP 1 The learner slows his pace and walks close to the desired edge of the sidewalk, using touch-trailing or touch-and-drag technique to follow the edge of the sidewalk and to explore features just outside the travel path or sidewalk area to locate a potential landmark or destination. Depending on the edge being followed and auditory (and visual, if possible) awareness of objects such as poles, bushes, trees, mailboxes, building lines, doorways, or other features near that edge of the sidewalk, the learner will preselect a potential landmark.

Rationale The learner slows his pace to maintain more awareness of features just off the sidewalk area. At locations with a curb or landscape strip along the edge of the sidewalk, using a widened arc with two-point-touch technique will allow the learner to locate objects outside the sidewalk area and slightly beyond the typical travel path area. Constant-contact or touch-and-drag technique may be most effective when there is a drop-off beside the sidewalk, but these techniques may miss objects that are beyond the edge of the sidewalk.

Variations A variation of three-point-touch technique with an extra wide arc for level surfaces may be used to check the area just beyond the sidewalk surface and still keep track of the edge of the sidewalk as needed. (See Chapter 5 for a review of the Three-Point-Touch Technique variation for level surfaces.) The learner may stop and explore with his cane when he visually or auditorily detects what he thinks is an object or landmark near the sidewalk that he has not previously detected while walking along the edge of the sidewalk. On wide commercial sidewalks, various features may be located within the sidewalk area, so the learner may need to explore the sidewalk area by using a systematic search pattern (gridline pattern) to locate features (see Chapter 10 for more information on systematic scanning patterns).

STEP 2 When an object is contacted, while maintaining his position on the sidewalk, if possible, the learner uses appropriate techniques to explore and identify the object (see Detecting and Moving around Obstacles in Chapter 5). In order to select an appropriate landmark, the learner must determine that the object is unique and permanently located so that it provides consistent and useful information about the learner's location.

Rationale In an unfamiliar area, the learner needs to identify a unique and permanent object, using safe techniques while doing so.

STEP 3 The learner determines if it is a good landmark to use, then makes a note (mental or recorded in some manner) about the location of the landmark in relation to other objects and destinations, or its location within the block. As connecting walkways are contacted, such as walkways to houses in residential areas, the learner makes note of the landmark's location in relation to these other features.

Rationale Knowing about features of the environment near the sidewalk can be helpful in future travel and reorientation. Recording information for a regularly traveled route or area assists in mapping and understanding the area and its features.

STEP 4 In order to find a known landmark, the learner repeats Steps 1 and 2, beginning the technique near the expected location of the landmark.

Rationale The learner does not need to search the entire sidewalk area each time to locate a landmark if he already knows its approximate location. He can begin searching when he is close to the intended destination or landmark.

CONSIDERATIONS FOR LOCATING LANDMARKS AND DESTINATIONS

- This technique may be used in self-familiarization to a new area, or to locate specific features such as an intersecting sidewalk, pole with a pedestrian pushbutton, bus stop, or other feature that is usually just outside typical sidewalk areas. In commercial areas, specific features may include doorways or walkways to buildings.

- Learners should be aware of potential protruding objects, such as signs, guy-wires, and tree branches, and use upper-body protective technique as necessary to avoid contact with these overhead obstacles.

- The O&M specialist and learner can discuss and categorize landmarks and their locations in relation to streets, cardinal directions, and other methods as appropriate to the age, experience, and intellectual capability of the learner.

- The learner can be provided with different opportunities to determine and practice appropriate methods of gathering and recording information about areas as well as methods for self-familiarization.

DETECTING THE STREET

Purpose: To help the learner consistently anticipate the approach to an intersecting street, recognize when he has arrived at the intersecting street, and stop before walking into the street.

PROCEDURE AT A GLANCE

1 Through a combination of distance awareness, understanding of pedestrian and vehicular traffic, and recognition of sound characteristics of intersections, the learner anticipates the approaching street corner.

2 The learner slows his pace slightly, switching to constant-contact technique while maintaining his approach alignment and awareness of traffic.

3 The learner detects the drop-off at the curb with his cane tip, or the combination of the ramp slope, detectable warning surface, and slight upslope of the street surface.

4 The learner stops, maintains his body and feet in the approach line of travel, and draws the cane back toward his body and against the curb, if present, checking the slopes during the maneuver. If there is a curb ramp or blended curb, the learner may apply slightly more pressure to the cane tip as he brings it back toward his body in order to find the slope difference between the sidewalk and the street.

5 Being aware of other pedestrians, the learner checks for a curb on each side of the ramp or sloped area.

METHOD

STEP 1 Through a combination of distance awareness, understanding of pedestrian and vehicular traffic, and recognition of sound characteristics of intersections, the learner anticipates the approaching street corner.

Rationale Awareness of his position and cues in the environment help the learner to maintain orientation and allow him to use the most effective techniques for detecting the street.

Variation Not all of these cues will be available in all locations, but learners should be taught to be aware of all possibilities potentially available on each street approach.

STEP 2 **The learner slows his pace slightly, switching to constant-contact technique while maintaining his approach alignment and awareness of traffic. If the learner uses constant-contact as his main cane technique, he will not need to switch.**

Rationale Using constant-contact technique allows the learner to quickly detect the curb or the slope of the curb ramp and texture difference of the detectable warning surface. Maintaining approach alignment is important to avoid losing potentially valuable alignment cues. It is also important to avoid searching around with the cane on the approach or moving so slowly that the line of travel is affected.

Variation Some learners may need to use touch-and-slide technique to gain additional information at curb ramps and blended curbs. Touch-and-slide technique can provide added information about the location of the edge of the street at curb ramps and blended curbs because there is a more prominent push forward of the cane tip in this technique, which may be more sensitive in locating expansion joints, if present, or slope differences between the sidewalk and street. (See Touch-and-Slide Cane Technique in Chapter 5 for more information.)

STEP 3 **The learner detects the drop-off at the curb with his cane tip, or the combination of the ramp slope, detectable warning surface, and slight upslope of the street surface.**

Rationale Either the drop-off of the curb, or at curb ramps or blended curbs, the ramp slope, the detectable warning surface, or the slight upslope of the street surface indicate the edge of the street in the absence of a curb.

Variation If the learner does not detect the curb or ramp and steps off into a location that seems to be the street, he should try to maintain his alignment and simply step backward. This should be practiced during lessons with an emphasis on maintaining body alignment while executing the move.

STEP 4 **The learner stops, maintains his body and feet in the approach line of travel, and draws the cane back toward his body and against the curb, if present, checking the slopes during the maneuver. If there is a curb ramp or blended curb, the learner may apply slightly more pressure to the cane tip as he brings it back toward his body in order to find the slope difference between the sidewalk and the street.**

Rationale The learner plants his feet to avoid losing his approach alignment information while confirming with his cane that he has reached the street. At curb ramps and blended curbs, locating the expansion joint (narrow gap found between sections of concrete or between the concrete of the curb ramp and asphalt of the street) or slope change with the cane tip helps the learner confirm that he is not standing in the street.

STEP 5 **Being aware of other pedestrians, the learner checks for a curb on each side of the ramp or sloped area.**

Rationale The learner checks for the curbs to confirm that he is at the edge of the street.

CONSIDERATIONS FOR DETECTING THE STREET

- Some learners may require corner and curb ramp familiarization first. O&M specialists can use guide technique to ensure learner safety, or they can use *tactile maps* or other orientation aids. With the current design of curb ramps and corners, learners need to develop an awareness of slight changes in slope and texture both underfoot and under the cane. Learners should be introduced to the detectable warning surfaces installed at ramps at the edge of the street, and work on detecting such surfaces—that consist of small truncated domes—with their feet as well as their canes.

■ Use of a particular cane technique (such as constant-contact or touch-and-slide) does not guarantee detection of the street, nor does the addition of environmental modifications such as detectable warning surfaces. Awareness of all the clues and a combination of information is needed for successful travel.

■ Initial practice may include walking the length of the block, detecting and stopping at the street, and then turning around and walking back to the other end of the block. Alternatively, the O&M specialist may wish to have the learner approach and detect the same location several times from different distances to build confidence.

■ Learners should be introduced to a variety of curb ramps and corners early in their experience of outdoor travel so they can detect the street and maintain their approach alignment at locations with different designs.

■ Some learners may need to trail a landscape strip or grass line at curb ramps that are very gently sloped or almost flat.

Street-Corner Familiarization

Often it is necessary to become familiar with the layout of a street corner in order to recognize the corner and to make the best decisions regarding street crossings and alignment for crossing, or for recovery from veer during street crossings. In completing this procedure, the learner explores all edges of the sidewalks near the corner. There are many possible configurations of sidewalks and corners. The illustration in Figure 6.2 shows the type of corner found in a residential area, with a landscape strip along each sidewalk, forming a plus shape. Figure 6.2 also provides labels for locations that are used in the procedure. Because this procedure consists of many steps, it has been presented in three separate parts, but these all constitute one technique.

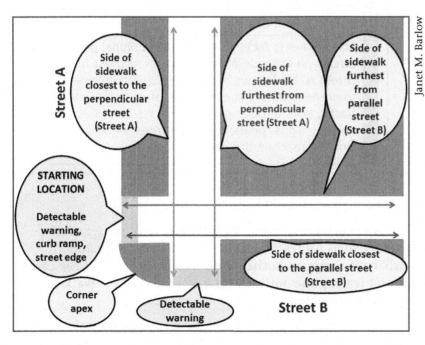

Figure 6.2

Labels Used in Description of Street-Corner Familiarization

STREET-CORNER FAMILIARIZATION

Purpose: To enable the learner to become familiar with the layout of a street corner—for initial concept development or for areas to be frequently traveled—in order to recognize the corner and to make the best decisions regarding street crossings and alignment for crossing, or for recovery from veer during street crossings.

I. Exploring Sidewalk Features along the Perpendicular Street

PROCEDURE AT A GLANCE

1 The learner approaches Street A. After detecting the street, the learner maintains his feet in a stationary position, listens for traffic on the streets parallel (B) and perpendicular (A), and explores the curb, curb ramp, and other features of the street sidewalk junction within reach of the cane.

2 The learner turns around 180 degrees and follows the edge of the sidewalk on the side furthest from the parallel street (B). The learner extends his cane arc along the landscape strip and into the area beside the sidewalk, using touch-trailing or a variation of the three-point-touch technique for level surfaces, maintaining awareness of alignment and location while noting the angle of the edge of the landscape strip (if available) and any signs, poles, hydrants, trees, or other features found near the sidewalk.

3 When the intersecting sidewalk is detected, the learner turns 90 degrees onto the sidewalk, away from Street B, and travels parallel to Street A, continuing to explore and note landmarks for 10 to 15 feet.

4 The learner squares off to the edge of the sidewalk and crosses the sidewalk. He then turns 90 degrees toward Street B.

5 The learner is facing Street B (the original parallel street) on the side of the sidewalk furthest from Street A. He follows along that side, maintaining awareness of alignment and location while listening to traffic, noting the angle of the grass line (if available), and any signs, poles, hydrants, trees, or other features until he reaches the intersecting sidewalk.

METHOD

STEP 1 The learner approaches Street A. After detecting Street A (see Figure 6.3), the learner maintains his feet in a stationary position, listens for traffic on the streets parallel (B) and perpendicular (A), and explores the curb, curb ramp, and other features within reach of the cane. This prepares the learner for exploring and tracing the outline of the intersecting sidewalks and recognizing the starting location on return to it in Step 10 or 12.

Rationale Holding a stationary position facing the street is important for characterizing features accurately and for ensuring safety at the edge of the street while exploring. Traffic on the streets is one of the

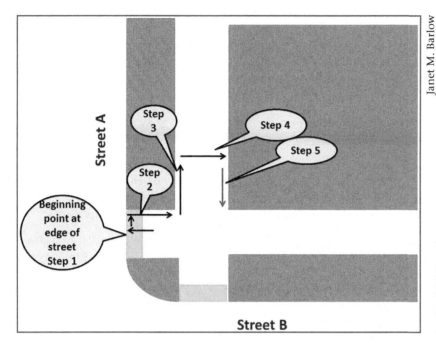

Figure 6.3

Steps for Exploring Sidewalk Area of the Perpendicular Street (Street A)

characteristics of the corner that the learner wants to assess, in addition to physical features like the curb ramp, detectable warning surface, poles, and curb.

STEP 2 The learner turns 180 degrees and follows the edge of the sidewalk on the side furthest from the parallel street (B). The learner extends his cane arc along the landscape strip and into the area beside the sidewalk, using touch-trailing or a variation of the three-point-touch technique for level surfaces, maintaining awareness of alignment and location while noting the angle of the edge of the landscape strip (if available) and any signs, poles, hydrants, trees, or other features found along the sidewalk.

Rationale Consistent search patterns are essential for accurate identification of landmarks and features for later use. Poles for *pedestrian pushbuttons* or potential landmarks may be located a foot or two off the sidewalk in the landscape strip. Learners with low vision may be able to locate such features by scanning along that edge of the sidewalk. The side of the sidewalk furthest from the parallel street and intersection is often more uniform and is the recommended location for pedestrian pushbuttons and other useful features (so it is better to check that side first, before the potentially more confusing apex of the corner).[1]

Variation In some situations, such as wide sidewalks in a business district, there may not be a detectable edge of the sidewalk to follow. In that case, the learner walks away from the street as straight as possible, checking for potential landmarks on the side furthest from Street B (with his back to Street A), about 10 feet away from Street A (approximately 3 to 5 steps).

STEP 3 When the intersecting sidewalk is detected, the learner turns 90 degrees onto the sidewalk, away from Street B, and follows the edge of the sidewalk and landscape strip parallel to Street A, continuing to explore and note landmarks for 10 to 15 feet.

---

[1]*While some texts call this the inside shoreline, traffic engineers consider it the outside edge of the sidewalk, crosswalk, and intersection, leading to confusing conversations about locations of pedestrian pushbuttons and other features. The term "inside shoreline" is not used in this description for that reason. The authors encourage the O&M discipline to align with traffic engineering terminology for these locations in the future.*

Rationale This exploration allows the learner to note features and landmarks along the sidewalk closest to Street A.

STEP 4 The learner squares off to the edge of the sidewalk, with his back to Street A, and crosses the sidewalk. He then turns 90 degrees back toward Street B.

Rationale Squaring off helps the learner to maintain orientation. The learner is now prepared to explore the side of the sidewalk parallel to and furthest from Street A.

STEP 5 The learner is facing Street B (the original parallel street) on the side of the sidewalk furthest from Street A. He follows along that side, maintaining awareness of alignment and location while listening to traffic, noting the angle of the grass line (if available) and any signs, poles, hydrants, trees, or other features until he reaches the intersecting sidewalk.

Rationale This approach allows the learner to note features along the sidewalk that is parallel to Street A and on the side of the sidewalk furthest from Street A.

II. Exploring Sidewalk Features along the Parallel Street

PROCEDURE AT A GLANCE

6 Continuing from Step 5, when the intersecting sidewalk is detected, the learner turns 90 degrees and follows the edge of the sidewalk on the side furthest from Street B, traveling parallel to Street B, and continuing to explore and note landmarks for 10 to 15 feet.

7 The learner squares off to the edge of the sidewalk and crosses the sidewalk. He then turns 90 degrees toward Street A.

8 The learner follows the landscape strip (if present) on the side of the sidewalk closest to Street B until the intersecting sidewalk is detected, maintaining awareness of alignment and location while listening to traffic, noting the angle of the edge of the landscape strip (if available), and any signs, poles, hydrants, trees, or other features found along the sidewalk.

9 When the intersecting sidewalk is detected, the learner turns 90 degrees onto the sidewalk, toward Street B, stopping when the street is detected and exploring the features of the location as in Step 1.

METHOD

STEP 6 Continuing from Step 5, when the intersecting sidewalk is detected, the learner turns 90 degrees and follows the edge of the sidewalk on the side furthest from Street B, traveling parallel to Street B, and continuing to explore and note landmarks for 10 to 15 feet (see Figure 6.4).

Rationale This approach allows the learner to note additional features along the side of the sidewalk furthest from the street, parallel to Street B.

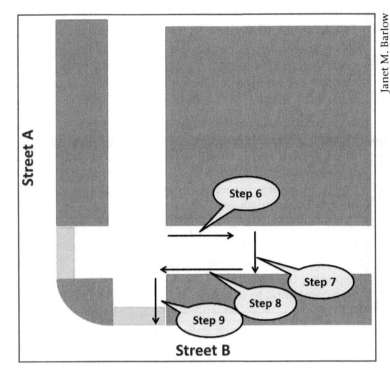

Figure 6.4

Steps for Exploring Sidewalk Area of the Parallel Street (Street B)

STEP 7 The learner squares off to the edge of the sidewalk and crosses the sidewalk. He then turns 90 degrees back toward Street A.

Rationale Squaring off helps the learner to maintain orientation. The learner is now prepared to explore the side of the sidewalk parallel to and closest to Street B.

STEP 8 The learner follows the landscape strip (if present) on the side of the sidewalk closest to Street B until the intersecting sidewalk is detected, maintaining awareness of alignment and location while listening to traffic, noting the angle of the edge of the landscape strip (if available), and any signs, poles, hydrants, trees, or other features found along the sidewalk.

Rationale This exploration allows the learner to note additional features along the side of the sidewalk closest to the street, parallel to Street B.

STEP 9 When the intersecting sidewalk is detected, the learner turns 90 degrees onto the sidewalk, toward Street B, stopping when the street is detected and exploring the features of the location as in Step 1.

Rationale The learner locates landmarks close to the crosswalk of Street B, then finds the edge of the street and familiarizes himself with the curb ramp and crossing location for Street B.

III. Exploring the Corner or Apex Area

> **PROCEDURE AT A GLANCE**
>
> **10** Using appropriate cane techniques and maintaining awareness of the location of Street B, the learner crosses the sidewalk at the edge of the ramp or curb, then turns 90 degrees, with his back to Street B.
>
> **11** The learner follows the edge of the sidewalk closest to the intersection, maintaining awareness of alignment and location while noting the angle of the landscape strip (if available) and any signs, poles, hydrants, trees, or other features found along the sidewalk.
>
> **12** When the intersecting sidewalk is detected, the learner turns 90 degrees onto the sidewalk, toward Street A, stopping when Street A is detected, exploring the features of the location as in Step 1, and comparing to information noted in Step 1.

METHOD

STEP 10 Using appropriate cane techniques and maintaining awareness of the location of Street B, the learner crosses the sidewalk at the edge of the ramp or curb, then turns 90 degrees, with his back to Street B (see Figure 6.5).

Rationale This turn positions the learner to explore the area at the apex of the corner while following the landscape strip (if present). The learner maintains awareness of the location of the street to avoid walking out into the street.

Variation In some locations where the crosswalks are close to the apex of the corner and no landscape strip is present at the apex, the area may have been explored with the original cane reach at the start of

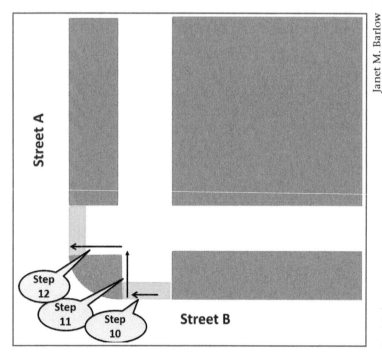

Janet M. Barlow

Figure 6.5

Steps for Exploring the Corner or Apex Area

the street-corner familiarization procedure. The learner may have already returned to an area very close to the crossing point for Street A.

STEP 11 **The learner follows the edge of the sidewalk closest to the intersection, maintaining awareness of alignment and location while noting the angle of the landscape strip (if available) and any signs, poles, hydrants, trees, or other features found along the sidewalk.**

Rationale This approach allows the learner to become familiar with the other features at the apex of the corner, which may be helpful in alignment or in recognizing the corner in future travel.

Variation At locations where the entire corner is paved, the learner may need to actually trail the curb or the edge of the street, making sure not to walk into the street.

STEP 12 **When the intersecting sidewalk is detected, the learner turns 90 degrees onto the sidewalk, toward Street A, stopping when the street is detected, exploring the features of the location as in Step 1, and comparing to information noted in Step 1.**

Rationale This step brings the learner back to the location where he started, along the intersection side of the sidewalk.

CONSIDERATIONS FOR STREET-CORNER FAMILIARIZATION

- Depending on the learner's understanding of concepts and level of travel experience, the O&M specialist may wish to break down this exercise into different segments and make use of tactile graphics to help the learner understand the spatial layout.

- For some learners, it may be best to begin by exploring both sides of the sidewalk when approaching Street A (parallel to Street B) first and recording that information, then exploring both sides of the sidewalk approaching Street B, and finally completing this order of familiarization to put the entire corner together. After some practice, the described procedure will work well for most learners and most corners. (Jacobson, 1993, 2013, describes a slightly different order of exploration for street-corner familiarization.)

- The most important aspect of street-corner familiarization is that it is systematic and can be generalized to a variety of other settings by the learner as needed.

- There are many variations of street-corner configurations of landscaping, curb ramps, and sidewalks, and many nontraditional intersecting sidewalks. The O&M specialist and learner need to work together at a variety of intersections to consider methods to analyze, explore for landmarks, and stay oriented in different situations.

- Learning and using this procedure early in an instructional program, at simpler intersections, makes it easier to use in later lessons at more complex or more open corners. Learners can be encouraged to take responsibility for identifying corner features and to develop their skills as their lessons and travel areas become progressively more complex.

- Staying oriented while completing this procedure is essential. Learning this procedure can also provide practice for the learner to get reoriented, using traffic and landmarks.

- In commercial areas, there may be no landscape strip or grass line to follow, so the O&M specialist and learner must consider other options, such as gridline patterns and methods to explore the corner and maintain orientation while locating landmarks.

- The O&M specialist needs to work with each learner to determine appropriate methods of recording information about landmarks to identify the corner, as well as cues that can be used for alignment for street crossing in the future (e.g., audio recordings, braille notes, tactile maps, or setting points of information in a GPS program for key corner landmarks). The O&M specialist should involve the learner in discussing and deciding what is most appropriate to use. The recording of information provides an opportunity for the learner to recognize usable landmarks and cues and make decisions in the future.

■ There are many variations in the types of corners and curb ramps that may be encountered. After the learner is comfortable with the procedure and understands the spatial layout of street corners, intersecting sidewalks, landscape strips, and grass lines, the O&M specialist should build in opportunities to experience a variety of curb ramps and corner configurations early in training, if possible, rather than providing all training in an area with consistent corner configurations.

■ There are many locations without a landscape strip along the street and with sidewalks located along the curb edge. At those locations, the learner may need to follow the curb while exploring. There will likely be many poles and possible overhead obstacles (such as signs) to avoid and upper-body protective technique should be used as needed. The learner and O&M specialist must also be aware of traffic and the location of the curb to avoid stepping off the curb.

■ These familiarization procedures will be used later in street crossings because they provide opportunities for the learner to practice detecting the street.

Tips for Teaching Block-Travel Skills

Integrating Orientation

O&M specialists may assign a "home" location within a residential area to provide a consistent base or reference point from which to build orientation skills and lessons. Some O&M specialists use a different home location for each learner, particularly if several learners are working in the same area. In other situations, O&M specialists may begin all lessons at a rehabilitation center, school, or at the learner's actual home. A home base can also be useful for self-familiarization and route-planning activities.

Jacobson's (1993, 2013) five-point travel system, which is described in Chapter 2, can be used to integrate orientation skills within a block-travel unit in a manner that is both systematic and logical. Prior to the start of each lesson, learners can be asked to identify or review cardinal directions, surrounding street names, key landmarks, route shapes to be traveled, and route reversals. A similar review can be conducted at the end of each lesson to further solidify learners' understanding of block layouts in the travel area. An important aspect of integrating orientation into mobility skills is to ensure that learners are thinking about how specific areas relate to the overall layout of the area.

Block travel will be part of numerous lessons in different environments. As learners become more proficient with cane-handling skills in the outdoor environment, various tasks can be added to their lessons, such as finding a specific landmark or address. If a learner is seldom disoriented, it may be important to introduce a route or activity in which the learner becomes disoriented in order to practice problem-solving skills necessary for reestablishing orientation.

When familiarizing themselves to a new area, learners who are blind or visually impaired may find that following the edge of the sidewalk is helpful for detecting each street and determining the location of the curb ramp. After locating the street and curb ramp, and developing an understanding of the configuration and layout of the area, the learner may re-approach the intersection, attending to various cues and clues that may assist in detecting the edge of the street efficiently and accurately.

The O&M specialist may record pertinent information about the grid pattern of blocks and streets in the area, as well as "hypothetical" problems related to travel in the area. This information may supplement material provided by the O&M specialist for planning and during the actual lessons.

Even without including street crossings, or when street crossings are done with a guide, there are many opportunities to give learners destinations and mini-routes to complete to integrate orientation and mobility techniques and to build skills and confidence during block travel. For example, a learner can be asked to find the walkway to the third house along the block, or to locate the house walkway that is made of gravel, or to perform other tasks that heighten the learner's awareness of features in the area.

Sequencing

Block travel and the techniques described in this chapter are essential parts of all travel activities. These techniques and procedures will be repeated and reinforced throughout O&M training. Lesson sequences may vary depending on the O&M specialist's preference and the learner's skills and needs. Some of the cane techniques described in Chapter 5, such as touch-trailing technique, can be introduced and practiced when locating destinations along the block or when exploring block features.

For initial practice in outdoor travel, smooth, wide sidewalks are usually best since they allow the learner to develop skills in handling the cane on different types of surfaces and deal with the cane tip contacting grass or other soft surface areas that are not typically found indoors. As the learner's skills develop, practice should include sidewalks with rough or uneven pavement, areas with narrow or very wide sidewalks, and sites with grass and with curb borders. Curb ramps are installed in most areas, so lessons should include various types of curb-ramp installations. In addition, consideration should be given to the reality that many neighborhoods are not laid out in an orderly grid pattern and may not contain sidewalks. (Travel in areas without sidewalks is covered in Chapter 9.)

O&M Specialist Positioning

The O&M specialist will need to be in various positions to assess, teach, and monitor learner skills and safety during block travel. When the learner is walking along a curb or drop-off, the O&M specialist should be positioned so she can stop the learner before the learner steps off the edge. This cautionary positioning may require the O&M specialist to walk in the street for short periods of time, but O&M specialists are advised to avoid this whenever possible as their visibility may be reduced and drivers' behavior can be unpredictable. The safety of both the O&M specialist and the learner are important during O&M lessons.

O&M specialists should be aware of the size and weight differential between themselves and their learners and plan their positioning accordingly. For example, a small female O&M specialist work-ing with a 6-foot-tall man may need to be in a different position than a taller O&M specialist, both to be able to adequately stop her learner from a misstep and to see around obstacles.

Strategies for Different Populations

Learners Who Have Low Vision

Learners who have low vision can be encouraged to practice visual skills, such as systematic scanning and eccentric viewing—while traveling with the long cane—to locate intersecting walkways, poles, and signs. Learners can practice visually identifying various environmental features while standing still at first, and then while traveling using a cane to preview the underfoot surface. Understanding of environmental context can help learners apply *blur interpretation* when integrating visual skills with cane usage. For example, understanding that stop signs are located close to corners can help a learner to interpret what he sees from a distance as a small red blur. That visual information can be used to determine that constant-contact cane technique should be used in anticipation of the approaching street corner. Upon approach, additional cues can be used to verify the assumption. Application of skills for the use of low vision devices, such as a monocular, can be easily integrated into a block-travel unit.

Age Differences

Due to shorter lesson length and travel-time factors, young children often start initial block travel in areas close to their preschool or elementary school. When possible, O&M specialists may work in the young child's home area, including other family members on occasion to make sure that everyone is reinforcing the same skills.

Integrating orientation and mobility within block travel is very important and young children will likely need structured instruction in concept development to understand how the environmental features of the block fit together into a cohesive whole. Young children may begin travel by thinking about whether they are walking with the street at their side and by applying directionality concepts of left and right. However, they will need to learn cardinal directions in order to have a consistent frame of reference for orientation as they get older and as route travel becomes more complex.

O&M specialists will need to create lessons that are highly motivating for younger learners, such as building a map together of familiar or unfamiliar blocks, planning treasure hunts, or creating challenges for small groups of children to embark upon together. (For further ideas about teaching and learning O&M with children, see Fazzi & Naimy, 2010; Fazzi & Petersmeyer, 2001; Knott, 2002.)

Adults who are adventitiously blind and who have a conceptual understanding and previous experience with the layout of blocks, intersections, and *vehicular traffic patterns* may progress quickly through these block-travel skills. O&M specialists can make use of analogies from possible past driving experiences to explain key concepts or use a variety of travel environments to support the generalization of block-travel skills for the future.

Older adults may benefit most from travel experiences on a familiar block or to a desired destination. The primary goals for O&M specialists when working with older adults is to improve travel safety and quality of life and to maintain levels of independence and interdependence. Therefore, working to increase safe travel in familiar areas can be highly motivating for older learners. When selecting training areas for older adults, the O&M specialist must take into consideration the physical stamina and possible health constraints of the older learner. Rest breaks may be needed for some learners, and areas with easy access to benches can be helpful for creating a positive learning situation. Some *support canes* come with folding seats and can be useful during block travel when rest breaks are needed. Older adults who may also have balance issues or a shuffling *gait* may need to avoid areas with broken sidewalks.

Learners with Additional Disabilities

Learners with additional disabilities may benefit from a variety of assistive technologies to promote as much independent travel as desired and possible. For example, a learner who uses a hearing aid may need adjustments based on the noise levels in the travel environment. O&M specialists will need to work with learners, families, and audiologists as appropriate to ensure that learners can make maximum use of their hearing for block travel. Similarly, learners who use communication devices may need to have their phrases and communication requests expanded to include brief statements and requests that would be applicable for travel in residential or

commercial areas, such as, "My house is 206 Dale Street" or "I don't need help, thank you."

Learners who use an additional mobility device for balance or to aid with limited physical stamina may need additional practice maintaining a straight line of travel or detecting curbs. O&M specialists may want to select initial training areas where benches are easily accessible for rest breaks or work with physical therapists to make sure that mobility devices are equipped with seats. Consultations with family members and related health professionals, such as physical therapists, in regard to the use of support devices (e.g., support cane, walker, or scooter) are essential to planning O&M lessons for block travel.

Learners with intellectual or learning disabilities who have challenges with memory functions may benefit from a memory aid during block-travel lessons. For example, homemade flip maps with photos or tactile cues for a sequence of landmarks can be used to help a learner with orientation during block travel. Commercially available recording and memory devices can serve a similar purpose. Mainstream technologies such as smartphones also have apps or tools for taking notes or setting points of interest that can be used to further enhance block travel.

Ambrose-Zaken, Calhoon, and Keim (2010); Lolli, Sauerburger, and Bourquin (2010); and Rosen and Crawford (2010) provide further ideas and strategies for teaching O&M to learners with additional disabilities.

Self-Advocacy

As learners begin to develop skills for travel on and around blocks, they will increasingly encounter other pedestrians and vehicular traffic. With these increased opportunities and with O&M specialists assuming less obvious monitoring positions as learners gain confidence in their travel skills, learners are more likely to interact with pedestrians and drivers. Some learners will have the confidence and prior experience necessary to interact with and maintain appropriate boundaries with strangers that they encounter. Learning to solicit information and assistance when needed and to politely and assertively refuse assistance and end conversations with strangers are important self-advocacy skills that learners will need to develop during block-travel instructional units. O&M specialists can work with learners to understand how moments of disorientation may attract greater interactions with the public than other aspects of travel. Being prepared to interact in these situations, through role-play and practice, can help learners to advocate for themselves as needed.

Another important aspect of self-determination is to be able to choose where one wants to travel to and what will be the best way to get there. Moving with purpose is key to O&M training. Basic route-planning activities can be introduced early on in block-travel training to build these important skills.

During block travel, initial routes can be planned by starting with and returning to an established home base. Tactile maps can be a useful aid in developing orientation and learner route-planning skills. Planning and traveling routes in both familiar and unfamiliar areas is an important skill for later independent travel. While initial travel may be within and around a block, as street-crossing and transit skills are added, route planning can become more and more complex.

CHAPTER

7

Street Crossings

In teaching street-crossing techniques to learners, the orientation and mobility (O&M) specialist needs a solid understanding of intersection layout and design (referred to as *intersection geometry* by traffic engineers and in this chapter) and traffic controls (e.g., signs, signals, and markings). Barlow, Bentzen, Sauerburger, and Franck (2010) provide extensive information about these topics as well as intersection and curb-ramp design and vehicular- and pedestrian-signal actuation. Barlow, Bentzen, and Franck (2010) provide information about intersection modifications that may be needed, such as detectable warning surfaces and accessible pedestrian signals. The authors of this book assume that the O&M specialist already possesses this basic knowledge or will refer to these resources as needed.

Taking and managing risks is a part of everyday life, whether a person is at home, at school, at work, or moving about the community. Children generally learn the items to be cautious about from their caregivers and teachers. Responsible adults allow children the level of freedom to perform tasks they feel the children are ready to handle, and balance keeping children safe with the need to provide them with experiences that will ultimately prepare them to function as a competent adult in a variety of environments. The same is true for children who are blind or visually impaired.

Programs to teach children and youth about the dangers of substance use, bicycle safety, and driver's education are generally available, but classes in pedestrian safety are uncommon. Crossing guards are strategically placed to ensure safe street crossings near elementary schools, but pedestrian-safety education is generally left up to families. As a result, many pedestrians lack basic knowledge about intersection geometry and traffic controls that would enable them to make informed choices about street crossings. In 2014 there were 4,884 pedestrians killed and an estimated 65,000 injured in traffic crashes in the United States; approximately 16,500 of those killed or injured were under 20 years of age (National Center for Statistics and Analysis, 2016).

This chapter is intended to provide O&M specialists with basic knowledge about intersections that learners with visual impairments, as pedestrians, may encounter, as well as the procedures for teaching those learners how to minimize risks by teaching them to:

- Analyze intersections so that they can make informed choices about given crossings, including where best to cross and when to find an alternate crossing or ask for assistance if they deem it necessary
- Prepare to cross at intersections with good alignment, visibility, and use of pedestrian controls
- Cross streets at the safest times
- Manage the crossing to reach the destination with consistency and confidence

It is important to note that each intersection and crossing is unique and that advances in technology or changes in the design and management of traffic controls and vehicles in the future require O&M specialists to continue to update their knowledge and skills. They will need to make informed decisions about how to teach learners to make crossings on an individual basis—that is, based on the cognitive and physical abilities and emotional maturity of the learner and the demands of a particular intersection.

For learners who are visually impaired, instruction in intersection analysis and street-crossing preparation and timing are essential elements of the O&M curriculum in both educational and rehabilitation settings. Instruction must be individualized and include teaching at actual intersections to help learners develop an understanding of how intersections work and how to manage personal risk when making crossing decisions.

Common Terminology

The terminology applied throughout this chapter is generally the same as that used by traffic engineers in describing streets and intersections, and is also used in the chapters referenced from *Foundations of Orientation and Mobility*. Some terminology used by O&M specialists in the past has been limited to use in the field of O&M, resulting in misunderstandings in discussions with those who design and operate the intersections that learners with visual impairments are taught to cross. For example, many traffic engineers are confused by O&M terminology such as "plus intersection" or "shoreline" since those terms are not used by transportation professionals.

Traffic engineers tend to use two separate parameters in describing intersections: geometry and traffic control. Recognizing these two separate aspects and their relationship to street-crossing decisions can be helpful to O&M specialists who teach intersection concepts and street-crossing techniques to learners with visual impairments.

Intersection Geometry

Terms relating to intersection geometry and the types of intersections with which O&M specialists and learners should be familiar are described in the following sections. In this text (and in the field of O&M), the terms "parallel street" and "perpendicular street" are used to describe the learner's direction of travel. The parallel street is alongside the learner when she is crossing the street; the perpendicular street is the street that the learner is preparing to cross or is crossing.

Four-Leg Right-Angle Intersections

A *four-leg right-angle intersection* is the traffic engineering term for a basic square intersection of two streets crossing at right angles to each other. O&M specialists have typically called this a "plus intersection," but this term is not used by transportation engineers and other transportation professionals. The number of lanes on either street can vary from one to seven or more, and the crossing distance will vary depending on the number of lanes. The corner radius, or how rounded the corner is, tends to increase as number of lanes and speed of vehicles on the road increase. Parallel and perpendicular traffic can usually provide alignment or heading (directional) information to the learner.

Three-Leg (T) Intersections

Three-leg intersections, also referred to as T intersections, usually involve two streets, with one street ending at the intersection with the other. Traffic engineers do use the term T intersection for this type of intersection geometry. Crossing the stem of the T may be relatively simple, while negotiating the other legs of the intersection—crossbar of the T intersection—may involve crossings with more than one turning vehicle and no parallel straight-through traffic to provide information about alignment or timing of crossing.

Offset Intersections

Offset intersections are similar to two T intersections that are located in close proximity, but not directly opposite each other, on opposite sides of a through street or other major street. Traffic movement, location of crosswalks, and traffic-signal timing can be quite confusing for the learner in this type of intersection.

Often, marked crosswalks and pedestrian signals are located furthest from the offset, on the outside edges of the intersection, as shown in Figure 7.1. Like three-leg intersections, parallel traffic is not available for auditory alignment or as an indication of time to begin crossing the through street.

Skewed Intersections

Skewed intersections are those in which two streets meet at an angle that is significantly less than a right angle (see Figure 7.2). Generally, skewed intersections

.

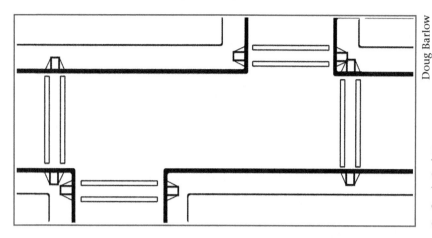

Figure 7.1

Offset Intersection
Typical markings at an offset intersection with marked crosswalks located on the outside edges of the intersection.

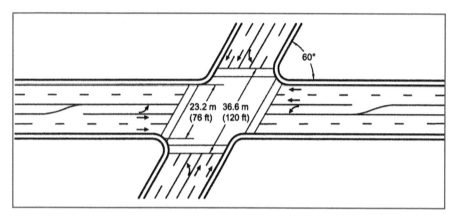

Figure 7.2

Skewed Intersection
The crosswalks at this skewed intersection are parallel to the traffic movement.

Source: Federal Highway Administration. (2004, August). Figure 15c. In Signalized intersections: Informational guide (Publication No. FHWA-HRT-04-091). Washington, DC: US Department of Transportation. Retrieved from https://www.fhwa.dot.gov/publications/research/safety/04091/04091.pdf

are found at four-leg intersections, but may also be present at three-leg intersections. Typically, for traffic engineers to define the intersection as skewed, one angle must be 75 degrees or less. At skewed intersections, the traffic on the parallel street often can be used for alignment, but neither the traffic nor the curb line of the perpendicular street (the street being crossed) can be used for alignment.

Multi-Leg Intersections

Multi-leg intersections are those in which more than two streets meet, resulting in five or six legs converging at the intersection. More than six legs are uncommon and more than four are discouraged according to traffic-engineering design manuals. Roundabouts may be installed in place of multi-leg intersections.

Roundabouts

A *roundabout* is a type of intersection in which traffic travels around a circular island in the middle of the intersection, with all entering vehicles yielding to the traffic traveling within the circulatory roadway around the center (see Figure 7.3). Older-style traffic circles, common in the northeastern United States, may have stop signs or signals, crosswalks to the central island, and different rules for vehicles and pedestrians; these are not considered roundabouts as outlined in the current definition from the Federal Highway Administration (2000). In the United States and other countries where vehicles travel on the right side of the street, traffic moves counterclockwise around the central island of the roundabout. In countries where vehicles travel on the left, traffic moves clockwise around the central island. Roundabouts may be installed at intersections of two or more streets and the pedestrian crossings may vary from one to four lanes in each direction. Splitter islands at roundabouts separate the two directions of vehicular traffic entering and exiting the roundabout on each leg. (Splitter islands may be raised or painted; however, paint on islands [as identified in Figure 7.3] is not typically detected and cannot be used by pedestrians who are blind.) Pedestrian crosswalks are located along the roadway before vehicles

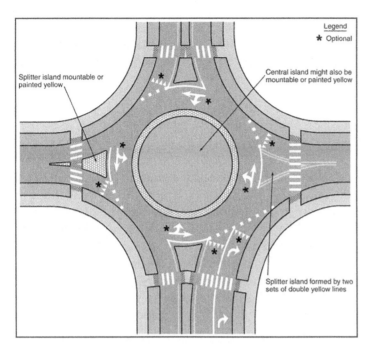

Splitter island mountable or painted yellow

Central island might also be mountable or painted yellow

Legend
★ Optional

Splitter island formed by two sets of double yellow lines

Figure 7.3

Single-Lane Roundabout
Pedestrians cross this type of roundabout one lane at a time on the outside legs and should not go to the center island.

Source: Federal Highway Administration. (2009). Figure 3C-3. In Manual on uniform traffic control devices for streets and highways. Washington, DC: US Department of Transportation. Retrieved from https://mutcd.fhwa.dot .gov/pdfs/2009r1r2/mutcd2009r1r2edition.pdf

enter or after vehicles exit the circulatory roadway. Pedestrians are usually expected to cross each leg in two stages, stopping at the splitter island in the middle of the crossing so they only cross traffic traveling in one direction at a time.

In roundabouts, pedestrians do not have parallel traffic movement to use for crossing or alignment, and the sound of traffic moving in the circle may mask the sound of approaching traffic. Perpendicular traffic also may not be aligned perpendicularly to the crosswalk direction.

Other Alternative Intersection Configurations

There are many new configurations being designed, such as diverging diamond interchanges, continuous-flow intersections, single-point urban interchanges, and median U-turns. Further descriptions and graphics are available on various websites and informational guides from the Federal Highway Administration (see the Resources section in the online AFB Learning Center). Potentially the most confusing feature of these new types of intersections is the diversion of left-turning traffic to the "wrong" side of the road. This can be discerned through careful analysis and listening to vehicles at each crossing. However, due to the angles at these intersections, using parallel traffic as a guide for alignment or a crossing is usually not possible.

Geometric Features within Intersections

Within intersections, there may be other geometric features that are intended to assist with the flow of vehicular or pedestrian traffic.

Traffic Islands or Medians

Traffic islands are intended to provide pedestrians with refuge areas during crossing and to simplify the task of crossing. They may be located in the center of the roadway between lanes of traffic traveling in two different directions; this type is usually referred to as a *median*. Other designs include triangular islands between a right turning lane and the main through lanes of traffic or the splitter islands that separate and direct traffic at roundabouts. The presence of islands can lead to disorientation for some pedestrians who are blind, particularly if the island is not well designed.

Boulevards

Boulevards are streets with wide medians separating the lanes of traffic. They may need to be crossed in two stages due to the width of the median. Pedestrians will stop at the median or traffic island for the first stage of the crossing and then complete the second stage of the crossing during the next walk phase or gap in traffic.

Alleyways

Alleyways, or alleys, are narrow lanes that usually run behind buildings or residences in older parts of towns and cities as rear-access or service roads. They are usually treated similar to driveways in terms of geometric features or traffic control for crossings.

Traffic Control

Traffic control refers to the signs, signals, and markings that dictate rules for vehicular traffic in a given area. At an intersection, how the vehicular and pedestrian traffic is managed at each crossing is referred to as the traffic control for that intersection.

While intersection geometry was previously discussed for full intersections, traffic controls are specific to each crossing at an intersection. For example, at an intersection controlled by a two-way stop sign, there are two different types of pedestrian crossings present: a controlled crossing with a stop sign and an *uncontrolled street crossing* without a stop sign.

Discussion of traffic control with learners should include the following:

- Uncontrolled crossings
- Stop sign–controlled streets
- Traffic signal–controlled streets
- Crosswalks
- Pedestrian signals

Uncontrolled Crossings

An uncontrolled crossing does not have a stop or yield sign or a signal at the crosswalk location. These locations may have a marked crosswalk with a beacon (a pedestrian-activated yellow flashing light), but are still considered uncontrolled by traffic engineers because the sign or signal does not require vehicles to stop or yield. Although vehicles should stop at pedestrian crosswalks, whether marked or unmarked, pedestrians should still treat them as uncontrolled crossings.

Stop Sign–Controlled Streets

Stop sign–controlled streets include crossings where two streets meet at an intersection but only vehicles on one street must stop before continuing (two-way stop) or where both streets have stop signs and all vehicles must stop (all-way or four-way stop). Note that crossing the street that does not have a stop sign for vehicles at a two-way stop is considered an uncontrolled crossing, not a stop sign–controlled crossing.

Traffic Signal–Controlled Streets

Traffic signal–controlled streets have some type of traffic signal, which can be pre-timed or fixed time, semi-actuated, or fully actuated. Various methods, ranging from video detection to magnetic loops to pedestrian pushbuttons, are used to call, actuate, or change the signal. The timing of signals can also be changed from traffic-management centers that are miles from the signal, so a signal timing plan may change at any time. Therefore, it may not be possible to categorize a crossing as having a specific type of timing plan.

- *Pre-timed or fixed time signals* run on a predetermined cycle that provides a predictable amount of time for each crossing. The amount of time may change according to the time of day. (A *cycle* for a traffic signal is one complete sequence of all possible traffic movements at an intersection, referred to as signal *phases.*)

- *Semi-actuated signals* provide green signals on the major street until there is a call to the signal, either by a pedestrian or a vehicle, for crossing that street, at which time the signal turns red (at the appropriate time after a yellow signal is displayed). The pedestrian usually actuates the signal by using the pedestrian pushbutton while the vehicle actuates the signal through one of several methods of vehicular detection, such as magnetic loops or video detection, among others. There is usually a long time provided to cross the side, or minor, street alongside a major street, but just barely enough time for a pedestrian to cross the major street. There may not be adequate time for a pedestrian to cross the major street (with the parallel traffic) if the signal change is actuated by vehicles. Activating the pedestrian pushbutton will usually result in a longer crossing time.

- *Fully actuated signals* change depending on the traffic in each lane at each cycle for all approaches to the intersection. This type of signal timing results in complex variations in the order and timing of traffic signal phases and often has protected left or right turns when pedestrians do not have the right-of-way to cross, even though some of the traffic on the parallel street is moving. (See Barlow, Bentzen,

Sauerburger et al., 2010, for more information.) Fully actuated signals may seem to act predictably at certain times of the day, such as rush hour when there is a lot of traffic in all lanes, but can vary greatly from cycle to cycle. Pedestrians usually need to use a pedestrian pushbutton to call a Walk signal to have adequate time to cross the road.

Crosswalks

Crosswalks, marked or unmarked, legally exist at most intersections of two roads where there are sidewalks, giving pedestrians the right-of-way at crossings that are unsignalized (have no traffic signals). However, yielding to pedestrians and enforcing pedestrian right-of-way at crosswalks varies greatly in different states and communities within the United States. In most states, unmarked crosswalks legally exist at every intersection where sidewalks are installed. However, the definition varies. Learners and O&M specialists will want to investigate the laws in their area. At crossings that are signalized (contain traffic signals) pedestrians only have the right-of-way when crossing with the signal, whether the crosswalk is marked or unmarked.

Pedestrian Signals

At intersections with signals, pedestrian signal timing is used to provide a calculated time for pedestrians to cross the street. This is referred to as the *pedestrian phase* and is the time when the pedestrian signal displays a walk interval (Walk or white walking-man symbol), then a flashing don't walk or pedestrian clearance interval (Don't Walk or flashing orange hand symbol). Where a pedestrian signal is installed, the pedestrian may be required to push a button to receive a Walk signal, and pushing that button will provide enough time for the pedestrian to cross the street. (Finding and using pedestrian pushbuttons is a required skill today, but was not commonly needed at the time the first edition of this book was published.) If there is no pedestrian signal, it is possible that the traffic signal phasing does not include an amount of time that is long enough for a pedestrian to cross the street.

At most intersections, pedestrian signals provide a pedestrian with a crossing time that begins at the same time as the movement of near-lane-parallel traffic. However, there are some types of pedestrian timing that provide for pedestrian movement at different times and are generally intended to improve pedestrian access and safety. Where there is a *leading pedestrian interval (LPI)*, the Walk signal begins three to six seconds before the green signal for vehicles, allowing pedestrians to establish their presence in the crosswalk before turning vehicles receive a green. Without an *accessible pedestrian signal (APS)*, pedestrians who are blind or visually impaired will not know the pedestrian phase has begun and the amount of time provided may not be adequate for pedestrians to cross if they wait to begin crossing after near-lane-parallel traffic begins moving. An *exclusive pedestrian phase*—also called Barnes Dance, scatter light, or pedestrian scramble timing—provides a wholly separate time for pedestrians to cross. When the pedestrian Walk signal is displayed, all vehicles have a red signal and pedestrians may cross in all directions, including diagonally. For pedestrians wishing to cross only one of the streets at an intersection, the exclusive phase can be a disadvantage because they must wait through both vehicular phases for their turn to cross. For blind or visually impaired pedestrians, exclusive phases can be difficult to recognize. Another drawback is that there is no parallel traffic moving to use for alignment during the crossing.

At any location where there is a pedestrian signal, an APS, if installed, can convey the information provided by the visual signal in an audible and vibrotactile manner. An APS usually has additional features such as pushbutton locator tones, tactile arrows, and automatic volume adjustment.

Crossing guard or police control may be present at intersections near schools, when an intersection is under construction, during special events, or when signals are malfunctioning. When present, it is important for the learner to follow the directions of the crossing guard or police officer. In order to determine if a crossing guard is present, the individual can consider the proximity to a school and the time of day with regard to school schedules, as well as changes in traffic patterns. It is likely that crossing guards or police officers, when present, will interact with the individual preparing to cross the street. There should also be ample pedestrians around the learner to ask for confirmation about the presence of a crossing guard.

For a more detailed discussion of traffic control, see Barlow, Bentzen, Sauerburger et al. (2010) and Barlow, Bentzen, and Franck (2010).

Street-Crossing Techniques

Crossing a street safely and efficiently requires a sequence of specific tasks and procedures:

1. Detecting the street.
2. Locating the crosswalk and appropriate crossing location.
3. Analyzing the intersection, including intersection geometry, traffic control, and movements.
4. Aligning for crossing, including locating a physical cue for realignment.
5. Assessing the crossing and determining when to begin crossing, taking into consideration intersection traffic control and whether it is
   a. uncontrolled, including through streets at two-way stop signs,
   b. stop sign–controlled, or
   c. signal controlled, including locating and using pushbuttons.
6. Initiating crossing and maintaining correct heading while crossing.
7. Recovering from street crossing (when the learner was misaligned or has veered).

In general, the tasks for detecting the street, locating the crossing location, aligning to cross, and maintaining alignment while crossing are affected by intersection geometry. Tasks such as using pedestrian pushbuttons and determining when to begin crossing are affected by traffic control features. There may be some overlap in these tasks. Although learners will be performing all tasks in conjunction with street crossings, for the purpose of this discussion, each task is described separately.

The street-crossing tasks just listed may be taught in various environments and sequences depending on the learner's readiness and abilities and experience and needs, and the availability of teaching environments. The O&M specialist and the learner also need to recognize that street and intersection designs change over time, with innovations in signals, markings, and geometric features. O&M specialists and learners must remain aware of developments in traffic engineering and vehicle design.

After years of emphasis on moving vehicular traffic more quickly and efficiently through intersections and communities to the detriment of the needs of pedestrians, the US Federal Highway Administration is beginning to focus more on pedestrian and cyclist access and safety. However, the increase in bicycle lanes and cycle tracks will likely present new challenges for pedestrians who are blind or visually impaired. In addition, the technology of vehicles and signals is advancing rapidly and may create additional challenges and opportunities.

O&M specialists may find it useful to focus on specific aspects of the crossing in each lesson. For example, crossing the street while walking with a guide may allow the learner to focus on listening to the traffic movement. These tasks should not be taught in isolation and may be sequenced differently depending on the situation, teaching area, or learner. Before mastery is attained, learners need to be able to combine all street-crossing tasks.

The *wayfinding* tasks of street crossing (detecting the street, locating the crossing, aligning to cross, and maintaining correct heading or alignment while crossing), which relate to intersection geometry or shape, are essentially the same, despite differences in traffic control at various types of intersections. For example, the same techniques may be used to align to cross at a small stop sign–controlled residential intersection or at a large actuated signalized intersection. The geometry may affect the crossing decision in terms of recognizing the location of threats in a lane-by-lane analysis, but it does not usually change the strategy or technique. On the other hand, the techniques for determining when to cross relate to the type of traffic control present and are different depending on whether the crossing is stop sign–controlled, uncontrolled, or signal-controlled.

The learner may also approach tasks somewhat differently at a familiar street crossing versus an unfamiliar street crossing. At a familiar location, the learner will know the basic layout of the intersection, the type of traffic control, and available features. However, even at very familiar street crossings, the learner should still be encouraged to analyze the intersection for current conditions, attend to traffic, and make sure the intersection is functioning as previously assessed. At an unfamiliar crossing, the learner needs to fully analyze the intersection to determine a cue for alignment, as well as examine intersection geometry, pedestrian visibility, and intersection traffic control for timing, and to familiarize herself with the corner and find a pedestrian pushbutton when available.

DETECTING THE STREET

See the procedure for Detecting the Street in Chapter 6.

LOCATING THE CROSSWALK AND APPROPRIATE CROSSING LOCATION

Purpose: To enable the learner to find the location to begin a street crossing. At an unfamiliar intersection, this may require some exploration and self-familiarization at the corner, as described in the procedure for Street-Corner Familiarization in Chapter 6.

PROCEDURE AT A GLANCE

1 After detecting the street, while holding her feet stationary, the learner explores to the right and left with her cane for a curb, curb ramp, landscape strip or grass line, pole, or other feature of the sidewalk.

2a If a curb ramp or other known feature is detected, the learner adjusts her position to the side of the curb ramp furthest from the parallel street or to another crossing location that has been previously determined.

2b If a curb ramp or other known feature is not detected, the learner turns away from the parallel street and checks for a curb ramp or other known feature on the side furthest from the parallel street. If the curb ramp is not found, she turns back toward the parallel street to search for the curb ramp, then positions herself near the curb on the side of the ramp furthest from the parallel street.

3 The learner listens to traffic on the perpendicular and parallel streets to ascertain whether she is in a good location to cross.

METHOD

STEP 1 After detecting the street, while holding her feet stationary, the learner explores to the right and left with her cane for a curb, curb ramp, landscape strip or grass line, pole, or other feature of the sidewalk. The learner maintains awareness of other pedestrians and nearby vehicles while exploring the area to locate known features of the crossing.

Rationale Each approach to a corner may result in a slightly different position within the sidewalk when detecting the street. The learner needs to determine her location in relation to known features at the intersection. Since curb ramps are now required to be within the width of the crosswalk, the ramp location can be a reliable cue to the location of the crosswalk. (Learners should understand that this is not true everywhere, but it is becoming more common.) On most residential sidewalks, the ramp should be within reach of the cane. While the ramp location may be a reliable cue to the location of the crosswalk, the ramp and the slope of the ramp are not reliable cues to the direction of travel on the crosswalk.

Variations At completely unfamiliar crossings where the curb ramp is not within cane reach, the learner may need to complete the procedure for Street-Corner Familiarization (see Chapter 6).

Learners with low vision may be able to visually identify the crosswalk and curb ramp location. Learners should be acquainted with different types of crosswalk markings and the differences between crosswalk markings and vehicle stop lines (called limit lines in some geographic areas).

STEP 2A If a curb ramp or other known feature is detected, the learner adjusts her position, if necessary, to the side of the curb ramp that is furthest from the parallel street or to another crossing location that has been previously determined.

Rationale In general, being on the side of the curb ramp furthest from the parallel street positions the learner within, or very close to within, the crosswalk and on the portion of the curb that is more in line with the crossing (less rounded). Crossing from the ramp may be preferable in some situations.

Variations Since curb ramps are required at all crosswalks as streets are repaved, the general expectation of learners should be to find a curb ramp within the marked or unmarked crosswalk area. Additionally, there are still some locations without curb ramps, and learners should be introduced to these environments.

STEP 2B If a curb ramp or other known feature is not detected, the learner turns away from the parallel street and checks for a curb ramp or other known feature on the side furthest from the parallel street. If the curb ramp is not found, she turns back toward the parallel street and searches for the curb ramp. When she finds the curb ramp, the learner adjusts her position to the side of the curb ramp furthest from the parallel street or to another crossing location that has been previously determined.

Rationale Crosswalks can be set back from the corner and sidewalk approach direction so checking first on the side away from the parallel street can help the learner find the location more quickly. If it is not found, she then can go back toward the corner apex to search for the ramp.

Variations The learner may realize from listening to traffic that she is too close or too far from traffic and search first in the direction suggested by that information.

At a roundabout or *channelized turn lane* (lane for vehicles turning right, separated from main traffic lanes by a triangular island) the crosswalk may be 40 to 50 feet from the point at which the street is first contacted. In such instances, the learner can use touch-and-drag cane technique to follow the curb or edge of the sidewalk on the side closest to the street as it curves around, looking for a curb ramp, detectable warning surface, or other cue to the crossing location.

The edges of grass lines or landscape strips may also provide cues to the proper location for crossings.

STEP 3 **The learner listens to traffic on the perpendicular and parallel streets to determine whether she is in a good location to cross. She should be particularly aware of the stopping location of cars on the perpendicular street in relation to her position. This will help her to confirm that traffic is not consistently stopping closer to the intersection than the location where she is standing and that she is likely positioned within the crosswalk.**

Rationale Traffic movement and positioning, perpendicular and parallel, can provide information about the crossing and crossing location that cannot be gained by tactile cues at the corner. Even at familiar corners, traffic congestion, construction, or illegally parked vehicles can change drivers' behavior and may affect the learner's crossing decisions.

Variation At roundabouts, channelized turn lanes, or mid-block crossings, parallel traffic may not be available to use as a cue for positioning. Learners may have to rely on tactile cues such as the location of the curb ramp, in combination with perpendicular traffic movement, to assess their position.

CONSIDERATIONS FOR LOCATING THE CROSSWALK AND APPROPRIATE CROSSING LOCATION

- The complex design of intersections can make locating the crosswalk or crossing location more difficult than it used to be. The lack of a curb ramp may be an indication of a crosswalk that is closed to pedestrian traffic, one that is set back much further from the intersection than anticipated, or a location with old infrastructure where curb ramps have not yet been added.

- The O&M specialist may need to work with the learner on suitable ways to move to the crossing location, using appropriate cane techniques and clearing with the cane.

- Learners should be aware of different types of curb ramps (e.g., perpendicular ramps, parallel ramps, ramps with shared *landings*, blended corners) and possible diagonal alignment of ramps at the apex of a corner.

- At residential intersections, a learner who maintains a straight line of travel along the sidewalk may be lined up in the correct location without searching or moving from the location where she first contacted the street on approach along the sidewalk. However, having the O&M specialist reinforce that she check her position at this point will prepare the learner for more complex crossing situations in later lessons.

- At roundabouts, the learner may need to look for the curb ramp by trailing the landscape strip or curb line on the side closest to the street to avoid crossing at the wrong location, toward the center island, or across the circulatory roadway. This procedure may also be necessary at locations with channelized right-turn lanes in order to reach the island and proper crossing location.

INTERSECTION ANALYSIS PROCEDURES

The lane designations used in intersection analysis and crossing decisions are always assigned in relation to the learner's position at the intersection when preparing to cross. Figure 7.4 shows the position of a learner preparing to cross counterclockwise and the lane labels used in this situation: near-lane-parallel traffic, far-lane-parallel traffic, near-lane-perpendicular traffic, and far-lane-perpendicular traffic. Figure 7.5 shows

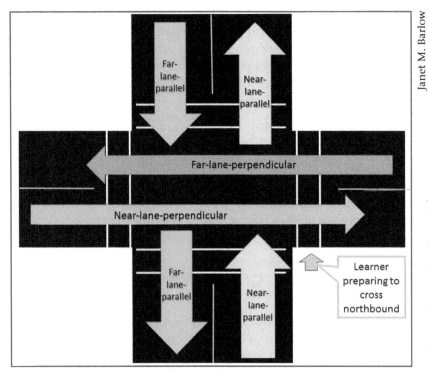

Janet M. Barlow

Figure 7.4

Lane Designations for a Counterclockwise Crossing

The lanes are labeled in relation to the learner's position. The learner is preparing to cross northbound on the east crosswalk (counterclockwise crossing). The near-lane-parallel traffic is the lane or lanes moving in the same direction as the learner, in this case traveling north through the intersection.

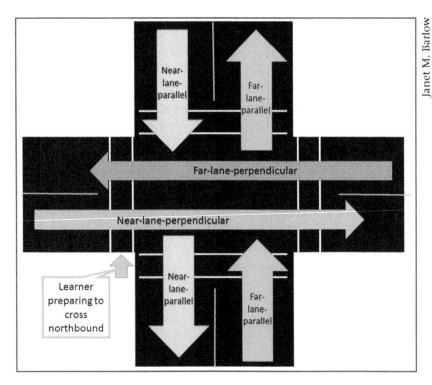

Janet M. Barlow

Figure 7.5

Lane Designations for a Clockwise Crossing

The lanes are labeled in relation to the learner's position. The learner is preparing to cross northbound on the west crosswalk (clockwise crossing). The near-lane-parallel traffic is the lane or lanes coming toward the learner and traveling south through the intersection in the opposite direction of the learner.

the position of a learner preparing to cross in a clockwise direction and the corresponding lane labels for that scenario. While these figures show a single lane in each direction, there may be two or more lanes traveling in that portion of the intersection. In general, the lane of traffic traveling straight through the intersection that is closest to the pedestrian's crosswalk is considered the most desirable to use for crossing.

Analyzing Intersection Geometry

Purpose: **To prepare the learner to make a street-crossing determination by analyzing the intersection geometry, visibility, and other features.**

	PROCEDURE AT A GLANCE
1	After detecting the street, the learner observes the movement of the traffic through the intersection.
2	The learner identifies the near-lane-parallel traffic, determines vehicles' travel paths, and estimates the number of lanes.
3	The learner identifies the far-lane-parallel traffic, determines vehicles' travel paths, and estimates the number of lanes.
4	The learner identifies the near-lane-perpendicular traffic, determines vehicles' travel paths, and estimates the number of lanes.
5	The learner identifies the far-lane-perpendicular traffic, determines vehicles' travel paths, and estimates the number of lanes.
6	The learner synthesizes the information gathered from the previous steps to determine the geometry and relative size of the intersection. The number of lanes counted for the perpendicular street crossing indicates the width of the crossing and the time needed to cross.
7	The learner explores features present at the corner to determine if any obstacles may negatively impact the visibility of pedestrian crossings, mask auditory information for crossings for the learner, or otherwise impact the decision for crossing.

METHOD

STEP 1 **After detecting the street, the learner observes the movement of the traffic through the intersection to determine the intersection geometry and relative size.**

Rationale Listening to traffic and observing other information will assist the learner in determining the geometry and relative size of the intersection. Knowledge of intersection geometry is essential to determining which street or combination of streets to cross to get to the desired destination and the appropriate timing for eventual crossing. The relative size of the intersection gives the learner information about the length of the crossing to be made and the time needed to cross to the other side.

Variation A learner with low vision can use visual information together with auditory information to determine the geometry and size of the intersection. (See Chapter 10 for more information on using vision for intersection analysis.)

STEP 2 The learner identifies the near-lane-parallel traffic (the lane traveling through the intersection closest to and parallel to the crosswalk being used; see Figures 7.4 and 7.5) and determines if the vehicles travel through the full intersection and whether they can make left or right turns. The learner counts or estimates the number of lanes.

Rationale This traffic information will be important for the crossing, and the learner needs to determine potential movements that may be used for a crossing indication or for alignment during her crossing. The movement of the traffic can also assist the learner in determining the intersection geometry.

STEP 3 The learner identifies the far-lane-parallel traffic and determines if the vehicles travel through the full intersection and whether they can make left or right turns. The learner counts or estimates the number of lanes.

Rationale The number of traffic lanes provides an idea of the width of the street and whether the movement of traffic will conflict with or assist the learner during the crossing. How and where the traffic travels can provide information about the intersection geometry.

STEP 4 The learner identifies the near-lane-perpendicular traffic and determines if the vehicles travel through the full intersection and whether they can make left or right turns. The learner counts or estimates the number of lanes and the time needed to cross them.

Rationale The learner needs to know as much as possible about the street she is crossing. The traffic provides an idea of the width of the street and how and where the traffic travels, and can provide information about the intersection geometry.

STEP 5 The learner identifies the far-lane-perpendicular traffic and determines if the vehicles travel through the full intersection and whether they can make left or right turns. The learner counts or estimates the number of lanes and the time needed to reach and cross them.

Rationale The learner needs to know as much as possible about the street she is crossing. The traffic provides an idea of the width of the street and the time needed to cross it. How and where the traffic travels can provide information about the intersection geometry. Because she will reach the far lanes later in the crossing, at an uncontrolled location, the learner will need to hear vehicles from that direction earlier to provide enough time to clear the lanes before the vehicles reach that location. It cannot be assumed that drivers of vehicles will see the learner crossing and stop to allow her to complete the crossing.

STEP 6 The learner synthesizes the information gathered from the previous steps to determine the geometry and relative size of the intersection and the time needed to cross. If both parallel and perpendicular lanes of traffic move fully through the intersection and can make left and right turns, then the intersection is a four-leg right-angle intersection. The learner may determine that it is a three-leg intersection if the traffic moving on either the parallel or perpendicular street is constricted to only left or right turns. For example, if the near-lane-parallel traffic does not travel through the full intersection and makes only right and left turns, then the learner would logically theorize that she is at a three-leg or offset intersection, facing the crossbar, resulting in no parallel traffic to use for alignment and with the possibility of poor visibility and parked cars for a potential crossing. The auditory or visual information from an offset intersection depends on the degree of offset, with mild offset intersections sounding more like a four-leg intersection and moderate or severe offsets sounding like a three-leg intersection. The number of lanes counted for the perpendicular street crossing indicate the width of the crossing and the time needed to cross it. The number of lanes in the parallel street may indicate traffic volume and complexity, with an increased number of lanes signifying a likely increase in volume, turning traffic, and intersection complexity.

Rationale The learner needs an idea of the intersection geometry and complexity before crossing. The number of lanes in the intersection gives the learner information about the length of the crossing and the time needed to cross, and alerts her to possible complex signal phasing for multiple lanes of traffic to factor into her analysis.

STEP 7 The learner explores features present at the corner to determine if any obstacles may negatively impact the visibility of pedestrian crossings, mask auditory information for crossings for the learner, or otherwise impact the decision for crossing. The learner may explore the area with the long cane (see Chapter 6 for a detailed description of Street-Corner Familiarization) to look for environmental features positioned near the corner that may impact visibility. These features include, but are not limited to, overgrown hedges or bushes, large postal boxes, covered bus benches and bus shelters, or crosswalks set back at a skewed intersection. The learner may also listen to determine if there is something that might compromise the use of sounds, such as identification of a sound shadow or the presence of a loud bus, plane, or construction site.

Rationale Learners should take the time to determine if there are any environmental features that might negatively impact the visibility of pedestrian crossings, especially for right-turn lanes for counterclockwise crossings. Instances of poor visibility or masked sounds at the corner may indicate the need to find an alternate crossing or to solicit assistance during the crossing.

Variation A learner with low vision can use visual information together with auditory information to determine traffic patterns and lanes in the intersection. (See Chapter 10 for more information on using vision for intersection analysis.)

CONSIDERATIONS FOR ANALYZING INTERSECTION GEOMETRY

- Young children should be encouraged to listen to traffic and identify the locations of vehicles, using simple terms such as "the cars in front of you" or "the cars beside you," paired with the more refined terms "perpendicular" or "parallel" to help build conceptual understanding.

- Identifying and recognizing the differences in movement of the various lanes of traffic, and labeling them near-lane-parallel, far-lane-parallel, near-lane-perpendicular, and far-lane-perpendicular will be particularly important when dealing with complex intersections and phasing plans, but the terms and concepts can be introduced and used first at relatively simple intersection configurations.

- If the learner is not properly aligned, it is very difficult to analyze the intersection, so alignment may need to be adjusted first. However, while listening to traffic in order to align, the learner can also analyze the traffic flow and make decisions about the roadway width and the type of traffic control present.

- Medians or islands may not be detectable by listening. At locations with medians or islands, the learner may be able to recognize that the far-lane-perpendicular traffic seems further away or hear what seems to be an empty lane in the middle of the street and surmise that it is a median or traffic island.

Analyzing Traffic Control and Movements

Purpose: To prepare the learner to make a street-crossing determination by analyzing traffic movement at the intersection as well as the vehicle and pedestrian controls. This step may be minimal at very familiar intersections, but the learner needs to always, at least briefly, reevaluate the intersection to ensure that controls or traffic patterns have not changed.

PROCEDURE AT A GLANCE

1. The learner observes vehicle movements to determine traffic patterns and sequence of traffic, and the type of vehicle controls, pedestrian controls, and actuations present. She also listens for other pedestrian activity and their patterns of movements (if present).

2. The learner begins by determining the pattern of traffic flow of the near-lane-parallel traffic.

3. The learner determines the pattern of traffic flow of the far-lane-parallel traffic.

4. The learner determines the pattern of traffic flow of the near-lane-perpendicular traffic.

5. The learner determines the pattern of traffic flow of the far-lane-perpendicular traffic.

6. The learner determines the sequence of traffic-flow patterns, including pairings of movement.

7. The learner examines other environmental features present at the corner or intersection that may indicate or confirm a stop sign–controlled crossing or traffic signal control at the intersection.

8. The learner continues her analysis to determine the appropriate time to cross based on the control present at the crossing (uncontrolled, stop sign–controlled, or signal-controlled).

METHOD

STEP 1 The learner observes vehicle movements to determine traffic patterns and direction of traffic movement through the intersection, the sequence of traffic moving through the intersection, how vehicles start and stop in either an alternating or continuous flow, and the type of vehicle controls, pedestrian controls, and actuations present at the intersection. She also listens for other pedestrian activity and their patterns of movement (if present).

Rationale Listening for traffic and other information will assist the learner in determining traffic patterns and the type of traffic, pedestrian controls, and actuations present at the intersection. Knowledge of traffic and pedestrian controls is essential for determining the appropriate timing for the street crossing.

Variations A learner with low vision can use visual information together with auditory information to determine traffic patterns and lanes in the intersection. (See Chapter 10 for more information on using vision for intersection analysis.) In certain situations, such as in smaller, less complex, or somewhat familiar intersections, some learners will be able to combine the intersection analysis for geometry and traffic control. However, separating the tasks in the beginning provides practice in a systematic order for analyzing the intersection that will prove useful at more complex intersections.

STEP 2 The learner begins by determining the pattern of traffic flow of the near-lane-parallel traffic, including whether vehicles continue without stopping (likely uncontrolled), stop and start before proceeding through the intersection (likely presence of a stop sign control), or wait and idle at the intersection and then proceed through as a group (likely presence of a traffic signal control).

Rationale The pattern of traffic provides information about the type of control present, which is essential in selecting and making an appropriate crossing decision. The near lane is the lane that often provides the best information about when to begin crossing, so it is analyzed first.

STEP 3 The learner determines the pattern of traffic flow of the far-lane-parallel traffic.

Rationale Focusing on a different lane or set of lanes provides confirmation (or lack thereof) of information gathered in listening to the pattern of the near-lane-parallel traffic.

STEP 4 The learner determines the pattern of traffic flow of the near-lane-perpendicular traffic.

Rationale Focusing on the movements of the perpendicular traffic lanes provides confirmation (or lack thereof) of information gathered in listening to the pattern of the parallel traffic.

STEP 5 The learner determines the pattern of traffic flow of the far-lane-perpendicular traffic.

Rationale Focusing on the movements of the perpendicular traffic lanes provides confirmation (or lack thereof) of information gathered in listening to the pattern of the parallel traffic.

STEP 6 The learner determines the sequence of traffic-flow patterns, including pairings of movement, such as noting that all northbound traffic moves together, including cars in the northbound lanes that turn east or west, or that northbound and southbound left-turning vehicles move simultaneously. The sequence of traffic movement may assist the learner in determining if there are dedicated left or right turning lanes, complex or simple phasing, slip lanes, and other features or controls. However, learners should be aware that signal phasing and sequence can change with each cycle depending on the traffic present in each lane.

Rationale An understanding of the traffic control present and the intersection movements is necessary for the next procedures of aligning to cross and determining when to cross.

STEP 7 The learner examines other environmental features present at the corner or intersection that may indicate or confirm a stop sign–controlled crossing or traffic signal control at the intersection. The learner may confirm the presence of a stop sign–controlled crossing at a clockwise crossing by extending her cane to the left and right to locate the stop sign pole for the perpendicular street. (The stop sign for a perpendicular crossing in a counterclockwise direction will not usually be located on the same corner as the learner.) The learner may confirm the presence of a traffic signal or pedestrian pushbutton pole (typically found on her left side on clockwise crossings and right side for counterclockwise crossings) by extending her cane to the left and right to locate the traffic signal or a pedestrian pushbutton pole for the street. (If the learner has completed the Street-Corner Familiarization procedure in Chapter 6, she should have found these landmarks previously.)

Rationale This analysis provides further confirmation of information determined by listening.

Variation A learner who has low vision can visually scan for the presence of a stop sign, traffic signal, or pedestrian control located at the same or opposite corner. She can also look for the word STOP, which may be painted in the street, or for a stop line or limit-line marking on the street. She can also look for a traffic signal or pedestrian signal across the street. The learner can visually trace the crosswalk line to the opposite corner and then scan horizontally to increase her chance of locating the vertical traffic-signal pole.

STEP 8 The learner continues her analysis to determine the appropriate time to cross based on the control present at the crossing (uncontrolled, stop sign–controlled, or signal-controlled).

Rationale Different strategies will be used to decide when to cross and will depend on the method of traffic control present at that street.

CONSIDERATIONS FOR ANALYZING TRAFFIC CONTROL AND MOVEMENTS

- This skill can and should be practiced at intersections before independent street crossing is even introduced.

- If a learner is not properly aligned, it is very difficult to analyze the intersection, so alignment may need to be adjusted first. However, while listening to traffic in order to align, the learner can also analyze the traffic flow and make decisions about the roadway width and the type of traffic control present.

- Listening to the traffic patterns before crossing is a good idea even at familiar crossings, but may be done quickly to confirm the intersection is operating as expected.

- At an unfamiliar crossing, the learner should listen for several minutes to ensure that she has heard cars on each street and the full traffic pattern. At a busy signalized intersection, she should understand that the pattern may change with each cycle.

- The learner should listen as long as necessary to determine the appropriate time to cross.

- In analyzing the crossing, the learner should evaluate the crossing by considering each lane (lane-by-lane analysis), either through listening or looking (if she has low vision), to determine where vehicles may come from during her crossing. The learner evaluates each lane to be crossed and the direction from which vehicles will be approaching while crossing that lane. For example, at a counterclockwise crossing of a street with four lanes, two in each direction, the near-lane-perpendicular traffic will be approaching from the left. Potential conflicts for this lane at a signal are cars approaching from the left, including

  □ a car running a red light;

  □ cars turning right or left on green from the parallel street in front of the pedestrian, which are supposed to yield to the pedestrian but may not;

  □ cars turning right or left on green arrows from the parallel street in front of the pedestrian (when the signal might not be displaying Walk for the pedestrian).

- The same conflicts are possible in the second lane. In the third lane of this crossing, the far-lane-perpendicular on a two-way street, potential conflicting vehicles are approaching from the right and should be stopped and waiting at the signal, providing alignment and heading information for the second half of the crossing. In the fourth lane, vehicles would again be approaching from the right, but drivers may be planning to make a right turn on red without coming to a full stop, or may be stopped across the crosswalk.

- It should not be assumed that either a clockwise or counterclockwise crossing is always safest. There are advantages and disadvantages for each direction of crossing and a decision about which way to cross at an intersection may depend on travel plans, street configurations, traffic patterns, or other considerations. (See Sidebar 7.1 for list of advantages and disadvantages of counterclockwise and clockwise crossings.)

Advantages and Disadvantages of Crossing Counterclockwise and Clockwise

Counterclockwise Crossing at a Two-Way Street (with Parallel Traffic on the Left)

Advantages

- Near-lane-parallel traffic (see Figure 7.4) is close and moving in the same direction as the learner, which is easier to hear and allows her to identify the surge quickly. It is usually also easier to use for alignment and heading information.
- Idling far-lane-perpendicular traffic on the second half of crossing can provide a sound cue that may assist with correcting alignment.
- Permissive left-turning traffic from the parallel street in front of the learner is usually blocked by near-lane-parallel traffic, providing enough time for the learner to clear the near lanes of the perpendicular street.
- Drivers attempting to turn right on red from the far lanes of the perpendicular street are looking toward an approaching pedestrian and may see the learner's cane or dog guide.

Disadvantages

- Near-lane-parallel traffic turning right on green can create an immediate conflict when stepping off the curb. The learner may not be within immediate view of drivers who may be aggressive in making their turn.
- The parallel traffic surge may be difficult to distinguish if there is a steady stream of traffic turning right on red from the near-lane-parallel. This may delay the learner's beginning to cross.
- Near-lane-perpendicular vehicles running a red light may arrive at the crosswalk just as the learner begins to cross.
- Far-lane-perpendicular traffic may pull into the crosswalk area when attempting to turn right on red, or may approach quickly, and the driver's visibility of the learner may be blocked by other vehicles in closer lanes.

Clockwise Crossing at a Two-Way Street (with Parallel Traffic on the Right)

Advantages

- Near-lane-perpendicular traffic (see Figure 7.5) waiting at the stop line or limit line can provide a sound cue for alignment as the learner begins her crossing.
- Parallel traffic cannot turn into the lanes as the learner is starting to cross.
- Far-lane-perpendicular traffic has a clear view of the crosswalk and the learner in the crosswalk during the last half of the crossing (which is helpful if the learner is late in completing the crossing).
- Cars turning right on green in the near-lane-parallel street should have a good view of the approaching learner and her cane and cane movement.
- Vehicles running a red light in the near-lane-perpendicular street are likely to be past the learner before she steps out into the street.

Disadvantages

- Near-lane-parallel traffic is coming from the other side of the perpendicular street, traveling toward the learner. The learner may be delayed in hearing the traffic surge if the perpendicular street is wide.
- Near-lane-perpendicular traffic attempting to turn right on red may be pulled forward across the crosswalk, with drivers likely looking to their left, away from the learner, for a gap in traffic (and may try to turn quickly before the traffic on the parallel street gets there from across the intersection).
- The learner reaches the middle of the street late in the phase, when far-lane-parallel traffic may be turning left from behind her right shoulder during gaps in near-parallel-traffic. The drivers' attention when turning left is often focused on approaching traffic.

ALIGNING FOR CROSSING

Purpose: To enable the learner to align accurately for a street crossing. At unfamiliar intersections, this procedure may include carefully exploring the area to find a tactile cue for alignment, as described in Chapter 6 (see procedure for Street-Corner Familiarization), particularly if pedestrian pushbuttons are present.

PROCEDURE AT A GLANCE

1 Maintaining awareness of her approach direction and alignment, the learner attends to traffic and other cues at the crossing location.

2a If traffic is available, the learner listens to the movement of parallel and perpendicular traffic, adjusting her heading as necessary to be aligned parallel to traffic movement on the parallel street.

2b If no traffic is available, the learner maintains approach alignment and awareness of approach trajectory and projects a mental line across the street. She may explore the curb and gutter to see if her alignment is perpendicular to the curb, particularly in a residential or small business area where corners may be relatively square.

3 After aligning to cross, the learner explores the alignment of the curb, curb ramp, or detectable warning surface in relation to her feet, the nearby landscape strip or grass line (if present), and other potential cues, and determines a cue for alignment to be used when preparing to cross.

4 The learner finds the cue, then turns slightly away from it, realigns with it, and checks her alignment using parallel and perpendicular traffic or other techniques.

METHOD

STEP 1 Maintaining awareness of her approach direction and alignment, the learner attends to traffic and other cues at the crossing location.

Rationale Listening to traffic and checking for other cues will assist the learner in determining if she is properly aligned for crossing.

Variation A learner who has low vision may be able to align visually using crosswalk lines and other features.

STEP 2A If traffic is available, the learner listens to the movement of parallel and perpendicular traffic, adjusting her heading as necessary to be aligned parallel to traffic movement on the parallel street. (See Auditory Alignment with Parallel Traffic and Auditory Alignment with Perpendicular Traffic in Chapter 6.)

Rationale Traffic on the parallel street will probably provide the most accurate alignment information and will likely be the traffic moving during the learner's street crossing. The near-lane-parallel traffic, which will be traveling in the same direction as the learner for counterclockwise crossings and approaching from across the intersection in the opposite direction for clockwise crossings, is likely to be most useful because of its relative proximity to the crosswalk and the learner. This traffic will be the lane closest to the crosswalk in most intersection configurations. The learner can also reconfirm the traffic control present at the intersection during this time (see procedure for Analyzing Traffic Control and Movements earlier in this chapter).

STEP 2B If no traffic is available, the learner maintains approach alignment and awareness of approach trajectory and projects a mental line across the street. She may explore the curb and gutter to see if her alignment is perpendicular to the curb, particularly in a residential or small business area where corners may be relatively square.

Rationale Without traffic, tactile and line-of-travel approaches provide information to help determine the direction to cross.

Variations Another method of establishing or reestablishing alignment at the curb is to utilize a landscape strip or grass line while approaching the curb. A slight variation of this method can be used while standing a few feet from the curb. The learner places her foot along the sidewalk edge, then, with the cane tip extended against the landscape strip in front of her foot, she projects this line forward and moves up to the curb. Common mistakes include the learner following the cane tip up to the curb, or failing to remember to move close enough to the edge of the curb. Learners with low vision may use crosswalk lines or other visual cues.

STEP 3 After aligning to cross, the learner explores the alignment of the curb, curb ramp, or detectable warning surface in relation to her feet, the nearby landscape strip or grass line (if present), and other potential cues, and determines a cue for alignment that she can use when preparing to cross.

Rationale Establishing a tactile alignment cue can be helpful for future crossings at the intersection, at times when there is little traffic, or particularly in locations where pedestrian pushbuttons are present. If there is a pedestrian pushbutton, the learner must push the button, then return and realign and be ready to cross with the next surge of traffic. She will not be able to wait to hear traffic move on the parallel street to realign for the crossing and will benefit from a tactile or visual cue to realign.

STEP 4 The learner finds the cue, then turns slightly away from it, realigns with it, and checks her alignment using parallel and perpendicular traffic or other techniques.

Rationale The learner checks her ability to accurately align with the chosen physical cue by realigning with it and confirming her positioning by listening to traffic and other cues.

Variation The learner may also ask another pedestrian for confirmation of her alignment at the intersection.

CONSIDERATIONS FOR ALIGNING FOR CROSSING

- If the learner is not properly aligned, it is very difficult to analyze the intersection, so alignment may need to be adjusted first. However, while listening to traffic in order to align, the learner can also analyze the traffic flow and make decisions about the roadway width and the type of traffic control present.
- Determining a tactile or visual alignment cue is essential at a signal-controlled intersection with pedestrian pushbuttons because the learner will need to begin crossing as soon as the signal is green for parallel traffic. There will not be time to realign with parallel traffic movement before beginning to cross.
- In a familiar environment, the learner may use the curb for alignment if she knows that the curb is perpendicular to the crossing direction. However, in many suburban locations, the curb radius may be so large and round that aligning with the curb will align the learner toward the center of the intersection.

- At familiar locations or after familiarizing themselves with a corner, some learners align themselves at a known angle in relation to the curb (when the curb is not perpendicular to the crosswalk) and use that as their tactile cue.
- Researchers found that learners align more accurately with underfoot cues that are perpendicular to their travel direction (Scott et al., 2011a).
- The O&M specialist can help the learner identify appropriate cues to use for intersections that will be crossed again and provide feedback as the learner practices realigning quickly, consistently, and efficiently with the chosen cue.
- Perpendicular traffic can be used for auditory alignment at some intersections, but not where the roads do not meet at a 90-degree angle (skewed intersections) or at most roundabout or channelized turn-lane crosswalks where the road is curved.
- Learners using vision to make alignment decisions need to be sure they are aiming for the correct target curb at roundabouts and other alternative intersection configurations. Sometimes an island that is not intended for pedestrian use can look like a sidewalk to an individual with low vision.
- The learner should not use turning vehicles as a means for checking or adjusting her alignment.
- Initially, the O&M specialist should check the learner's cane position, relation of feet to the curb, and total body alignment.

DECIDING WHEN TO CROSS

Deciding When to Cross at Uncontrolled Crossings

Purpose: To enable the learner to evaluate the crossing situation and determine whether she can hear or see traffic with enough warning to know when it is clear to cross and to make the correct timing decision for the crossing (Sauerburger, 1999, 2005, 2006, n.d.).

	PROCEDURE AT A GLANCE
1	The learner estimates the width of the street and the amount of time it will take to cross the street.
2	The learner waits for a quiet period, then listens for approaching vehicles on the perpendicular street.
3	The learner notes the warning time of each vehicle (the time between when it was first heard or seen and when it passed in front of her) and compares that to her crossing time.
4	The learner repeats Steps 2 and 3 for numerous vehicles until she can draw a conclusion about whether vehicles can be heard with enough warning to be confident as to when it is clear to cross.
5	If vehicles are not detected with enough warning, the risk of crossing is assessed.
6	If it is too risky, the learner considers alternatives to crossing at that location.

METHOD

STEP 1 The learner estimates the width of the street and the amount of time it will take to cross the street.

Rationale This is a necessary step for the learner to be able to compare her crossing time to the gap in traffic and her ability to hear approaching vehicles.

STEP 2 The learner waits for a quiet period, then listens for approaching vehicles on the perpendicular street.

Rationale To begin to evaluate how much warning time there is for vehicles approaching the crossing location at that time, there needs to be a gap in traffic. Also, when using hearing, it is ideal for the setting to be as quiet as it can be (Wall Emerson & Sauerburger, 2008). If there is no clear or quiet time and the learner cannot evaluate the situation and its risk, she may need to consider alternatives.

Variation A learner with low vision may look for vehicles in addition to listening. Practice should include where to look and how to scan effectively.

STEP 3 The learner notes the warning time for each vehicle (the interval between hearing or seeing the vehicle and the vehicle passing in front of her) and compares that to her crossing time. Both near- and far-perpendicular lanes need to be assessed (e.g., eastbound and westbound cars on the perpendicular street). Crossing can present different situations at different times, each of which must be considered individually and treated as a separate crossing situation and decision. The same is true of each direction of crossing (e.g., crossing from the south side of the street to the north side, crossing from the north side of the street to the south side).

Rationale Understanding whether the warning time is as long as the crossing time is a part of making the crossing decision. The warning time is the interval of time it takes for the vehicle to reach the crosswalk from the time the learner hears or sees it. If the warning time is longer than the crossing time, the learner will be able to complete the crossing if she starts crossing just before she hears or sees the vehicle from her location. The range of warning time of approaching vehicles can vary at different times at the same crossing, depending on the acoustic or visual conditions.

STEP 4 The learner repeats Steps 2 and 3 for numerous vehicles from each direction until she can draw a conclusion about whether vehicles can be heard with enough warning time to establish with confidence that it is clear to cross at that location and in that situation.

Rationale The learner should listen or watch for enough approaching vehicles from each direction to assess the range of warning times for the vehicles. This observation is essential to determining if it is safe to cross when she detects nothing coming and to ensure that no vehicles can reach her before she completes her crossing. If she assesses the warning time of only one vehicle from each direction, she may get the wrong impression because the speed of a single vehicle may be significantly faster or slower than other vehicles. Because she will reach the far lanes later in the crossing, she needs to hear or see vehicles earlier from that direction to clear the lanes before the vehicles reach that location. The learner should never assume that drivers will see her crossing and yield to allow her to complete her crossing.

STEP 5 If vehicles are not detected with enough warning, the risk of crossing is assessed. The learner considers the features of the crossing, such as the speed of vehicles, visibility of the crosswalk, general visibility of the learner (nighttime and rainy conditions may result in less visibility to drivers), number of lanes to be crossed, familiarity with the crossing, and typical yielding behavior of drivers in the area, among other factors.

Rationale There are some situations where the learner may feel the risk is low, or that there are strategies (see following Variations section) she can use to lower the risk, even though she cannot detect the vehicles with enough warning to make the complete crossing.

Variations If the location is a single-lane crossing, such as a single-lane roundabout entry or exit or a channelized turn lane, and there is not enough warning of approaching vehicles to be confident that it is clear to cross, the learner may choose to use a strategy to encourage the vehicle to yield. After confirming that the vehicle has yielded, the learner can cross in front of the vehicle. Before using the strategy, the learner should confirm, either through knowledge of the location or by asking questions of other pedestrians, that there is only one lane and not enough room for another vehicle to come around the stopped vehicle. Strategies to affect vehicle yielding include:

- Flagging with the cane - moving the cane back and forth before beginning to cross.
- Hand up - putting one hand up toward the driver in a stop position while flagging with the cane.
- Reversible step - flagging while taking one step into the street at the gutter, then pausing to reevaluate the traffic movement. Reversible step was found to be most effective for getting right-turning vehicles to yield at signalized crossings and research at roundabouts has indicated it is also effective at unsignalized crossings (Bourquin, Wall Emerson, Sauerburger, & Barlow, 2014, in press).

Other learners may feel that the crossing has an acceptable risk—even if they are not sure they can hear all vehicles—if the vehicle speed is low and visibility is good, or if they know that a high percentage of drivers yield to pedestrians crossing in that area. Rather than a pronouncement by the O&M specialist that a crossing is unsafe, discussing options and decision making with learners may result in a better understanding of traffic and driver behavior. These variations should be considered by adults with the ability to manage personal risk and safety decisions in consultation with the O&M specialist and are not recommended for younger learners. However, O&M specialists should discuss the risks involved in various crossings with younger learners with whom they work and emphasize intersection analysis throughout O&M training. This will ensure that as adult learners they will be able to make informed choices for their own personal risk management.

STEP 6 **If the crossing is too risky for the learner, the learner considers alternatives to crossing at that location.**

Rationale Alternatives to crossing are an appropriate option if the situation is too risky and the possibility of injury is not acceptable to the learner in that situation. The learner cannot be confident that it is clear to cross due to the inadequate warning time of approaching vehicles.

Variations Alternatives may include choosing another location at which to cross, soliciting assistance, getting a ride, using a shared-ride service, riding a bus to the end of the line and back to avoid crossing at that location, or avoiding making the trip by ordering online and having goods delivered.

Sometimes just moving 25 to 50 feet down the roadway, particularly along a residential street with a hill or curve, can make a difference in the ability to hear vehicles from adequate distances.

CONSIDERATIONS FOR DECIDING WHEN TO CROSS AT UNCONTROLLED CROSSINGS

- Uncontrolled crossing locations include a through street (a street without stop signs) at a two-way intersection, an intersection with no traffic controls at all (usually found only in residential areas), roundabouts and channelized turn lanes, and mid-block locations. While vehicles are supposed to yield to pedestrians at marked and unmarked crosswalks, crosswalks are considered uncontrolled crossings if there is no signal or stop sign facing the vehicles traveling on the street to be crossed. In most US states, unmarked crosswalks legally exist at every intersection where sidewalks are installed. (For further discussion of uncontrolled crossings see Barlow, Bentzen, Sauerburger et al., 2010; Sauerburger, 1999, 2005, 2006, n.d.; and Schroeder et al., 2016.)
- At locations with more than one lane of traffic in the same direction, the learner must understand that one car stopping to allow her to cross may mask the sound of another car approaching in the next lane. The stopped vehicle may also block the approaching driver's view of the pedestrian crossing. Crashes due to this type of situation are often referred to as "multiple-threat" crashes (see Figure 7.6).
- It is important for the learner to have an understanding of the time needed to cross the street, so that comparisons with warning times can become natural and automatic rather than require any mental calculations (see the Tips for Teaching Street-Crossing Techniques at the end of this chapter).

Richard Blomberg

Figure 7.6

Example of a Multiple-Threat Crash
The vehicle that has stopped in the first lane to allow the pedestrian to cross masks the sound of the approaching vehicle in the second lane while also blocking the view of the approaching driver.

- Each direction of traffic must be analyzed separately, then both considered together to determine if there is enough warning to be confident that it is clear to cross the entire street. For example, there may be enough warning from vehicles approaching from one direction but not the other, and both must be considered when making a crossing decision for that situation. Because vehicles approaching from each direction may vary greatly in range of warning times, and because the learner needs longer warning times for vehicles in far lanes than for those in the near lanes (she will reach the far lanes later in the crossing), traffic from each direction may present a very different situation. Warning times for both directions must be assessed, and both must have a range of warning times that are longer than the crossing time for the learner to be confident about when it is clear to cross.
- At roundabouts, designers assume pedestrians will stop on the splitter island in the middle of the crossing and make a separate crossing for each direction of vehicle travel on the street.
- When crossing an uncontrolled street, near-lane-parallel traffic, at either a stop sign–controlled street, a two-way stop intersection, or a fully uncontrolled intersection, cannot be relied on as an indication of the appropriate time to begin crossing. Whether vehicles come to a complete stop and then surge through the intersection or are in continuous motion through the intersection, these parallel street vehicles can clear the intersection before a pedestrian has crossed even one lane of traffic, no longer offering any buffer to vehicles moving on the uncontrolled perpendicular street. These parallel vehicles can also block other drivers' view of the pedestrian crossing and mask the sound of a fast-moving vehicle approaching on the street being crossed.

Deciding When to Cross at Stop Sign–Controlled Intersections

Purpose: To enable the learner to evaluate the crossing, determine when to cross, and assess if adequate information and gaps in traffic are available at that location.

PROCEDURE AT A GLANCE

1 The learner listens to the pattern of traffic movement.

2a If there are regular detectable quiet periods in traffic on both streets, the learner can decide to cross in those quiet periods.

2b If there are not consistent quiet periods in traffic on both streets, the learner may choose to cross with a near-lane-parallel vehicle traveling straight through the intersection.

3 If Steps 2a and 2b are not available or are difficult to determine, and the learner feels the risk is unacceptable, the learner considers alternatives to crossing that location at that time.

METHOD

STEP 1 The learner listens to the pattern of traffic movement, listening for approaching vehicles and whether all vehicles come to a stop before proceeding through the intersection, how long she can hear vehicles approaching, whether there are long gaps between vehicles, what direction or directions most traffic is traveling, and whether there are a lot of vehicles turning in a particular direction.

Rationale Having decided this is a stop sign–controlled crossing, the learner needs to determine more details about the traffic patterns to decide when to cross.

STEP 2A If there are regular detectable quiet periods or gaps in traffic on both streets (when there is no traffic on either street), as may be common in residential areas, the learner determines that she can cross in those quiet periods.

Rationale A simultaneous gap in all traffic provides an opportunity to cross. A quiet time at a stop sign–controlled crossing provides the learner with an opportunity to initiate the crossing prior to a potential vehicle reaching the stop sign, and creates a clear right-of-way for the pedestrian and ample time to make the crossing since once a car reaches the intersection, it is required to stop and proceed only if the intersection is clear.

STEP 2B If there are not consistent quiet periods or gaps in traffic on both streets, the learner may cross with a near-lane-parallel vehicle traveling straight through the intersection, which may prevent perpendicular traffic from moving. It is important for the learner to complete the lane-by-lane analysis described in the Intersection Analysis Procedures earlier in this chapter and be aware of the direction from which conflicting traffic might approach.

Rationale A near-lane-parallel vehicle traveling through the intersection, if not turning, prevents perpendicular traffic from moving during that time because the perpendicular vehicle must wait for the parallel vehicle to pass before beginning to move into the intersection. Depending on the speed it is traveling, the parallel vehicle may or may not block traffic from turning left across the crosswalk from the opposite side of the parallel street (at a two-way stop).

Variation A vehicle stopping before the crosswalk in the near-lane-perpendicular street to be crossed is used by some as an indication of the time to cross. However, it is important to be sure the vehicle driver is coming to a full stop and likely to be looking toward, and is therefore aware of, the learner. This behavior may be common at heavily traveled pedestrian areas.

STEP 3 If Steps 2a and 2b are not available or are difficult to determine, and the learner feels the risk is unacceptable, the learner considers alternatives to crossing that location at that time.

Rationale Alternatives to crossing are an appropriate option if the crossing situation is considered too risky by the learner or the decision is too difficult for the learner.

Variations Alternatives may include choosing another location at which to cross, soliciting assistance, getting a ride, using a shared-ride service, riding a bus to the end of the line and back to avoid crossing at that location, or avoiding making the trip by ordering online and having goods delivered.

CONSIDERATIONS FOR DECIDING WHEN TO CROSS AT STOP SIGN–CONTROLLED INTERSECTIONS

- Stop sign–controlled crossings may include two-way and four-way stops. At two-way stops, the learner is crossing the street where vehicles are required to stop before proceeding, usually the minor street. While vehicles are required to stop before proceeding, learners should understand that "rolling stops" are common and drivers may not be paying enough attention to pedestrians preparing to cross.

- As with all crossings, the situation may change at different times of day and with different traffic patterns. Learners should assess the crossing and the crossing decision each time they need to cross.

- As part of the assessment of the crossing, the O&M specialist and the learner should discuss and consider the direction of travel of the vehicle and where the driver's attention may be focused.

- Crossing in front of stopped perpendicular traffic can be risky unless the learner is confident that the driver is aware of her presence and not looking in the other direction. The O&M specialist can help the learner understand the driver's typical scanning behavior for gaps in traffic and which direction the driver may be looking.

- Even though all cars are supposed to stop before continuing, four-way stops can be quite busy and at times it can be difficult for some learners to find a time when they feel the crossing risk is acceptable. Four-way stops with two lanes of traffic from each direction may be difficult to cross because of constant traffic movement. Busy stop sign–controlled crossings should be considered only for learners with advanced skills.

Deciding When to Cross at Signal-Controlled Intersections: Locating and Using Pushbuttons

At traffic signals, the learner must first find and use the pushbutton, if present, to determine the appropriate time to begin crossing.

Purpose: **To enable the learner to find and use a pedestrian pushbutton to provide adequate time to cross. At signalized intersections, with the various signal timing plans in use, pedestrians must use a pedestrian pushbutton, if one is installed.**

PROCEDURE AT A GLANCE

1. The learner listens for and notes if there is a pushbutton locator tone (once per second) or a tone or speech Walk indication from an APS.

2. The learner searches for the pushbutton using a systematic pattern, beginning on the side furthest from the parallel street.

3. Once the pushbutton or APS is located, the pushbutton or APS device is explored to locate the actual pushbutton and determine if there are other features installed.

4. The learner holds the pushbutton down for more than two seconds to see if more information is provided.

5. The learner listens to the APS, if available, and the traffic at the intersection for a full cycle to make sure that tones or speech correspond with traffic movement. If there is no APS, the learner listens for a full cycle of traffic after the button is pressed to confirm information regarding traffic patterns determined earlier during the intersection analysis.

6. As traffic on the perpendicular street begins to move, the learner presses the pushbutton again, returns to the predetermined spot at the curb, realigns with the previously determined tactile cue, and prepares to cross.

METHOD

STEP 1 The learner listens for and notes if there is a pushbutton locator tone (once per second) or a tone or speech Walk indication from an APS. At older installations of audible signals, if there is no pushbutton locator tone, there may be a tone or message indicating the walk interval.

Rationale If there is a pushbutton locator tone, it assists with finding the pushbutton. Knowing whether there is an APS installed at the intersection can be helpful.

STEP 2 The learner searches for the pushbutton using a systematic pattern (see the Street-Corner Familiarization procedure in Chapter 6), beginning on the side furthest from the parallel street.

Rationale Even where there is a pushbutton locator tone, a systematic search pattern is needed to maintain orientation. US standards now call for the pushbutton to be located near the crosswalk line furthest from the parallel street, so that is the best place for the learner to begin looking.

Variation Dog guides are trained to avoid obstacles and may be reluctant to approach poles supporting pedestrian pushbuttons. It may be more efficient for the handler to use a cane to search initially before teaching the dog to locate the pole.

STEP 3 Once the pushbutton or APS is located, the pushbutton or APS device is explored to locate the actual pushbutton and to determine if there is a tactile arrow, braille street name, or another feature. If there is a tactile arrow, the learner confirms that the arrow is pointing in the direction of the street being crossed. If not, she may have found the pushbutton for the other street crossing at the corner, rather than the crossing she intends to make.

Rationale Various types of pushbuttons and APS devices are used in the United States. Learners need to familiarize themselves with the type installed at that intersection. There will be a pushbutton locator tone if a newer type of APS is installed.

Variation Some signalized intersections do not have pushbuttons. If the learner searches and determines there is no pushbutton, she returns to the curb and reevaluates traffic for crossing. At some locations without pushbuttons, usually in suburban or rural areas, there may not be adequate time provided for a pedestrian to cross the road, so the learner must carefully reevaluate the traffic movement and time available.

STEP 4 The learner holds the pushbutton down for more than two seconds to see if more information is provided about the intersection through a speech message.

Rationale Some APS devices provide street names, increased volume, or an increase in typical pedestrian crossing time if the button is held for an extended period (1 second or more). Two seconds is a good rule of thumb to be sure it has been pressed long enough. The main indicator that there are other features installed will likely be a speech message after the learner holds the button down. It is important to note that some cities require a longer press of the button to call the audible Walk indication, so O&M specialists and learners may need to investigate local policies.

Variation This step is not necessary if it is not an APS and there is no pushbutton locator tone.

STEP 5 If an APS is present, the learner listens to the APS and the traffic at the intersection for a full cycle to make sure that tones or speech correspond with traffic movement. If there is no APS, the learner listens for a full cycle of traffic after the button is pressed to confirm information regarding traffic patterns determined earlier during the intersection analysis. Consider the streets and their placement and reconfirm the traffic movement for the planned crossing.

Rationale Although pushbutton placement is currently subject to standards, it has not always been standardized, and as a result, variations in placement still exist. It is relatively easy to find and use the wrong pushbutton. Listening through the traffic cycle can help the learner prepare for crossing and reorient if necessary, particularly if she has listened carefully before beginning to look for the pushbutton.

STEP 6 As traffic on the perpendicular street begins moving, the learner presses the pushbutton again, quickly returns to the predetermined spot at the curb, realigns with the previously determined tactile cue, and prepares to cross.

Rationale If the pushbutton is pressed during the walk interval for the street being crossed, it may not call the pedestrian phase and Walk signal for the next signal cycle, leaving inadequate time for a pedestrian to cross. Pressing the button as the perpendicular street traffic begins moving prevents accidentally pressing it during the Walk interval. The learner must return to the crossing location and be ready to cross before the parallel traffic begins to move, or she will have to wait for the next signal cycle and press the button again.

CONSIDERATIONS FOR DECIDING WHEN TO CROSS AT SIGNAL-CONTROLLED INTERSECTIONS: LOCATING AND USING PUSHBUTTONS

- Signal-controlled intersections can include intersections with a variety of timing schemes as well as relatively simple pedestrian crossings with signals. There are also pedestrian crossings at unsignalized locations with pushbuttons that activate beacons such as *pedestrian hybrid beacons*.
- Learners should understand that the walk indication of an APS means that the pedestrian signal is displaying Walk. This does not mean that it is necessarily safe to cross. The learner should always attend to traffic movement and information determined in intersection analysis and not rely on the APS indicator alone.
- There are different types of APS devices installed in the United States. Standards set in 2009 require APS devices to have a pushbutton locator tone, a tactile arrow, automatic volume adjustment, and both audible and vibrotactile walk indicators (Federal Highway Administration, 2009).
- If the learner has determined that there is no pedestrian pushbutton or APS installed at the intersection, she can skip this procedure.

Determining the Time to Begin Crossing at Signal-Controlled Intersections

Purpose: To enable the learner to evaluate the crossing after pushing the pedestrian pushbutton and determine traffic or signal information to use to time and begin the crossing.

	PROCEDURE AT A GLANCE
1	The learner again determines the location of the near-lane-parallel traffic.
2a	Counterclockwise crossing: The learner listens for the surge of near-lane-parallel traffic moving in the same direction the learner will be crossing, noting other traffic movement just before the surge of traffic, and whether a clear surge of traffic is evident. At a one-way street, the near-lane-parallel traffic may be moving in the opposite direction of the learner.
2b	Clockwise crossing: The learner listens for the surge of near-lane-parallel traffic, noting other traffic movement just before the surge of traffic, and whether a clear surge is evident. At a two-way street, the near-lane-parallel traffic will be coming toward her from across the intersection, moving in the opposite direction to the learner's crossing, and she will need to note whether she can clearly hear the beginning of the surge. At a one-way street, the near-lane-parallel traffic may be moving in the same direction as the learner.
3a	If there is an APS, the learner confirms that its walk indication and the near-lane-parallel traffic surge coincide. If so, both can be used as an indication of the time to begin crossing.
3b	If the APS walk indication and the near-lane-parallel surge do not coincide, the learner evaluates the intersection further to determine what information to use to decide when to cross.

METHOD

STEP 1 The learner again determines the location of the near-lane-parallel traffic.

Rationale The learner has identified this lane earlier in intersection analysis but needs to consider the information available to determine when to begin crossing. The surge of near-lane-parallel traffic is usually at the time when the Walk signal for pedestrians is displayed.

STEP 2A Counterclockwise crossing: The learner listens for the surge of near-lane-parallel traffic moving in the same direction the learner will be crossing, starting to move as the signal changes, noting other traffic movement just before the surge of traffic, and whether a clear surge of traffic is evident. At a one-way street, the near-lane-parallel traffic may be moving in the opposite direction of the learner. The learner will plan to initiate her crossing with traffic moving straight through the intersection in that lane. For counterclockwise crossings of two-way streets, that traffic will be on her left and traveling in the same direction and she must be certain that the vehicle is traveling straight through the intersection and not turning right on red. She notes whether there is heavy left-turning traffic just before the movement of the near-lane-parallel traffic—which probably indicates a protected left turn (green arrow) across the crosswalk—and whether there are a lot of right-turning cars. She also listens for the walk indication of the APS, if present, and confirms whether it coincides with the near-lane-parallel traffic movement.

Rationale The learner needs to carefully evaluate the traffic surge and determine if it provides adequate information. For counterclockwise crossings, cars may still turn right across the crosswalk during the walk interval, and although they are supposed to yield to pedestrians in the crosswalk, they may not do so. If an APS is present, it may provide an earlier indication of the beginning of the Walk signal than can be discerned using near-lane-parallel traffic. However, if there is a left-turn arrow and cars complete their turns after the end of the arrow, stepping out too quickly can be hazardous.

STEP 2B Clockwise crossing: The learner listens for the surge of near-lane-parallel traffic, noting other traffic movement just before the surge of traffic, and whether a clear surge is evident. The learner will plan to initiate her crossing with traffic moving straight through the intersection in that lane. At clockwise crossings of two-way streets, the near-lane-parallel traffic will be on her right and traffic will be coming toward her from across the intersection in the direction that is opposite to her crossing. She notes whether she can clearly hear the beginning of the surge. She also attends to the near-lane-perpendicular traffic to determine if traffic turning right on red is regularly pulling into the crosswalk just before the near-lane-parallel surge. At a one-way street, the near-lane-parallel traffic may be moving in the same direction as the learner.

Rationale The learner needs to carefully evaluate the traffic surge and determine if it provides adequate information. For clockwise crossings, near-lane-perpendicular vehicles that intend to turn right on red may pull into the crosswalk and turn just before the near-lane-parallel traffic surge. Those drivers may typically not be looking toward the learner's position, so she will need to take that into consideration. If an APS is present, it may provide an earlier indication of the signal change than the near-lane-parallel traffic, particularly at very wide intersections.

STEP 3A If there is an APS, the learner confirms that its walk indication and the near-lane-parallel traffic surge coincide. If so, the combination of both can be used as an indication of the time to begin crossing.

Rationale An APS can provide confirmation of the information provided by the traffic. It may provide a slightly earlier walk indication than the surge and can assist the learner to begin crossing ahead of right-turning traffic on a counterclockwise crossing. Whether the APS indicates the crossing at the same time as the near-lane-parallel traffic surge must be confirmed before crossing.

STEP 3B If the APS walk indication and the near-lane-parallel surge do not coincide, the learner evaluates the intersection further to determine what information to use to decide when to cross.

Rationale If the APS and near-lane-parallel surge do not coincide, it is likely that some type of innovative pedestrian timing is installed at the intersection. The APS may be providing the walk indication because a lead pedestrian interval or exclusive pedestrian phase is installed at that location. If lead pedestrian intervals or exclusive pedestrian phases are installed, the near-lane-parallel traffic will not begin moving at the same time as the Walk signal. If the learner crosses with the near-lane-parallel traffic, she may be crossing against the Walk signal, when drivers do not expect pedestrians in the crosswalk and pedestrians do not have the right-of-way.

CONSIDERATIONS FOR DETERMINING THE TIME TO BEGIN CROSSING AT SIGNAL-CONTROLLED INTERSECTIONS

- If a pushbutton is present, it must be used, even if it does not seem to make a difference. (See Barlow, Bentzen, Sauerburger et al., 2010, for a detailed description of pedestrian pushbutton timing plans and requirements.) If the learner does not know whether a pushbutton is present at the intersection, she should search carefully or ask another pedestrian.

- In downtown areas there may not be pedestrian pushbuttons, and Walk indications may be provided in every signal cycle. Even in downtown areas, proposed regulations by the US Access Board (United States Access Board, 2011) will require the installation of APS devices with tactile arrows aligned with the crosswalk that provide both audible and vibrotactile indications at the locations where pushbuttons are typically placed. Additional features, such as a longer crossing time, an audible beacon, or a street-identification message, if installed, may be provided after holding down the pushbutton on an APS device (Barlow, Scott, Bentzen, Guth, & Graham, 2013; Harkey, Carter, Bentzen, & Barlow, 2007).

- If there is an APS installed, the learner will explore its functioning when locating and using the pedestrian pushbutton. It may not provide a walk indication if the button has not been pressed, so APS functioning cannot usually be evaluated and correlated to the near-lane-parallel traffic surge unless the pushbutton is used.

- Downtown and small business areas may not have the complexity of signals found along major commuting arteries and suburban intersections. Instruction should also include these complex types of intersections along transit lines, because residential apartments as well as employment opportunities are commonly located in this type of environment.

- Learners with low vision may be able to see the pedestrian or vehicular signals. Scanning and checking the traffic should be part of their routine before stepping into the street. Instruction needs to include effective scanning techniques and where to look for vehicles as noted in the lane-by-lane analysis discussion (see also Chapter 10 for more on scanning).

- Transit stops may be positioned relatively close to the corner and a bus stopped to pick up passengers may move through the intersection on a green or a yellow signal that is about to change to red. The surge of a bus can easily be mistaken for the beginning of a parallel traffic surge, and should not be used as an indication of street-crossing timing due to the unpredictability and masking of other traffic sounds.

- The stopping of perpendicular traffic may be used to anticipate the signal change, but should not be used as an indication of an appropriate time to begin crossing. This can be unreliable and dangerous for several reasons:
    - If traffic is intermittent, the signal may have changed several seconds before a vehicle stops and the signal may be about to change again.
    - A vehicle may be stopping for a different reason, such as waiting to make a left turn or letting a passenger out.
    - Traffic on the parallel street may have a left- or right-turn arrow, giving vehicles the right-of-way when crossing the crosswalk.

- Learners should not use signal indications for the perpendicular street (e.g., a red signal for perpendicular traffic) as an indication of the time to cross. Variations in signal functioning and the use of various protected phasing (green arrows) can make this a dangerous choice.

- Where there are dual-protected turn lanes, or split phasing, it can be difficult to distinguish the difference between the traffic moving in the turn lanes on the perpendicular street from the near-lane-parallel traffic surge when making a clockwise crossing. Learners should experience such situations and O&M specialists and learners should discuss and note the subtle difference in sound and traffic movement information with this type of signal phasing.

INITIATING CROSSING AND MAINTAINING CORRECT HEADING OR ALIGNMENT WHILE CROSSING

Purpose: To enable the learner to begin crossing in a systematic way and travel across the street efficiently.

PROCEDURE AT A GLANCE

1 While standing in an aligned position at the crossing location, the learner checks with her cane that the street surface in front of her is clear, then returns her cane to a ready position, with the tip near the edge of the street and the top of the grip and hand extended forward and angled toward the parallel street to be visible to traffic. She maintains awareness of traffic movement and other pedestrians, and reevaluates whether there are masking sounds that may prevent her from hearing traffic.

2 Determining it is time to begin crossing, the learner flags with her cane, moving it across her body and back again in an exaggerated arc, touching the tip to the street on each side, with the cane slightly above knee height at the apex of the arc.

3 Continuing into constant-contact technique, the learner steps into the street, maintaining awareness of her intended direction of travel and traffic movement on the parallel street.

4 The learner crosses the street, maintaining alignment with traffic traveling parallel to the crosswalk and waiting perpendicular cars, while continuing to listen for cars turning across the crosswalk.

5 Walking at a steady, normal pace, the learner concentrates on maintaining a straight line of travel until she contacts the opposite curb, curb ramp, or detectable warning surface on an island or median.

6 When the cane contacts the curb, curb ramp, or detectable warning surface, the learner continues in a straight line while vertically positioning or anchoring the cane.

7 The learner brings the cane onto the sidewalk, clearing the area for her next step, and continues into the touch technique or other desired cane technique.

METHOD

STEP 1 While standing in an aligned position at the crossing location, the learner checks with her cane that the street surface in front of her is clear of obstacles or holes, then returns her cane to a ready position, with the tip near the edge of the street (against the curb if there is a curb), with the top of the grip and hand extended forward to be visible to traffic, particularly near-lane-parallel traffic when making a counterclockwise crossing. She maintains awareness of traffic movement and other pedestrians, and reevaluates whether there are masking sounds that may prevent her from hearing traffic.

Rationale The learner checks the street to ensure that her first step is into a clear area and to determine the height of the step down in preparation for crossing. The cane is held in a position that will be visible to drivers, particularly to encourage yielding and enhance their awareness and recognition of the learner. If there are masking sounds as she is preparing to cross, such as a loud truck, bus, lawnmower or other equipment, it may be difficult to hear traffic adequately at that time and she may choose to wait for the next crossing opportunity.

Variations When a vehicle is idling nearby, it may mask traffic sounds that are needed for the crossing. The learner and O&M specialist should discuss options for this situation. The learner may turn her head away from the street crossing, while maintaining foot position and alignment, to signal to a waiting driver that she is not crossing yet. Some have used a strategy of pretending to answer a phone call or just looking away and moving the cane in close to their bodies. At a signalized location with a pedestrian pushbutton, if the learner misses the surge of traffic, she must push the button again.

STEP 2 Determining it is time to begin crossing (see procedures for Deciding When to Cross earlier in this chapter), the learner flags with her cane, moving it across her body and back again in an exaggerated arc, touching the tip to the street on each side, with the cane slightly above knee height at the apex of the arc. At signalized locations with an APS, the learner must confirm that traffic on the perpendicular street is stopping or stopped and listen for initial parallel traffic movements when the walk tone or message is heard. Vehicles may still be legally clearing the crosswalk when the walk indication begins, so careful listening is important.

Rationale The movement of the cane may alert drivers to the learner's presence and intention to cross. Flagging has been found to result in somewhat improved yielding by right-turning drivers when learners are making counterclockwise crossings (Bourquin et al., 2014). It has not been specifically evaluated in clockwise crossings. Using both the APS and traffic to confirm that it is the appropriate time to cross provides more certainty about the signal and confirms that traffic is following signal indications.

Variations Other strategies for improving driver yielding have been evaluated and can be used in conjunction with flagging. These include:

- Hand up - putting one hand up toward the potential right-turning driver in a stop position while flagging with the cane.
- Reversible step - flagging while taking one step into the street at the gutter, then pausing to reevaluate the traffic movement. Reversible step was most effective at getting vehicles to yield, but more research is needed (Bourquin et al., 2014).

STEP 3 Continuing into constant-contact cane technique, the learner steps into the street, maintaining awareness of her intended direction of travel and traffic movement on the parallel street.

Rationale Irregularities in the street surface, possible vehicles within the crosswalk, and other potential hazards require appropriate cane techniques during the crossing. Constant-contact cane technique may also provide greater tactile information about the crosswalk if the crosswalk is made of a contrasting material to the street and may help the learner notice if she veers from the crosswalk. The parallel traffic movement can provide continuous alignment or heading information while crossing.

Variation Touch technique may be preferred by some learners and O&M specialists.

STEP 4 The learner crosses the street, making corrections as necessary to maintain alignment with traffic traveling parallel to the crosswalk and waiting perpendicular cars, while continuing to listen for cars turning across the crosswalk.

Rationale If traffic is present, it can provide a continuous clue to the appropriate travel direction. Both parallel traffic and idling perpendicular traffic can form a "wall of sound" on one half of the crosswalk for the learner to make use of. Small adjustments during the crossing prevent larger errors.

Variation Learners who have low vision may use the vehicles, as well as crosswalk lines, to maintain alignment while crossing.

STEP 5 Walking at a steady, normal pace, the learner concentrates on maintaining a straight line of travel until she contacts the opposite curb, curb ramp, or detectable warning surface on an island or median. On approach to the last lane, if an APS is present, she listens for the pushbutton locator tone of the APS on the corner for additional alignment information and corrects her heading as necessary. To avoid tripping, the learner may slow her pace or change to constant-contact cane technique (if not already using it) when she anticipates contact with a curb. Reaching the crown of the street—the high point of the street, usually at the center of the crossing—may give the learner an awareness of how far she has traveled within the street.

Rationale The learner wants to clear the intersection quickly, but should maintain a reasonable pace and good cane technique. The tactile cue of arrival at the other side of the street or a median may be a curb, but could also be a curb ramp or a 2-foot-deep section of a detectable warning surface (truncated domes).

Variation If the side of a vehicle is contacted, it may be in the crosswalk or the learner may have veered away from the parallel street. The learner should trail around the vehicle, toward the parallel street, and contact the vehicle with her cane (loudly) to alert the driver to her presence, then continue with the crossing.

STEP 6 When the cane contacts the curb, curb ramp, or detectable warning surface, the learner continues in a straight line while vertically positioning or anchoring the cane.

Rationale By approaching the curb in this manner, the learner is properly positioned to clear the area for her step out of the street. The learner should not conform to the line of the curb, as this may change her direction.

STEP 7 The learner brings the cane onto the sidewalk, clearing the area for her next step, and continues into the touch technique or other desired cane technique.

Rationale This clearing with the cane provides a preview for the next step, facilitates smoothness, and hastens the resumption of the touch technique.

Variation Learners with good kinesthetic awareness may initiate this procedure while moving up to the curb.

CONSIDERATIONS FOR INITIATING CROSSING AND MAINTAINING CORRECT HEADING OR ALIGNMENT WHILE CROSSING

- It is good practice to review the lane-by-lane intersection analysis just before making each crossing.
- If there are many pedestrians in a busy commercial district, it can be quite difficult to locate the appropriate crossing location or a pedestrian pushbutton or APS device. The learner may wish to practice waiting for the signal to change and making her approach to the crosswalk after the main group of pedestrians has cleared, positioning herself and crossing on the next signal cycle. Some learners may prefer to solicit assistance from another pedestrian in such situations. In either case, a congested-area cane technique is appropriate and careful search techniques, with awareness of other pedestrians, should be used.
- Tall buildings in a commercial district can affect traffic sounds and other auditory information.
- The street-crossing techniques should be taught in segments to ensure that each step of the technique is mastered in various types of environments.

- Audible beaconing on APS devices or tactile guidestrips are features that may be installed at some wide intersections to assist with maintaining a proper heading (Barlow et al., 2013; Scott et al., 2011b).

- When the learner is preparing to cross, the O&M specialist should position himself so that he can monitor the learner and the entire intersection, as well as potentially stop the learner from stepping forward. The O&M specialist should also not stand in a position that may block sounds his learner needs to hear (see the O&M Specialist Positioning section later in this chapter.)

STREET-CROSSING RECOVERY

Recovering from Veer or Alignment Error Away from the Parallel Street

Purpose: To enable the learner to locate the desired sidewalk in an efficient and systematic manner following a veer or alignment error away from the parallel street (in-block) during a street crossing.

PROCEDURE AT A GLANCE

1 After completing the crossing and failing to locate the sidewalk with the initial clearing procedure, the learner checks both sides with the full length of the cane.

2a If the sidewalk is located through extension of the cane, the learner negotiates the curb, corrects toward the sidewalk, and upon reaching the sidewalk continues in her desired direction.

2b If the sidewalk is not located with extension of the cane, the learner either turns toward the parallel street and walks along the curb utilizing three-point-touch technique until she locates the sidewalk, or steps up onto the curb, crosses the grass or other surface to the perpendicular sidewalk and, if necessary, locates the appropriate sidewalk.

METHOD

STEP 1 After completing the crossing and failing to locate the sidewalk with the initial clearing procedure, the learner checks both sides with the full length of the cane.

Rationale The learner checks with the full length of the cane to facilitate location of the sidewalk in the event she has only veered a few feet from her intended line of travel.

STEP 2A If the sidewalk is located through extension of the cane, the learner steps up out of the street, corrects toward the sidewalk, and upon reaching the sidewalk continues in her desired direction. The learner should be aware of the potential for signs, guy-wires, or tree branches at head height if she steps up outside the sidewalk area and use appropriate protective techniques (see Chapter 4).

Rationale The learner steps out of the street to remove herself from the danger of passing traffic. The learner corrects toward the sidewalk to ensure that the sidewalk is reached smoothly and quickly. The learner continues in the desired direction to facilitate location of her objective.

Variation The learner may take a step or two in the street to the sidewalk before stepping up on the curb, particularly on a quiet street.

STEP 2B If the sidewalk is not located with extension of the cane, the learner either turns toward the parallel street and walks along the curb using three-point-touch technique to locate the sidewalk, positioning herself as close to the curb as possible, or steps up onto the curb, crosses the grass or other surface to the perpendicular sidewalk and, if necessary, locates the appropriate sidewalk. The learner should be aware of the potential for uneven footing or signs, guy-wires, or tree branches at head height if she steps up outside the sidewalk area and use appropriate protective techniques.

Rationale The three-point-touch technique is used because it detects where the curb and the sidewalk intersect and prevents the learner from stepping up onto areas that may be uneven or contain head-level objects. The procedure to step up onto the curb immediately removes the learner from the danger of passing traffic or accidentally walking into a gutter that may have debris, and provides the learner with a systematic method of locating the sidewalk.

CONSIDERATIONS FOR RECOVERING FROM VEER OR ALIGNMENT ERROR AWAY FROM THE PARALLEL STREET

- If the curb is on the right side as the learner contacts it, she typically should turn right to locate the sidewalk.
- If the curb is on the left, she generally should turn left to locate the sidewalk.

Recovering from Veer or Alignment Error toward the Parallel Street

Purpose: To enable the learner to locate the desired sidewalk in an efficient and systematic manner following a veer or alignment error toward the parallel street during a street crossing.

	PROCEDURE AT A GLANCE
1	Realizing she has walked too far or that traffic is too close and she has veered into the parallel street, the learner executes a sharp turn toward the curb and continues, utilizing constant-contact technique.
2	Upon contacting the curb, the learner walks up to the curb and extends her cane beyond the curb to check for the sidewalk.
3a	If the sidewalk is located through extension of the cane, the learner negotiates the curb, corrects toward the sidewalk, and upon reaching the sidewalk continues in her desired direction.
3b	If the sidewalk is not located with extension of the cane, the learner either turns and walks along the curb utilizing three-point-touch technique to locate the sidewalk, or steps up onto the grass or other surface and travels across the surface to the sidewalk, reorienting herself using traffic, the sun, and other clues, and locates the appropriate sidewalk.

METHOD

STEP 1 Realizing she has walked too far or that traffic is too close and she has veered into the parallel street, the learner executes a sharp turn toward the curb and continues, utilizing constant-contact cane technique.

Rationale A sharp turn toward the side of the street enables the learner to get out of the street as quickly as possible. Environmental clues, such as distance traveled, traffic, and pedestrians, help the learner to realize that she has veered into the parallel street. If the parallel street was on her left when she began crossing, she turns right to reach the curb, and if the parallel street was on her right when she began crossing, she turns left to move out of the street.

STEP 2 Upon contacting the curb, the learner walks up to the curb, extends her cane beyond the curb, and checks for the sidewalk.

Rationale The learner walks up to the curb to move out of travel lanes quickly. Extending the cane and checking for a sidewalk prevents stepping up into tree branches or other obstacles and allows the learner to determine if the sidewalk is close to the street.

STEP 3A If the sidewalk is located through extension of the cane, the learner steps up out of the street, corrects toward the sidewalk, and upon reaching the sidewalk continues in her desired direction. The learner should be aware of the potential for signs or tree branches at head height if she steps up outside the sidewalk area and use appropriate protective techniques (see Chapter 4).

Rationale The learner steps out of the street to remove herself from the danger of passing traffic. The learner corrects toward the sidewalk to ensure that the sidewalk is reached smoothly and quickly. The learner continues in the desired direction to facilitate location of her objective.

STEP 3B If the sidewalk is not located with extension of the cane, the learner either turns and walks along the curb utilizing three-point-touch technique to locate the sidewalk, or steps up onto the grass or other surface and travels across the surface to the sidewalk, reorienting herself using traffic, the sun, and other clues, and locates the appropriate sidewalk. The learner should be aware of the potential for signs or tree branches at head height if she steps up outside of the sidewalk area and use appropriate protective techniques.

Rationale The three-point-touch technique is used because it detects where the curb and the sidewalk intersect. The procedure removes the learner from the danger of passing traffic and provides the learner with a systematic method of locating the sidewalk.

Variation If, by using environmental clues, the learner is sure of the location of her sidewalk, she may proceed directly to the desired sidewalk. Environmental settings (e.g., trees, embankments) may prevent the learner from stepping up onto the grass or another surface.

CONSIDERATIONS FOR RECOVERING FROM VEER OR ALIGNMENT ERROR TOWARD THE PARALLEL STREET

- By checking directly to her right and left the learner may contact the street and mistake this for the sidewalk. Therefore, she should be taught to check the area to her front right and front left.
- If the curb is on her right side as the learner contacts it, she typically should turn right to locate the sidewalk. If the curb is on the left, she generally should turn left to locate the sidewalk.
- Pedestrian clues may render this procedure unnecessary. If the learner hears pedestrians, she should correct naturally in that direction and continue in her desired direction.
- On heavily traveled streets, the learner should step up out of the street immediately, if possible, and locate the sidewalk.

Tips for Teaching Street-Crossing Techniques

Learners should be exposed to and learn to recognize the different patterns of traffic with various types of traffic control and geometry, moving from relatively simple to complex patterns. While street-crossing instruction often begins in residential areas, traffic movement patterns and traffic directions can be easier to hear and see in small business areas with regular traffic. The simplest intersection movement patterns to discern though hearing are at signalized intersections of two one-way streets, an intersection of streets with one lane traveling in each direction, or the intersection of a major street and a minor street. O&M specialists and learners can develop checklists for intersection analysis that can be reviewed prior to a lesson or used during a lesson to make sure that each step is followed.

Integrating Orientation

In mastering the techniques of street crossing, orientation enters into every aspect of the learner's activities. Establishing the correct heading for a crossing, maintaining that heading while crossing, and recovering from misalignment or veers during a crossing requires constant awareness of the street and traffic location and the learner's position in relation to that traffic. Cardinal directions can be used to keep track of which corners of the intersection the learner intends to initiate her crossing from and complete the crossing to (e.g., southwest corner to northwest corner for a clockwise crossing or southeast corner to northeast corner for a counterclockwise crossing.) Similarly, using cardinal directions to analyze the movement of vehicles through the intersection helps to develop a full picture of traffic patterns during intersection analysis.

After learning the basic skills, short routes can be planned and traveled. They should involve street crossings of increasing difficulty that require decisions about routes based on crossing locations, type of control, and other features that the learner can consider.

Tactile maps can be used in conjunction with listening and exploring intersections to help learners understand the intersection geometry and the movement of traffic through the intersection. Traffic movement through an intersection can be practiced by having students simulate traffic movement in an indoor hallway, or in a room with tables rearranged, with each student assigned to make various turns and movements at the intersection by the O&M specialist.

Soliciting information from other pedestrians may be part of route planning and travel in new areas. Making sense of that information and asking appropriate follow-up questions is an orientation skill that can be developed with practice in more familiar areas and then extended to unfamiliar areas.

Sequencing

In addition to considering the complexity of intersections and optimal intersections to select for introducing various aspects of street-crossing techniques, O&M specialists can consider how to sequence the procedures. For example, teaching the fundamentals of intersection analysis can precede teaching the physical cane mechanics for crossings. If the O&M specialist decides to focus on intersection analysis as the first part of the sequence, he can complete crossings together with the learner, focusing on listening skills and concept development.

It is important that learners who have congenital visual impairment spend as much time as needed to fully understand the geometry, size and distance, and traffic patterns and controls at intersections. For example, understanding each of the elements below helps the learner to make sound decisions about where and when to cross a four-leg signal-controlled intersection:

- Relative width of four lanes of perpendicular cross traffic
- Relative time it takes to cross the lanes
  - Time to cross when the line of travel is straight
  - Time to cross when the line of travel has a minor veer
- Length of time provided within the signal cycle for crossing
  - When pushing the pedestrian pushbutton (e.g., pedestrian phase time)
  - Without pushing the pedestrian pushbutton (e.g., green-light time for near-lane-parallel traffic)

School-age learners can employ the scientific inquiry method used in the academic curriculum to hypothesize distances and timings and then test each hypothesis to develop a plan of action for later crossings. Crossings can be simulated with the O&M specialist serving as a guide and the learner managing the stopwatch for crossings when a pushbutton is used. The O&M specialist may also time crossings and the crossing time available at intersections where pushbuttons are not installed, possibly at some that have pedestrian signals and at some where pedestrian signals are not installed. Each data point can be recorded digitally and then analyzed to determine the timing differences that result from using the pedestrian pushbutton, how much time is available to cross the intersection at different times of day and with different traffic volumes, and how fast the crossing needs to be in order to complete it within the pedestrian phase. This strategy can be repeated at new or novel street crossings to engage learners in the intersection-analysis process and to promote critical thinking for independent travel. Similarly, adults who have adventitious visual impairment can apply the concepts and previous experiences they had as pedestrians or drivers to understanding and assessing crossing situations. For example, they can be asked to describe anticipated driver behavior of near-lane-parallel traffic when right on red is allowed. By doing so, they can begin to pair the location of the vehicle in the near lane (by auditory or visual cues) with an estimation of whether they will be making a right turn on a red light and how that will affect the crossing.

With practice and feedback, learners can develop an understanding of the time needed to cross uncontrolled streets (Sauerburger, n.d.). As the learner crosses the street, the O&M specialist measures how many seconds it takes from the beginning of the crossing to reach the middle, and how many seconds from the beginning to complete the crossing. This is repeated several times. If the crossing times vary, the longest recorded time is used as the learner's crossing time. After the O&M specialist reports that crossing time to the learner, the O&M specialist asks the learner to imagine herself starting to cross that street. The specialist reports when the stopwatch indicates that the learner would have been halfway across the street and when the learner would have completed the crossing. Repeat this until the learner feels ready to try it herself. It is important for learners to avoid trying to count seconds or steps to complete the task, and instead simply imagine themselves crossing. When the learner thinks that her perception of crossing time is accurate, she imagines herself

crossing and reports when the imaginary crossing begins and ends. She should also report when she would have reached the middle. The O&M specialist starts a stopwatch when the imaginary crossing begins, and notes when the learner reports she is in the middle and across the street within a second of the same time that the stopwatch indicates that she should have reached those points. This feedback regarding accuracy of crossing-time estimates can help improve the learner's accuracy. This is repeated until the learner is consistently within one second of accuracy in reporting when she thinks she would have reached the middle and when she would have completed the crossing. The same activity is repeated until the learner can consistently and accurately report crossing time for streets of various widths.

There is little research on the sequence of instruction, particularly for street crossings. O&M specialists may plan a sequence based on the location and their learner's needs and experience. It is important for the program of instruction to include experience with variations in intersection geometry and signalization, remembering that learners may move to new areas and not have the opportunity for further O&M instruction.

Learners should be exposed to and learn to recognize the different patterns of traffic at stop signs versus intersections with signals or roundabouts, moving from relatively simple to complex patterns. It can be helpful to expose learners to intersections in small business areas to listen to traffic patterns before beginning street crossings at residential intersections. Some O&M specialists begin teaching street-crossing skills at a small signalized intersection of a minor street with a more major street, crossing the minor street alongside the regular traffic of the major street, which provides a good parallel surge as well as alignment information and veering feedback.

Street crossings of increasing difficulty can be introduced as the learner progresses in skill development. As with all techniques, different learners will have difficulties in different aspects of the skills and the O&M specialist will need to creatively design lessons that address each learner's needs.

O&M Specialist Positioning

The O&M specialist should position himself to react appropriately and consider the direction of vehicle threats. Verbal cues can be established in advance, with physical contact used only when necessary. In street-crossing lessons, the O&M specialist should be able to stop the learner from stepping in front of a vehicle, if possible. The O&M specialist's position may also vary somewhat depending on the relative size of the learner and the O&M specialist, and the responsiveness of the learner to verbal direction. For example, for a small woman (the O&M specialist) to stop a large man (the learner) from stepping out, she may need to be slightly in front of the learner, with one foot in the street, to use her weight to stop the learner's movement, while an O&M specialist who is taller than the learner may be able to stand behind the learner and grasp his shoulder, if needed. A series of verbal cues can be agreed upon before starting the lesson to quickly communicate during street crossings and to minimize the need for physical intervention.

Counterclockwise Crossings (Parallel Street on the Left)

Initial Positioning. The O&M specialist stands on the curb to the direct right of or slightly behind the learner. Distance is determined individually, depending upon learner skill and size. This positions the O&M specialist to see cars that are most dangerous to the learner upon initiating the crossing (cars turning from the parallel street or running a red light) *and* to see the learner without turning his head. The O&M specialist can monitor remaining traffic in the intersection with careful scanning. This position also ensures that the O&M specialist is not blocking sounds or the view of traffic that the learner is trying to hear or see.

Prior to Learner Reaching the Second Half of the Crossing. The O&M specialist, still behind the learner, moves toward the left side of the learner. This positions the O&M specialist to see approaching cars that pose the greatest threat to the learner (perpendicular traffic) prior to initiating the second half of the crossing, and keeps the learner within the same line of vision. This position also ensures that the O&M specialist is not blocking sounds or the view of traffic that the learner is trying to hear or see. If the learner has veered toward the parallel traffic, the O&M specialist may move closer and more to the left as needed to monitor the learner's safety.

Upon Learner Approach to the Curb. The O&M specialist, staying behind the learner, moves close to the learner to offer aid if needed.

Clockwise Crossings (Parallel Street on the Right)

Initial Positioning. The O&M specialist is behind and slightly to the right of the learner. Distance is determined individually, depending on the learner's skill. This positions the O&M specialist to see cars that are most dangerous to the learner upon initiating the crossing (near-lane-perpendicular cars) and to see the learner without turning his head. The O&M specialist can monitor remaining traffic in the intersection with careful scanning. This position also ensures that the O&M specialist is not blocking sounds or the view of traffic that the learner is trying to hear or see.

Diane L. Fazzi

Prior to Learner Reaching the Second Half of the Crossing. The O&M specialist, still behind the learner, moves toward the left side of the learner. This positions the O&M specialist to see approaching cars that pose the greatest threat to the learner (perpendicular traffic and parallel traffic that may be turning) prior to initiating the second half of the crossing, and keeps the learner within the same line of vision. This position also ensures that the O&M specialist is not blocking sounds or the view of traffic that the learner is trying to hear or see. If the learner has veered toward the parallel traffic, the O&M specialist may move closer and more to the right as needed to monitor the learner's safety.

Diane L. Fazzi

Upon Learner Approach to the Curb. The O&M specialist, staying behind the learner, moves close to the learner to offer aid if needed.

The O&M specialist's positions may vary from those described at one-way streets in order to efficiently monitor the learner and traffic and to avoid blocking traffic sounds that the learner needs to hear. At roundabouts and channelized turn-lane crossings, the O&M specialist should be on the downstream side of the learner—the side away from the approaching traffic—where he can see the approaching traffic and the learner at the same time and is in a position to stop the learner efficiently if there is a mistake in judgment of approaching vehicles. Positioning is often different when working with a learner using a dog guide (see strategies for Learners Using Dog Guides later in this chapter).

Strategies for Different Populations

General Strategies

There are many steps that need to be recalled from memory and followed for intersection analysis, alignment, preparation for crossing, and actual timing and completion of safe crossings. Checklists and verbal rehearsal of the procedures help the learner and O&M specialist ensure that no important step is left out. After initial instruction on the mechanics of street crossing, the O&M specialist

may develop several practice drills involving clockwise and counterclockwise street crossings, or routes that require practice of specific skills, depending on the needs, strengths, and weaknesses of the learner. The O&M specialist provides prompts and guidance as needed until the learner can execute all aspects of the crossing independently.

The introduction of independent street crossing should consider the age of the learner and her understanding of the environment. O&M specialists must balance their knowledge of age-appropriate activities and the importance of encouraging independence as much as possible with safety and awareness of the learner's decision-making ability.

Learners Using Dog Guides

Learners using dog guides may find that alignment and maintaining alignment during the crossing are aided by their use of the dog guide, however, they will still need well-developed listening and traffic-analysis skills. The O&M specialist working with a learner who is using a dog guide must also be positioned in a manner that is not distracting or confusing for the dog guide. In general, the O&M specialist should be off the right shoulder of the learner, not behind the dog guide, or with the dog guide between the O&M specialist and the learner. The O&M specialist and learner may benefit from contacting the dog guide school for assistance and suggestions.

Billie Louise Bentzen

Learners with Additional Disabilities

For learners who are deafblind, the O&M specialist must address communicating with the public and making decisions as well as soliciting assistance for

Eugene Bourquin

crossings. Communication cards have successfully been used by learners who are deafblind to solicit aid from the public for street crossings. The cards can be prepared with succinct phrases that are relevant to the learner's travel (see Lolli, Sauerburger, & Bourquin, 2010, for additional information).

When teaching street-crossing skills to learners who use wheelchairs or walkers, the learners' residual vision and ability to use a cane in conjunction with their mobility device, if necessary, detect curbs or drop-offs, and negotiate curb ramps are issues to consider and evaluate carefully. For wheelchair users, their seated position may result in reduced visibility to vehicle drivers. (Rosen & Crawford, 2010, provide extensive information regarding necessary skills and evaluation.)

Learners with cognitive disabilities may need to learn street-crossing skills in a more rote manner than described in this chapter. For some learners, a consistent verbal rehearsal of the procedures used to analyze and cross at appropriate intersections can be combined with a thoughtful level of graduated guidance (verbal prompting and reinforcing) from the O&M specialist to learn the skills necessary for safe street crossings (Wright & Wolery, 2014). (See Ambrose-Zaken, Calhoon, & Keim, 2010, for additional information.)

Self-Advocacy

As noted in Chapter 6, interacting with other pedestrians is an important skill and will need to be developed further in preparing for and making street crossings, particularly when lessons are in a business or commercial area where there are many other pedestrians. Learners need to understand that observers may interpret their waiting and listening at a new crossing as indecision or confusion and may try to help. Learners exploring a corner or crossing location, repositioning, or looking for a pushbutton may be seen by other pedestrians or drivers as disorientation. Practice in responding to other pedestrians, as well as in asking appropriate questions of pedestrians to gather information, should be incorporated into street-crossing lessons, particularly as the lessons move to busier areas. Role-playing interactions and responses can be incorporated into lessons and can also be an excellent group activity for learners.

Recognizing and understanding drivers' behavior and actions is another area for the learner and O&M specialist to discuss and consider. A group discussion among learners, for example, at an adult rehabilitation center that includes some who have been drivers and some who have never driven can be a very useful way to address these interactions. Drivers' attention can be attracted by certain types of actions. It can be useful for the learner to let the driver know her intentions when preparing to cross the street. Standing passively may convey to the driver that the learner is not crossing.

With the complexity of current signal phasing and traffic patterns, learners may find it necessary to request an APS or timing changes at certain intersections to provide adequate time for or information about the crossing. In the United States, public information meetings are required for most planned improvements of major intersections or sidewalk and streetscape changes in an area. Learners and O&M specialists may find that attending meetings and bringing up questions before construction occurs can result in positive changes to intersection designs and features. This advocacy can be an opportunity to educate traffic-engineering and planning professionals about the travel skills of pedestrians who are blind and the fact that people who are visually impaired do travel independently.

CHAPTER

8

Transportation Systems

Public transportation systems, such as *local bus services*, *trolley* or *streetcar* systems, *rapid rail transit*, *commuter rail*, and *paratransit services*, as well as taxis and taxi-like services, figure prominently in the travel of individuals who are blind or visually impaired. Orientation and mobility (O&M) specialists play a vital role in helping learners with visual impairments develop the problem-solving skills essential to using a wide range of transportation systems (Crudden, 2015). These transportation systems allow individuals to reach destinations in their communities that are not within easy walking distance, including schools, workplaces, community services, and recreational opportunities. Transportation type and availability will vary in rural, suburban, and urban areas. Transit buses are the most common form of transportation and are available even in relatively small cities and most suburban areas. An overview of airport travel is also provided in this chapter, but specific procedures are not included due to security-related restrictions on airport access. For a detailed description of the various types of systems, see Dodson-Burk, Park-Leach, and Myers (2010).

Public Transit Systems

Scheduling

The learner should have access to the website address and telephone number of the transit company to obtain scheduling information. Other options and information sources should also be ex-

plored, such as mapping programs, apps, and accessible global positioning system (GPS) units.

When planning a trip, the learner should research the following general information concerning bus and train scheduling:

- The consistency of a bus or train's schedule: whether it changes during different periods of the day, especially during rush hours and at night
- How the schedule may differ on weekends, nights, and holidays
- The number and name of the bus or train on which the learner wishes to travel
  - Some buses are named according to a major street, end point, landmark along the route, or major destination
  - Train lines may have color designations and often the route is named after the final station
- If the bus or train is express and which stops along the route are express stops

For a specific trip, the learner should find out the following:

- The exact locations for boarding and disembarking for travel to the destination and for the return trip (e.g., which side of the street the bus stop is on and its proximity to the corner; area landmarks)
- Whether transfers are necessary, and whether available for the planned route and travel time

The learner should be aware that bus and train schedules and bus routes may change. (See the section on Route Planning for Travel on Transit Systems later in this chapter for methods to obtain information.)

Rail transit travels on a fixed schedule, which may vary at different times of the day and week. Rail transit typically travels on a more frequent schedule than buses. Train time in the station is usually quite short, so boarding must be completed quickly and efficiently.

Fares

Cities utilize different systems by which *fares* are paid. Many systems have a token, ticket, or fare-card system whereby a passenger can purchase tokens or tickets in advance or add money to a fare card or *smart card* that is inserted into or touched to a fare box to pay for each trip. Most bus drivers do not carry money to make change, and passengers who do not have exact change may be denied passage. Discounted weekly or monthly passes may be available for students or for individuals with visual impairments.

When paying cash, transfers may be supplied to passengers who need to take more than one bus to arrive at their destination. Transfers are usually color-coded slips of paper that may be used only on the date of issue and within a specified time period.

Transfers may not be used for return trips. If needed, the learner should ask for the transfer when boarding the first bus and then hand it to the driver of the next bus. In some cities, there may be an additional charge for bus transfers. Many larger cities have implemented fare-card systems that eliminate the need for paper transfers.

On rail systems, fares are usually paid before boarding, either at gates at the entry to the station or at vending machines or card readers on the platform. In many newer *light rail* systems, there is no gate, per se, but each rider is expected to have a valid card or ticket in case transit officials ask to see it. On some commuter rail trains, tickets may be purchased on board or in advance. Some systems have developed apps for purchasing fares on smartphones.

O&M lessons should include familiarization with local transit-fare systems and discussion of the different types of ticket machines and collection devices. Practice in using the fare payment devices at less busy times of day can be very important to build learner confidence and independence in using the devices and any accessibility features of the fare collection or payment device.

ROUTE PLANNING FOR TRAVEL ON TRANSIT SYSTEMS (BUS OR TRAIN)

Purpose: To enable the learner to plan and gather necessary information to complete a trip on public transportation.

PROCEDURE AT A GLANCE

1 The learner and O&M specialist determine a method for the learner to record information.

2 The learner calls the destination and asks for and records the full address.

3 The learner asks for details about the entrance.

4 The learner asks the personnel if they know if there is a bus stop nearby and, if so, which bus route stops there.

5 The learner calls the transit company route-planning service and gives them the starting address and ending address and approximate travel time. The learner should ask for available transit options (bus or train) and routing information including details regarding the bus stop location.

6 The learner requests the same information for the return route.

7 The learner calls again and asks the same questions, making sure he receives the same answers, and asks follow-up questions as necessary.

METHOD

STEP 1 The learner and O&M specialist determine a method for the learner to record information.

Rationale There are a lot of details for the learner to gather and he needs to be prepared to record them in some manner. Bus or transit routing information includes more details than most people can remember after the call.

STEP 2 The learner calls the destination and asks for and records the full address, including the town and zip code. The learner may also ask for the nearest major cross streets or any significant landmarks.

Rationale The full address, including town and zip code, ensures that the learner has called the correct location. There may be more than one office or site of a business. Getting directions from the transit operator may require knowing the town of the destination.

Variation The learner may look up this information online, but it is still a good idea to confirm.

STEP 3 After the learner tells the person at the destination that he is blind and planning to travel there, the learner asks for details about the entrance. Specific questions are more likely to elicit accurate and helpful information, for example, "Is the entrance in the center of the block or on the corner? Is the doorway recessed? Is there a sign near the door?" If so, and if the learner has low vision, he can ask, "What color is the sign and what does it say?" Sometimes the personnel can provide helpful information and the learner will become more adept at judging that as he practices.

Rationale Details about the location of the entrance make it easier to locate the doorway and access the facility. Specific questions are more likely to result in usable information about the location.

Variation Some learners with low vision may be able to use the "street view" in mapping programs to view entrance details in advance.

STEP 4 The learner asks the personnel at the store or other destination if they know if there is a bus stop nearby and, if so, what bus route stops there. If the person at the location is not familiar with the bus routes, the learner should ask if there is someone else who might be able to help.

Rationale Business personnel may be able to provide more detailed information than the transit system can provide about the nearest bus stop in relation to the building entrance.

Variation Computerized mapping programs may provide this information.

STEP 5 The learner calls the transit company route-planning service and gives them the starting address and ending address and approximate time of travel (this could be the time that the learner needs to arrive at the destination or the time he plans to leave from starting point, depending on factors such as the purpose of the trip). The learner should ask for available route options, either by bus or train, and for detailed information on bus stop locations at either end of the trip, which may not be available, depending on the system. The learner then compares information about the bus stop locations with the information received from the personnel at the destination. A detailed list of questions to ask for either bus or rail travel can be found in Dodson-Burk et al. (2010).

Rationale Full information about the time and destination is needed to get accurate route information. Some bus and train routes run only at certain times of the day. Detailed information makes the trip easier.

Variation A lot of information is also available through online mapping programs, transit websites, and other route-planning resources and phone apps.

STEP 6 The learner requests the same information for the return route.

Rationale It is important to plan the return trip before departure to make sure the overall plan is feasible within the given time period and to get all the information down at once.

Variation The learner may not need return information if he is continuing to another destination from that location or is being picked up from that destination.

STEP 7 The learner calls again and asks the same questions, making sure he receives the same answers, and asks follow-up questions as needed.

Rationale This gives the learner a chance to check the information recorded about the route. It is not unusual to get slightly different route information from different customer-service personnel.

CONSIDERATIONS FOR ROUTE PLANNING FOR TRAVEL ON TRANSIT SYSTEMS

- Making calls for information at times that are less busy for the destination often results in better information. For example, if calling a restaurant, it is best to call between prime meal service times when there is often a lull in activity and the personnel there will have more time to answer questions. In calling either destinations or transit information lines, learners may sometimes get a person who is unable to provide accurate information. Sometimes it may be necessary to ask if another person is available to help or to call back at another time.
- Worksheets or digital recordings of destination or transit information can be used to help the learner organize and recall important information when needed for planning and travel.
- In planning for lessons using buses or rail transit, the O&M specialist and the learner should develop and confirm a contingency plan in case there are problems or they become separated during travel. Use of cell phones for maintaining contact is common but the learner and the O&M specialist need to discuss communication in advance, make sure their devices are charged and turned on during the trip, and consider other scenarios and possible emergency contact needs.
- Group lessons in route planning encourage camaraderie and help learners recognize that it can be challenging to solicit accurate information.
- Learners need to consider the street-crossing situation when planning their route and planning to reboard the bus for the return trip. Crossing the street is often required and crossing without a signal may not be possible, depending on the size of the street. The learner may need to plan to walk a couple of blocks to a crossing that is acceptable. Where there is no acceptable street crossing available, an alternate plan may be to board the bus and ride around to return to the starting point. For example, to avoid crossing a major arterial street without a signal, a learner may travel to his destination on a northbound bus on the east side of the street and, when returning, reboard at the same stop and travel northbound on the bus to the end of the line, where the bus turns and travels southbound.

Bus Systems

Each bus and transit system is locally run and may be set up somewhat differently. Each system has its idiosyncrasies and O&M specialists and learners should become familiar with the systems in their area. O&M instruction should make it clear that not all systems are the same.

Bus transit systems typically provide *fixed-route services* and run on regular schedules. Those schedules and routes may change at different times of day; buses on some routes may run more often at rush hour or may not run at night. Schedules may also vary on weekends or holidays. *Express bus service* will skip stops along the route. Most transit systems have websites with trip-planning information and individuals providing schedule information by phone. Various mapping programs also include transit options in their route-planning features. Trips may require a transfer from one bus route to a different bus route, or from a bus to a light rail or rapid rail system, which might take place at a transfer station or at an intersection.

Bus Vehicle Characteristics

School-age learners may be familiar with school buses, but the layout of doors, stairs, and seats is typically different than that used on public transit buses. It can be helpful for O&M specialists to schedule lessons that provide familiarization to transit buses before actual bus travel. The O&M specialist can contact the city bus garage to arrange for use of a bus for this purpose. This can be a good group lesson for several learners at the same time, which may be preferred by the bus system and allow them to easily provide staff assistance. O&M specialists may sometimes choose to ask a bus driver to allow them to familiarize a learner to the bus while it is on an extended layover, often at either end of a route. Layovers can last from five to fifteen minutes and while drivers usually are not required to allow bus familiarization, they may be willing to comply.

The following characteristics of the bus should be explored:

- Bus size and shape
- Door placement
- Steps or wheelchair lifts
- Handrails
- Fare box
- Seating arrangements
- Vertical poles and horizontal handrails
- *Stop announcements*
- *Stop request system*
- Operation of the rear door

Bus Size and Shape

Depending on learners' experience with buses and other vehicles, O&M specialists may wish to explore the outside of the bus with their learners, examining the bumpers, tires, location of the engine, and location of doors in relation to other features.

Door Placement

On city buses the front door is usually located just behind the front bumper of the bus, between the front wheel and front bumper. The rear door is located on the same side in front of the rear wheels. In most systems, all boarding of the bus takes place at the front door, while individuals may exit from both front and rear doors. The door usually folds into the bus area as it opens. The driver's seat is usually just opposite the front door.

Steps or Wheelchair Lifts

There are usually stairs at the entry to the bus, although there are some low-floor buses with one-step entry or a lowering feature that brings the bus level with the curb. In some places, buses with a lowering feature are called *low-floor buses* or "kneeling buses." Most buses are equipped with wheelchair lifts at the front door (in older bus models, the lift may be located at the rear door). When the *bus lift* is deployed, it extends straight out past the side of the bus and there is usually a beeping warning.

Handrails

Handrails are usually located beside the stairwells to aid in getting on and off the bus. They are usually positioned so that they can be contacted when stepping up onto the bus. There may be a short handrail attached to the door, then another handrail just past the door in the area of the second step.

Fare Box

The fare box is usually located on the learner's right when boarding and can be located by trailing the handrail until it is contacted. The driver is usually seated just behind the fare box. In most systems, the fare may be paid in cash with exact change (no change will be provided by the driver), however, the use of some type of fare-card system is becoming increasingly common, particularly in systems that provide transfers between rail and bus services.

Seating Arrangements

Most buses have long seats along the walls, facing each other and the center aisle, at the front of the bus, followed by rows of seats facing the front divided by an aisle down the middle. There are usually two seats on each side of the aisle, although newer bus models may have slightly different configurations, such as a single seat on one side of the aisle and two seats on the other side. Some newer buses also have a step up to the seats in the back section of the bus that is located behind the rear door. The seats near the front are generally reserved for people with disabilities. On school buses and long-distance coach buses, all of the seats usually face the front of the bus.

Vertical Poles and Horizontal Handrails

Vertical poles, sometimes called stanchions, are usually positioned near the front and rear doors and behind the driver. Overhead parallel handrails usually run the full length of the bus on the left side (when facing forward), starting approximately 2 feet behind the driver, and on the right side to the left of the front door as the learner enters, with a break where the rear door is located. There may be a type of grab rail built in as part of the back of each seat near the aisle. Some buses also include hanging straps suspended from the ceiling or parallel handrails as an additional, slightly lower handhold.

Stop Announcements

There are ADA requirements for announcing major cross streets, facilities, and transfer locations. In many systems this is provided by automated announcements as the bus travels its route. In other systems, or when the automated announcement system is not working, the driver may make these announcements.

Stop Request System

Stops may be requested by use of a pull cord or a raised bar (often yellow) that you push. The request cord or bar is usually located parallel to the floor, just above the windows inside of the bus, and may be reached by trailing up the window. The bar can also be positioned vertically between two windows on the inside of the bus. On newer bus models, stops may also be requested by pressing stop buttons located at the bottom of vertical poles. On coach buses, the stop request button is usually situated overhead, in the passenger service unit, where personal reading lights and air conditioning ducts are controlled.

Operation of the Rear Door

To keep passengers from boarding through the rear door, the driver can control the operation of the rear door. On some buses a green light (located above the door) is turned on, indicating that a passenger

may push the door open to leave. A learner who is blind should apply continuous pressure with one hand to the door, which will open when the light is turned on. If the driver fails to activate this mechanism the learner can call to the driver, "back door!" or may signal with the stop request system near the door to alert the driver to his needs.

Additional characteristics of long-distance coach buses include overhead luggage racks, footrests and armrests, restrooms, and additional steps within the bus.

Bus Stop Characteristics

Features

Bus stops may be open areas along a sidewalk that are unobstructed and paved to the curb; however, there are many bus stops along arterial or connector roads where there is no sidewalk and the bus stop area is not paved. Some municipalities improve bus stops by adding a pad of sufficient size for a wheelchair user to disembark, but for the foreseeable future many stops will be designated only by a sign or pole.

Stops may be identified by a bus bench or shelter, or by poles at the stop with signs. There is no standard position for benches or shelters and bus poles. Different sizes and shapes of poles are used in different cities, so it is important for learners to become familiar with the style used in the current area and to understand that such features vary. Signs may include the bus route number or name. Some poles have a box attached with the bus schedule displayed in small print. Another possible indication of a bus stop is the presence of a group of pedestrians, especially in commercial areas.

Location

The location of bus stops will vary due to the route, or may change without notice due to construction, special events, or other issues.

Along streets, bus stops may be located in one of these positions:

- Near the corner of a block, before the intersection in the direction in which the bus is traveling, often called a nearside stop by transit agencies
- At least a full bus length from the intersection after the bus has passed through an intersection, called a far-side stop by most transit agencies (although that terminology may not be used by customer service representatives)

- In the middle of the block
- On a specific transit island, possibly on a median in the middle of the street, or separated from the curb by a single vehicle lane or bike lane

Bus stop locations vary depending on the bus route, street configuration, and local transit-area policy. Traditionally, most stops were located along the route before intersections. With transit signal priority—which uses a device or signal emitted from the bus or transit vehicle to extend the green light to allow the transit vehicle to continue moving along a roadway—a stop located before the intersection may cause the green light to be held for an unacceptable length of time. Partly as a result of this, there is a recent trend to move stops to locations just past the intersection, which also encourages passengers to cross the street behind the bus or rail vehicle rather than in front of the bus, and which minimizes multiple-threat crashes where the bus blocks the passing car driver's view of the crossing pedestrian. Bus stops may also be located in the middle of the block if the bus has made a left turn just before the stop. Careful questioning of transit personnel may result in more detailed stop information; some bus systems provide detailed stop location information to accessible GPS programs.

Other common bus stop locations include:

- Transit stations
- Parking areas near major entrances to malls or other shopping facilities
- Airport locations in general proximity to arrival or departure areas

TRAVELING VIA BUS

Locating Bus Stop and Positioning at the Bus Stop

Purpose: To enable the learner to locate a bus stop efficiently, and to be properly positioned and ready to detect and board the bus when it arrives.

PROCEDURE AT A GLANCE

1 The learner uses prior information to determine the likely bus stop location in relation to the intersection and travels to that corner.

2 If the stop is located before an intersection, the learner walks to the perpendicular street, then, using touch-and-drag or constant-contact technique, follows the curb back along the parallel street looking for the bus pole or shelter. If the stop is located after the intersection, the learner completes the same process (on the other side of the cross street), but must follow the curb further because the stop will be approximately a bus length past the crosswalk.

3 After locating the bus pole, the learner trails the curb back in the direction that the bus approaches from (upstream) for approximately 3 feet.

4 The learner positions himself one to two steps back from the curb, facing the street.

5 While positioned at the bus stop, the learner holds the cane in a diagonal position.

METHOD

STEP 1 The learner uses prior information to determine the likely bus stop location in relation to the intersection and travels to that corner.

Rationale Bus stops can be located in a variety of positions near intersections and the learner can narrow the search area by obtaining information from the transit company, setting a point of interest in his GPS, or asking an individual in the area.

STEP 2 If the stop is before the bus crosses the intersection, the learner walks to the perpendicular street, then, using touch-and-drag or constant-contact cane technique, follows the curb back along the parallel street looking for the bus pole or shelter. If the stop is located after the intersection, the learner follows the curb (on the other side of the cross street), using touch-and-drag or constant-contact cane technique, but must follow the curb further because the stop will be approximately a bus length past the crosswalk.

Rationale The bus stop pole is usually situated close to the curb of the street. The use of touch-and-drag or constant-contact cane technique along the parallel street increases the likelihood that the bus pole will be contacted with the cane tip and that other possible obstacles will be detected while the learner maintains awareness of the location of the curb and street.

Variations The learner may have already located the stop as part of his familiarization to the corner (see Street-Corner Familiarization in Chapter 6) and may be able to more directly locate the stop without going all the way to the perpendicular street first.

The learner may also need to locate a bus stop for a bus route that is perpendicular to the initial line of travel. In such cases, the learner will need to make one or more crossings to the appropriate corner to initiate this step. After completing the final crossing, the learner will need to make a 90-degree turn toward where he thinks the bus stop is located and continue with the process as described.

STEP 3 After locating the bus pole, the learner trails the curb back in the direction that the bus approaches from (upstream) for approximately 3 feet.

Rationale This positioning places the learner in a location where the bus will typically stop, on the "upstream" side of the pole (the side the bus is approaching from). Buses typically stop with the front bumper, not the door, at the pole, since the bus pole may be an obstruction to passengers entering or disembarking the bus.

Variation At some locations, such as bus rapid transit stops or some types of transit shelters, there may not be an actual bus stop pole. The sign may be integrated into the design of the bus shelter. In this case the learner may position himself in a similar manner in relation to the shelter, facing the street. At busy shelters, or in bad weather, the learner may wish to wait within the shelter area and solicit information or assistance from other bus riders about the arrival of the bus.

STEP 4 The learner positions himself one to two steps back from the curb, facing the street.

Rationale A location one to two steps from the curb positions the learner out of the way of bus mirrors, doors that open outward, and exiting passengers as the bus pulls into the stop for disembarking and loading of passengers.

Variation If the learner just misses the bus and realizes he may have a long wait, he may choose to find a seat on the bus bench and reposition himself a few minutes before the next bus is due to arrive.

STEP 5 While positioned at the bus stop, the learner holds the cane in a diagonal position, with his arm slightly extended so the grip and top of the cane are about a foot in front of his body to be more visible.

Rationale If the cane is visible to the bus driver, he is more likely to stop directly in front of the learner.

Variation Some O&M Specialists recommend transferring the cane to the left hand while waiting to be ready to follow the handrail on the right side of the door to the fare box. The learner can position the cane either diagonally or in the left hand once he hears the bus approaching.

CONSIDERATIONS FOR LOCATING BUS STOP AND POSITIONING AT THE BUS STOP

- The learner may use other landmarks, such as a bus bench or shelter, to aid in positioning himself for the bus. In some cases, a bus pole or other landmark may not be present and the learner will need to use distance awareness and traffic clues to position himself properly.

- Other passengers who may be waiting can also provide visual and auditory cues to the location of the bus stop. However, in some cities, there may be stops for different types of services in close proximity, such as a tour bus and a public transit bus.

- Within a unit lesson on commercial areas, the O&M specialist may ask the learner to locate a bus stop as an objective. This prerequisite skill will help the learner be more successful when the unit on bus travel is introduced.

- At the beginning of a unit on bus travel, or during lessons on block travel, the O&M specialist may choose to run several lessons in which the learner's objective is simply to locate and position himself at a stop. Once this has been mastered, additional steps of bus travel can be introduced.

- In planning for lessons using buses or rail transit, the O&M specialist and the learner should develop and confirm a contingency plan in case there are problems or they become separated during travel. Use of cell phones for maintaining contact is common, but the learner and O&M specialist need to discuss communication in advance, make sure their devices are charged and turned on during the trip, and consider other scenarios and possible emergency contact needs.

Boarding a Bus

Purpose: To enable the learner to board a bus and find seating in an efficient and safe manner.

	PROCEDURE AT A GLANCE
1	Properly positioned at the bus stop, the learner determines the arrival and position of the bus from available auditory or visual clues.
2	The learner localizes the sound of the door and proceeds to the bus.
3	Upon locating the steps, the learner verifies whether the bus is the one he wishes to take by asking the bus driver.
4	The learner ascends the steps of the bus, utilizing a stair technique with his cane in his left hand while simultaneously trailing the handrail with his right hand.
5	The learner deposits his fare and asks the driver (a) to inform him when his stop has been reached; (b) whether the seat behind the door is vacant or, if needed, where the nearest vacant seat is; and (c) to provide a transfer to a connecting bus, if needed.
6	If the seat behind the door is vacant, the learner turns, locates the seat, and sits down.
7	If travel within the bus is required, the learner employs a congested-area constant-contact technique with the cane in his left hand and with his right hand trails the overhead handlebar as he proceeds to the vacant seat.

METHOD

STEP 1 Properly positioned at the bus stop, the learner determines the arrival and position of the bus from available auditory or visual clues. As the bus arrives, the learner attends to the bus position, stopping location, and the sound of the tires coming to a stop to determine his location in relation to the door.

Rationale The learner must be prepared to board when the bus arrives, so he needs to attend to the bus arrival and position in relation to his waiting position so that adjustments can be made accordingly.

STEP 2 The learner localizes the sound of the door as it opens and proceeds to the bus. If uncertain about its location, he extends his cane and contacts the stopped bus, then turns toward the door. The opening bus door, which is typically on hydraulics, creates a somewhat unique sound and movement of air pressure that can provide the learner with multiple clues as to its location.

Rationale The sound of the door opening provides a clue to its location. An automatic announcement and the sound of other passengers disembarking may also provide a clue. Inadvertently contacting the tire or bumper will also help the learner determine the door location if the learner knows the position of that feature relative to the door position.

Variation At busy stops, the learner may need to stand back to allow individuals to disembark from the bus.

STEP 3 Upon locating the steps, the learner verifies whether the bus is the one he wishes to take by asking the bus driver to confirm. The learner may use a phrase like, "Is this the northbound 280 stopping at Azusa Avenue?"

Rationale More than one bus may stop at any given stop. The learner needs to confirm that it is the bus he wants before boarding. While the assumption is that the bus can only be going in one direction, verifying directional information helps to reconfirm that the learner has not become disoriented at the corner. Including the name of the specific stop confirms that the bus is not an express that would bypass the desired location.

Variation Many systems now have automatic announcements outside the bus that provide the route number and other information as the door opens.

STEP 4 The learner ascends the steps of the bus, utilizing a stair technique with his cane in his left hand while simultaneously extending his right hand to the right to locate and grasp the handrail. The handrail may not be continuous and it may be necessary to reach forward to relocate the handrail after taking one step onto the bus.

Rationale The handrail provides a guide to the fare box on most buses and provides support when stepping up onto the bus. The depth of the stairs may also be uneven and the flattening out of the handrail helps to indicate the landing.

STEP 5 Upon locating the fare box at the top of the steps, the learner pays his fare and asks the driver (a) to inform him when his stop has been reached; (b) whether the seat behind the door (across from the driver) is vacant or, if needed, where the nearest vacant seat is; and (c) to provide a transfer to a connecting bus, if needed.

Rationale The fare usually must be paid when boarding. While there may be automatic announcements on the bus, asking the driver to inform the learner of his stop can reconfirm that the learner is on the correct bus and provide him with additional notification of the stop. The seat behind the door is a location where it is easy to talk to the driver and where the learner is visible to the driver and less likely to be forgotten. It is also the easiest seat from which to disembark quickly and efficiently and from which the handrail is typically within reach. Often, a passenger seated in that location will move if he overhears the learner asking about the seat. The learner can also ask or reconfirm with passengers if there is a vacant seat. Transfers are not needed on many systems now, but may still be needed on some.

STEP 6 If the seat behind the door is vacant, the learner turns, locates the seat with a modified diagonal technique—with the cane tip on the floor and a slow, careful extension of his cane, or with the constant-contact cane technique—and sits, clearing the seat as he sits down.

Rationale The learner extends his cane carefully to avoid tripping someone or hitting another passenger with his cane as he turns to take his seat. He maintains the tip on the floor to detect the stairs in case he turns too far.

STEP 7 If travel within the bus is required, the learner employs a congested-area constant-contact cane technique with the cane in his left hand and with his right hand trails the overhead handrail as he proceeds to the vacant seat. He may confirm the seat location verbally with other passengers as he travels toward the seat.

Rationale It is generally best to travel on the right (in the United States). Other passengers can be a source of additional confirming information. The overhead horizontal handrail is grasped to provide balance while the bus is moving.

CONSIDERATIONS FOR BOARDING A BUS

- Listening to several buses pull up to a stop can help the learner recognize the sound of the bus arriving. Some learners will be confused by the differences between public transit buses and school buses. The engine of most public transit buses is located at the rear of the bus, so the audible cues are of the bus tires, wind noise, and size of the vehicle pulling up. Many electric buses are relatively quiet when approaching.
- Visual cues can be confusing in some systems due to the prevalence of advertising on the outside of buses, meaning they can be a variety of colors, or change from time to time.
- While seated on the bus, the learner should either partially fold his cane or lean his cane against his shoulder to prevent other people mistaking it for a pole and grabbing it.

Disembarking from a Bus

Purpose: To enable the learner to disembark from a bus in an efficient and safe manner.

PROCEDURE AT A GLANCE

1. Upon being informed of or recognizing his stop, the learner grasps a vertical pole or horizontal handlebar and stands, listening for and localizing the sound of the opening doors.

2. Employing constant-contact technique in his left hand and grasping the vertical pole or horizontal handrail with his right, the learner proceeds toward the door, allowing the cane tip to slide along the floor.

3. Upon detecting the steps, the learner positions himself to descend. Before exiting, the learner may ask the bus driver for information regarding the position of the bus in relation to the intersection, as well as the location of the transfer bus (if needed).

4. Utilizing stair technique with the cane in his left hand and grasping the handrail with his right hand, the learner descends the steps.

5. The learner clears the area for his step off the bus and moves away from the bus, stepping up onto the curb if necessary.

METHOD

STEP 1 Upon being informed of or recognizing his stop, the learner grasps a vertical pole or horizontal handlebar and stands, listening for and localizing the sound of the opening doors.

Rationale Grasping a handrail or pole provides balance while the bus is moving. Localizing auditory information facilitates proper location of the door.

Variations The learner may activate the stop request system (pull the cord or push the stop) to further indicate to the driver that he wants to exit.

Passengers may prepare to disembark prior to the bus coming to a stop and form a line in the open area between the seats. The learner will need to be ready to join this line of people.

STEP 2 Employing constant-contact cane technique in his left hand and grasping the vertical pole or horizontal handrail with his right, the learner proceeds toward the door, allowing the cane tip to slide along the floor.

Rationale Constant-contact cane technique provides protection while moving inside the bus. Maintaining contact with the cane tip on the floor ensures location of the steps. The learner may exit through the rear doors on a familiar route, or on very busy routes when riders are expected to exit from the rear. However, it is desirable to stay near the front of the bus on an unfamiliar route and exit through the front door, where additional information can be solicited from the driver.

STEP 3 Upon detecting the steps, the learner positions himself to descend. Before exiting, the learner may ask the bus driver for information regarding the position of the bus in relation to the intersection, as well as the location of the transfer bus (if needed). Questions may include the direction the bus is facing, the name of the street the bus is traveling on, and the direction of the intersecting street (in front of or behind the bus). He may also wish to confirm the location of the return stop before disembarking.

Rationale The learner needs to be appropriately balanced and aware of the location of the first step. His position at this point is close to the driver and it can be advantageous to get as much information as possible before disembarking. Asking the bus driver for information prior to disembarking can provide additional essential orientation information and confirm the learner's location. In busy areas or on buses with double-wide entrances, passengers getting on the bus may initiate the boarding process while passengers are still disembarking, and it may be difficult to ask the driver questions.

STEP 4 Utilizing stair technique with the cane in his left hand and grasping the handrail with his right hand, the learner descends the steps.

Rationale Holding the handrail on the right positions the learner on the right side of the doorway; most passengers will be entering on their right (or the learner's left as he disembarks).

STEP 5 The learner clears the area for his step off the bus and moves away from the bus, stepping up onto the curb if necessary. He should be aware that there may be passengers waiting to board near the doorway as he steps out.

Rationale The learner clears for safety and moves away from the bus to allow other passengers to exit. The learner clears the area to determine if he will be stepping into the street and if it is clear, or if he will be stepping directly onto the sidewalk if the driver has pulled up close enough.

CONSIDERATIONS FOR DISEMBARKING FROM A BUS

- While independent bus travel requires that the learner be able to manage bus planning, bus stops, boarding, and disembarking from the bus, early interdependent bus experiences with families, on field trips, and together with the O&M specialist can help to build a comfort with and strong foundation for bus travel in the future.

- Learners may prefer to exit through the rear door on familiar routes or when seated near the back of the bus. On unfamiliar routes, exiting through the front door provides an opportunity to solicit more information from the driver.

- The learner's first step off the bus may be either into the street or onto the curb, and he should be aware of the possible difference. A useful lesson before the first experience with bus travel may be exploration and consideration of all the possible locations a bus may stop in relation to the marked stop or shelter.

- Having the learner obtain the scheduling and stop information in advance can be a helpful part of the lesson, reinforcing the information that should be gathered and helping the learner to realize the importance of some of the information as he travels the route.

- The O&M specialist can sequence lessons by first giving the learner a destination that requires a short and simple bus trip, and then expanding to longer, more involved trips that may involve obtaining a transfer or locating a bus stop at a transfer station or shopping mall. Some learners may have an immediate demand for a more complex bus route and the O&M specialist will need to sequence lessons accordingly.

- The learner should be aware of his personal orientation in relation to the doors and streets when entering, finding a seat, and exiting the bus.

- The learner can attempt to keep track of his orientation while on the bus to ensure that he will not end up too far out of his way if the driver forgets to call out his stop. The passing of certain landmarks, such as railroad tracks, a busy intersection, or a location where many passengers exit the bus may aid in this process. GPS and other electronic orientation devices can be used for this purpose. The learner may choose to remind the driver of his destination at some point along the route.

Light Rail, Rapid Rail, or Commuter Trains

Many of the components of travel using light rail, rapid rail (subways or elevated trains), or commuter trains are similar to bus travel, and the bus transit systems are commonly integrated with rail systems. There is also bus rapid transit (BRT) service in some US cities. In BRT systems, the buses usually have off-board fare collection and travel in dedicated lanes with stations that are typically in the center of the road, making them more similar to light rail than to typical bus service.

Light rail may travel by right-of-way within the street or on separated tracks. It is often on the street level with low platform stations located either in the center of the street or on curbs in similar locations to bus stops. Light rail trains usually have some type of boarding ticket, which is purchased in advance or in the station. Light rail trains are typically shorter than rapid rail trains. Some airports employ a type of light rail train to move passengers between areas of the airport.

Trolley or streetcar systems are present in many cities and are a hybrid of light rail and bus service, running on the roadway, but with a great deal of variation in types of stops, fare systems, and boarding features.

Rapid rail usually refers to train systems that are electrically powered, run on a dedicated line, and have stations that are above (elevated) or below street level (subway). Usually there is a station entry area that includes fare gates for fare payment and stairs, escalators, or elevators to the rail platform. There may be more than one entrance for a station, for example, with one on each end of the station, possibly separated by several blocks above ground. The typical rapid rail train platform is approximately 600 feet long, so station entries can be several blocks apart. New types of rail systems (such as MARTA in Atlanta, the Washington, DC, area

Metro, and BART in the San Francisco Bay Area) run trains that can be anywhere from two to eight cars long depending on the time of day, so the train may fill the whole platform area at some times of day and only fill a small portion of the platform area at other times.

Commuter trains are a type of passenger train transit service that utilizes diesel-electric or electrically propelled trains that operate over existing railways along with intercity freight. Fare is typically collected on board the train, usually through cash, a ticket, or a fare card, and boarding is normally from low platforms. Commuter rail is typically found in large metropolitan areas in the United States, such as New York City, the Chicago area, and the Washington, DC-Baltimore corridor.

Rail Vehicle Characteristics

Vehicles for light rail and rapid rail are quite similar in that they are usually electrically powered, with level boarding from the platform area, sliding doors that open, and a gap between cars that must be considered and avoided. It can be helpful for learners to schedule a lesson that provides familiarization to the rail vehicles before actual travel on the systems. Some systems provide regular training sessions or work with agencies that serve individuals who are blind to allow training activities on a railcar that is out of service, possibly at an end-of-the-line station. The O&M specialist can contact the transit system to see if a familiarization opportunity can be arranged. The O&M specialist should familiarize the learner with the following characteristics:

- Doors
- Seating
- Stop announcements
- Station layout

Doors

Each railcar has two or three sets of doors. Doors typically open with some type of tone when the vehicles stop in the station. Light rail vehicles may have a button to push to open the doors, which can be challenging to locate, especially when crowded. Doors are closed by the train operator when most passengers have boarded. At busy times, there may be more people on the platform than the train can accommodate and the doors may be closed before everyone can board. In most systems, the doors spring back if someone is within the doorway opening when it is closing, and trains cannot move if the doors are not secured. However, the doors often close with some force to discourage people from stepping in while the doors are closing.

Seating

Near each set of doors there may be seats along the wall, facing the center aisle of the train, or an open standing area with vertical poles. Vertical poles may also be located throughout the car. Rows of seats facing either the front and back of the train are located along the aisle between the door areas. Like buses, there is often an overhead handrail as well as handholds on the backs of the seats.

Stop Announcements

An automated announcement is usually provided as the train approaches a station and just before the doors open at the stop. Sometimes the announcement also includes additional information, such as "transfer point to the Red Line" or "doors open on the right."

Station Layout

Transit stations (including BRT stations) are often characterized as center platform or side platform stations, although there may be a combination of both center and side platforms in larger transfer stations. A *center platform station* is a boarding platform that is between two trains or buses. Travelers in both directions board from the same platform, with vehicles typically traveling in opposite directions on each side of the platform. A *side platform station* has two separated platforms with the trains or buses running on trackways between the platforms. Entry to the platform area may be from different locations, different stairs or escalators, or potentially even from opposite sides of the street for light rail systems. A person who goes to the wrong platform in a subway or elevated station with side platforms must go back to the faregate level and cross over to get to the other platform.

TRAVELING VIA TRAIN

Traveling within a Station and Positioning for Boarding

Purpose: To enable the learner to enter a train station and position himself for boarding a train.

PROCEDURE AT A GLANCE

1 After locating the station entrance, the learner enters the station, pauses briefly out of the flow of pedestrian traffic, and listens to the movement of passengers and for location of escalators or stairs and fare gates or turnstiles.

2 The learner localizes the stairs or fare gates and travels toward that feature, maintaining careful awareness of orientation and direction of travel. If there are stairs or escalators, he ascends or descends, then again listens for the fare-gate area.

3a Center platform stations: The learner listens for cues from other passengers traveling in the station and localizes the sound of stairs or escalators and, while maintaining awareness of orientation and using constant-contact technique, travels to the stairs, escalators, or elevators.

3b Side platform stations: The learner listens for cues from other passengers traveling in the station and follows the wall to the stairs or escalators after determining the expected location of the platform in relation to the direction he is facing and direction of travel on the train.

4 Upon reaching the platform level, the learner turns 90 degrees and, using constant-contact technique, travels to the edge of the platform.

5 Upon contacting the edge of the platform (or the detectable warning strip), the learner checks that he is aligned perpendicularly to the edge of the platform, steps back one step so he is approximately 3 to 5 feet from the edge of the platform, and waits for the train.

METHOD

STEP 1 After locating the station entrance, the learner enters the station, pauses briefly out of the flow of pedestrian traffic, and listens to the movement of passengers and for location of escalators or stairs and fare gates or turnstiles. If needed, the learner may solicit assistance.

Rationale The pause allows the learner to reorient and plan his travel within the station and locate his first destination, which may be stairs or escalators or turnstiles or fare gates, depending on the type of station and other features. Lighting is often much dimmer inside the station and learners with low vision will benefit from pausing to allow their eyes to adjust.

STEP 2 The learner localizes the stairs or fare gates and travels toward that feature, maintaining careful awareness of orientation and direction of travel. If there are stairs or escalators, he ascends or descends, then again listens for the fare-gate area. (Negotiating Escalators is covered in Chapter 9.)

Rationale Some stations have a set of stairs or escalators just inside the entrance, then fare gates at another level. Other stations may have fare gates just inside the street-level entrance. In either case, the learner needs to get to the fare gates to continue to the platform level. The learner pays the fare with a fare card, ticket, or other means and enters through the turnstiles or fare gates.

Variation There may not be a fare gate or stairs at a light rail station or stop. The learner may need to find a fare machine if the fare has not been purchased in advance. The location of fare machines varies greatly from system to system and the O&M specialist will need to address this skill in O&M lessons specific to the system. The learner also may solicit aid to locate the fare vending machine. Whenever possible, it is better to use a fare card to avoid the fare vending machine, which may or may not be fully accessible. In unfamiliar locations, the learner may find it necessary to trail a wall or fence to find an opening to the station area or fare gates or to solicit assistance from another transit rider.

STEP 3A Center platform stations: The learner listens for cues from other passengers traveling in the station and localizes the sound of stairs or escalators and, while maintaining awareness of orientation and using constant-contact cane technique, travels to the stairs, escalators, or elevators. If the stairs or escalators cannot be located by listening, it is usually possible to find them by following a wall, but that will often require following a U-shaped route to reach the stairway or escalator entrance. Maintaining orientation is essential for determining the correct train to board when reaching the platform. The learner determines on which side of the platform the train he desires will be located through orientation information (direction of travel) or by asking another passenger.

Rationale The stairs, escalators, and elevators are often centrally located for a center platform and will lead to a platform used by trains traveling in both directions. Other passengers often provide good auditory cues to the appropriate path of travel to reach the stairs, escalators, or elevators. The entry area is typically a restricted space and following a wall usually leads to at least one way to reach the platform, which may be the elevator.

STEP 3B Side platform stations: The learner listens for cues from other passengers traveling in the station and follows the wall to the stairs or escalators after determining the expected location of the platform in relation to the direction he is facing and direction of travel on the train. For example, if he is facing south and wants to board a northbound train, that train platform and the stairs to that platform will typically be along the east side of the station.

Rationale The stairs are almost always along the wall in side platform stations, so following the wall is an efficient way to find them, however, it is essential to identify the correct set of stairs or escalators for the platform and direction of travel the learner desires before going to the platform level.

STEP 4 Upon reaching the platform level, the learner turns 90 degrees and, using constant-contact cane technique, travels to the edge of the platform he desires. If the learner is uncertain of orientation in relation to the train, he may wait until a train comes into the station to discern the track location. (This will mean waiting and boarding the next train to allow adequate time to locate the door and board safely.) At center platform stations, the learner makes his turn based on the direction to the appropriate track for his train.

Rationale It is critical to avoid approaching the drop-off of the platform edge at an angle because the drop-off may not be detected quickly enough to avoid stepping off. Maintaining awareness of the location of the edge or edges of the platform can prevent missteps off the edge.

Variations In a side platform station, the learner can trail the wall to a known location, then turn and walk to the platform edge as described.

While the platform edge is consistently parallel to the direction of stairs or escalators in newer systems, this is not always true in the design of older systems and stations, so the learner may not need to turn 90 degrees to locate the edge. Elevator doors may also open facing the platform edge, so learner awareness of orientation is critical.

STEP 5 Upon contacting the edge of the platform or the detectable warning strip, which may not be present in all stations, the learner checks that he is aligned perpendicularly to the edge of the platform, steps back so he is approximately 3 to 5 feet from the edge of the platform, and waits for the train. If the train does not stop in front of that point on the platform, or he desires to move to a different position on the platform, he turns when there is no train in the station and travels parallel to the edge of the platform, using constant-contact or touch-and-drag cane technique and a wide arc to carefully follow the edge of the platform or the detectable warning strip to the location within the area that he prefers. If obstacles are contacted during this process, such as poles or stanchions, the learner goes around the obstacle on the side away from the platform edge, maintaining constant-contact cane technique, and returns to trail the edge. If a train comes in during this process, he steps away from the edge of the platform and waits for the train to leave before continuing to his waiting location.

Rationale Waiting for the train near the edge of the platform positions the learner to board efficiently and avoids the need to rush toward the platform edge with the flow of passengers boarding and disembarking from the train. Finding and following the platform edge or detectable warning strip when there is no train approaching or in the station can be the most efficient method of traveling and positioning oneself, particularly on a center platform since edge areas are typically kept clear. In side platform stations, signs, seating, and stairs are usually located along the wall, making it difficult to trail, although such objects can provide useful orientation. On center platforms, signs, seating, and stairs are located in the center between the two tracks and it can be difficult to maintain orientation when traveling around such objects as well as other passengers.

CONSIDERATIONS FOR TRAVELING WITHIN A STATION AND POSITIONING FOR BOARDING

- Some stations have an attendant booth near the fare gates; other systems may have cameras monitoring fare gates and various sections of the station. There are usually assistance telephones or intercoms near the fare gates if there is no staff present. O&M specialists should adjust their lessons and information provided to learners based on their local system, but it can be important for learners to know that each system is different and many systems may not have staff available near the entrances of train stations.

- Learners should have the opportunity to thoroughly explore several stations and find common elements such as ticket or fare machines, assistance phones, fare gates, and platform edges.

- Positioning on the train can be important for easy access to destinations as well as for security. This may be determined through familiarization to the station or by asking other passengers about the location of stairs in relation to the length of the train (near the front, in the middle, near the back). With practice, the learner can usually determine his position in relation to the train length by listening as the train enters the station to hear how many cars pass, where the train stops, and so on.

- At some transfer stations, the learner's position on the train can make the transfer route easier. In other cases, if the learner knows that he wants to exit from the north end of the destination station, he may position himself to be near the north end of the train waiting area when boarding at the departure station.

- Individuals are more visible to the train operator when boarding or disembarking if they are near the front of the train. When traveling at night, many passengers, including individuals who are blind, prefer to be near the front of the train where the train operator is usually located. Other passengers may prefer to be near the conductor (if the train has one), who is usually located in the middle car of a train.

- Efficiently planning routes may include considering the type of station platform and the location of stairs, escalators, or elevators. Most learners are more comfortable traveling on side platforms, where a wall can be followed to and from the stairs or exit. On familiar routes, learners may wish to position themselves for the most convenient or safe travel, for example, at a location that is well aligned to the stairs at their transfer station or by walking further into a side platform station to be near the stairs at their destination station, which is a center platform station.

- Elevators are provided in most newer stations to access all levels of the station. However, learners must keep in mind that use of the elevator can require entering or exiting the station at a different location than the main entrance or exit.

- O&M specialists and their learners may want to meet with train officials to learn about security issues in stations and safe places to wait. For example, in one city system, customers are always visible on the station video monitoring system when they are near the platform edge, but may not be visible when waiting along the wall. In that system, fare-gate areas are monitored on video, but stairs and bus waiting areas may not be.

Boarding a Rail Vehicle

Purpose: To enable the learner to board a rail vehicle and find seating in an efficient and safe manner. (*Note:* This procedure is not appropriate for commuter rail vehicles, but is used on both rapid rail and light rail transit vehicles with level boarding.)

	PROCEDURE AT A GLANCE
1	Properly positioned at the platform, the learner determines the arrival and position of the train from available auditory and visual clues.
2	The learner verifies whether the train is the one he wishes to take by listening to station or train announcements, reading train-identification signs, or asking another passenger.
3	When the train stops, using constant-contact technique, the learner steps forward and locates the edge of the platform and the side of the rail vehicle.
4	The learner turns toward the front of the train, contacting the train with his free hand and transferring the cane to his left hand if turning to the left (on a center platform).
5	The learner travels along the train to locate the door, using constant-contact technique to maintain awareness of the location of the platform edge and trailing the outside of the car with his free hand.
6a	Upon contacting an opening, the learner confirms it is a door by placing his hand on the doorframe and cane tip on the floor of the car, and turns into the door, grasping the handle or edge of a seat just inside the door.
6b	If the opening is the gap between cars and not a door, the learner continues past the opening and trails the car until a door is located, then completes Step 6a.
7	The learner may investigate with his cane to determine if a seat near the door is vacant or ask another passenger if a nearby seat is available.
8	If travel within the train is required, the learner employs a congested-area constant-contact technique with the cane in his left hand, and with his right hand trails the overhead handlebar as he proceeds to the vacant seat.

METHOD

STEP 1 Properly positioned on the platform, the learner determines the arrival and position of the train from available auditory and visual clues. Train arrivals seem obvious from auditory, visual, and air-pressure cues, but it is important that the learner not mistake a train on another track for his train. This is done most accurately if the learner is relatively close to the platform edge as the train arrives.

Rationale The learner must be prepared to board when the train arrives, so he needs to attend to the arrival and position of the train in relation to his waiting position and must be certain he is not mistaking a train on another track for his train. Trains have a maximum time in the station and the learner must board within that time or step back and wait for the next train. Trains are usually programmed to stop at the same location within the station, although that position in relation to the steps or escalators can vary depending on the length of the train.

STEP 2 The learner verifies whether the train is the one he wishes to take by listening to station or train announcements, reading train-identification signs, or asking another passenger.

Rationale In rapid rail systems, several trains may stop at the same platform, with only a couple of minutes between train arrivals, so the learner needs to confirm that he is boarding the correct train. Announcements are typically made in the station before the train arrives and at the doorway as the train stops. These announcements do malfunction at times, so learners may need to confirm with another passenger as the train pulls into the station. Visual train-identification signs may be located on the train car near each door, and some learners may be able to use these signs to determine if they are boarding the correct train.

Variation Learners with low vision may be able to see the signs at the front of the train or beside the door that usually provide the train identification, but lighting can be poor or signs can malfunction. The learner should be prepared to use another method to confirm the train identification.

STEP 3 When the train stops, using constant-contact cane technique, the learner steps forward and locates the edge of the platform and the side of the rail vehicle.

Rationale Knowing the exact location of the platform edge prevents stepping off accidentally between cars or at the front or back of the train. Contacting the vehicle confirms its location and provides guidance while locating the door.

Variation Learners with low vision may be able to visually detect the doorway and travel to it without contacting the train.

STEP 4 The learner turns toward the front of the train, contacting and trailing the train with his free hand and transferring the cane to his left hand if turning to the left (on a center platform).

Rationale On many systems the train operator looks out a window from the front of the train toward the back of the train before closing the doors. Turning toward the front of the train makes the cane more visible to the train operator and may result in his holding the door until the learner locates it and boards. It also gives the learner a consistent action to take when boarding; making a decision about the location of the doors and which direction to turn by listening in a noisy rail station can be problematic for some learners and may lead to rushing and unsafe maneuvers.

Variation Learners with low vision may not need to contact and trail the train, but should be certain that they have accurately identified a doorway; in aboveground stations, the sun shining through the gap between cars can look like a doorway.

STEP 5 The learner travels along the train to locate the door, using constant-contact cane technique to maintain awareness of the location of the platform edge and trailing the outside of the car with his free hand. This whole maneuver needs to be completed quickly and efficiently. Depending on the train system, learners may need to be prepared to trail around potential obstacles, such as barriers to prevent stepping between cars or pillars near the edge of the platform.

Rationale Constant-contact cane technique is used to maintain awareness of the location of the platform edge and to prevent tripping over or running into obstacles. Barriers are used in some systems on the platform to prevent stepping into the opening between cars. The learner needs to avoid tripping over such objects or running into pillars that are sometimes located alongside the trackway. Contact with the hand as well as the cane is the most efficient and certain method to ensure that the learner has located a doorway and not the gap between cars.

STEP 6A Upon contacting an opening, the learner confirms that it is a door by placing his hand on the doorframe and cane tip on the floor of the car, turns 90 degrees, and steps inside the train, grasping the handle or edge of a seat just inside the door. The learner should turn accurately and take a large step into the train to avoid stepping into the gap between the platform edge and the train car.

Rationale Using both the hand and cane tip provides more accurate identification to ensure that the learner is stepping into the doorway and not into the gap between cars. Accidentally stepping between cars can be a life-threatening mistake. The train's time in the station is limited and the train may start moving quickly after the doors close so it is best to find a handhold when stepping in.

Variations If the learner hears the closing-door tone before locating the doorway, he should turn 90 degrees away from the train and take at least two steps away from the train, repositioning himself after the train leaves to wait for the next train.

A button must be pressed to open the doors on some light rail trains, particularly at night. The train operator, if observing along the car, may open the door for a learner with a long cane or dog guide. The button location and style should be covered in a general orientation to the system, in case it is needed.

STEP 6B If the learner locates the gap between cars rather than the door, the learner continues past the opening and trails the car until a door is located, then boards as noted in Step 6a. The gap between cars curves in more than the door in most systems and there may be a barrier chain between cars or a barrier along the edge of the platform at that point. Some light rail systems do not provide any kind of barrier and the gap is large enough to step into, which may result in the learner being out of sight of the train operator.

Diane L. Fazzi

Rationale The learner needs to get to the door as quickly as possible and bypass any gap between cars. Recognizing the difference between the gap and a boarding door is an essential safety skill.

STEP 7 While holding onto a vertical pole or handhold, the learner investigates with his cane to determine if a seat near the door is vacant or asks another passenger if a nearby seat is available.

Rationale It is best to be seated near the door, rather than further back in the car, to facilitate disembarking from a crowded car. Investigating carefully with a cane often encourages someone to vacate a seat near the door. Other passengers are often the best source of information since most trains do not have attendants on each car.

STEP 8 If travel within the train is required, the learner employs a congested-area constant-contact technique with the cane in his left hand, and with his right hand trails the overhead handlebar as he proceeds to the vacant seat. He may confirm the seat location verbally with other passengers as he travels toward the seat.

Rationale It is generally best to travel on the right (in the United States). The overhead horizontal handrail is grasped to provide balance while the train is moving. Other passengers can be a source of additional confirming information.

CONSIDERATIONS FOR BOARDING A RAIL VEHICLE

- Orientation to the rail system and the rail vehicle should cover emergency evacuation procedures, station emergency call boxes and video monitoring of station area, track design, location of electric rails, and the track refuge area (usually under the platform edge) in addition to thorough familiarization to the railcar, doors, seating, and location of the in-car intercom.

- Other passengers are likely to attempt to assist the learner during boarding, and it is important for the learner and O&M specialist to practice ways in which the learner can take control of the situation.

- Gaps between cars and between the platform edge and the car vary from system to system and from station to station. Learners should be aware of the differences and, together with the O&M specialist, practice boarding at different times of day and with different passenger loads.

- It is often best to stand just inside the train door, particularly on a short route, rather than try to find a seat that requires travel back to the door to exit. It can be quite difficult to negotiate a crowded aisle of standing passengers in the minimal time allowed for boarding and disembarking in most rail stations.

- Doors may open on either side of the train. If the learner knows the type of station where he is disembarking, it can be helpful to move to a location near that door. For example, if he is boarding at a side platform station but knows he is disembarking at a center platform station, crossing the train when boarding can position him for a more efficient departure.

Disembarking from a Rail Vehicle and Leaving the Station

Purpose: **To enable the learner to exit the train and station safely and efficiently.**

PROCEDURE AT A GLANCE

1	Upon recognizing that he is approaching his stop, the learner stands, holds onto a vertical pole or overhead handrail, and faces toward the location of the door he will use to exit.
2	After the doors open, he proceeds to the door using congested-area constant-contact technique. If he was seated close to the door, he may trail the seat edge as he exits.
3	Upon detecting the doorway and train edge with his cane, he steps over the gap between the platform and the door and onto the platform.
4	The learner takes two or three steps forward away from the train, then stops to reorient before continuing out of the station.
5a	Center platform station: After the train leaves the station, the learner returns to the platform edge or detectable warning strip and trails along it with his cane using constant-contact technique. When stairs or escalators are detected, he turns 90 degrees. Using constant-contact technique, he travels to the stair or escalator enclosure.
5b	Side platform station: The learner walks straight ahead toward the wall, then turns 90 degrees in the direction he wants to exit. Using constant-contact technique, he follows the wall to the stairs or escalator.
6	Upon locating the stairs or escalator to exit, using the appropriate cane technique, the learner ascends or descends to leave the platform area.
7	After reaching the fare gate or concourse level, the learner listens to the sound of the fare gates and exits the station.

METHOD

STEP 1 Upon hearing his stop called, or recognizing that he is approaching his stop, the learner stands, holds onto a vertical pole or overhead handrail, and faces toward the location of the nearest door he can use to exit. The doors will usually open on the right side of the train (when facing forward) at side platform stations and on the left side of the train at center platform stations. At transfer stations, there may be two platforms and doors may open on both sides of the train. The learner should maintain his grasp on the pole or handhold until the train comes to a full stop and the doors open.

Rationale Standing indicates to others that the learner is planning to exit and allows him to position himself facing the door before the train stops. He holds on until the doors open because trains sometimes stop with a jolt or stop and move again to get into the correct position.

Variation If he is not sure which door will open, the learner faces the middle and turns toward the correct door as he hears the doors opening.

STEP 2 After the doors open, he proceeds to the door using congested-area constant-contact technique. If he was seated close to the door, he may trail the seat edge with one hand as he exits.

Rationale He waits for the doors to open because that provides a clear indication that the train has stopped moving and gives him an auditory cue to the location of the doors. He uses constant-contact cane technique to reliably detect the edge of the train at the door, but shortened to avoid interfering with other passengers who may be moving toward the door. If seated right next to the doors, it may be quite easy to trail the seat edge for another good cue to the train edge and doorway.

STEP 3 Upon detecting the doorway and train edge with his cane, he steps over the gap between the platform and the door and onto the platform.

Rationale Depending on the system and loading of the train car, the gap between the platform and the train car can be wide enough to catch a foot, so it is important for the learner to attend to the gap when stepping out.

STEP 4 The learner takes two or three steps forward away from the train, then stops to reorient before continuing out of the station.

Rationale Moving away from the door allows other passengers to exit the train. The learner stops to get oriented before walking into the platform area.

Variation At a familiar station, the learner may proceed without stopping, particularly at a side platform station.

STEP 5A Center platform station: After the train leaves the station and passengers clear somewhat, the learner returns to the platform edge or detectable warning strip, trails along it with his cane using constant-contact cane technique, and listens for stairs, escalators, and the movement of other passengers. When stairs or escalators are detected, he turns 90 degrees in the direction of the stairs or escalators and, using constant-contact cane technique, travels to the stair or escalator enclosure. The learner should contact this within 20 feet and should be aware that he is walking toward the other edge of the platform and utilize excellent constant-contact cane technique to find the detectable warning surface or platform edge if the stair or escalator enclosure is not contacted.

Rationale Many center platforms are quite narrow and contacting the platform at an angle when disoriented can lead to a fall from the platform. Maintaining contact with the edge allows parallel travel and awareness of its location. Stairs or escalator enclosures are often fewer than 10 feet back from the edge of the platform and can be detected aurally, but it is important for the learner to remember and anticipate the other platform edge.

Variation Other passengers can be an excellent source of information in unfamiliar stations. Soliciting assistance and information may be helpful for orientation.

STEP 5B Side platform station: The learner walks straight ahead toward the wall, then turns 90 degrees in the direction he wants to exit. Using constant-contact cane technique, he follows the wall to the stairs or escalator.

Rationale The stairs or escalator are generally located along the wall at a side platform station. Traveling straight toward the wall and turning in the desired direction is generally most efficient and avoids possible misalignment in locating the exit stairs or escalator.

STEP 6 Upon locating the correct stairs or escalator to exit, using the appropriate cane technique, the learner ascends or descends to leave the platform area. He should confirm the destination of the stairs or escalators with other passengers first. If the learner has low vision, he should check for signs above the stairs or escalators to confirm that they go to his destination.

Rationale Some stations may have several different sets of stairs or escalators, exiting to different streets or platform areas, so confirming that he is at the proper set of stairs or escalators is good practice before traveling to the wrong place. A level change is usually necessary to exit rapid rail stations, but not many light rail stations. The learner should use good cane technique to detect obstacles and other passengers when ascending or descending stairs or escalators.

Variations Some learners may need to locate and use elevators in stations. At transfer stations, learners may reach another platform level before the concourse or fare-gate level. In many older systems, the fare gates may be on the platform level; most stations in newer systems have fare gates and platforms on separate levels.

In some rail stations, particularly on-street light rail, the platform is at sidewalk level and there are no fare gates or other barriers to pass through when leaving. Passengers are typically directed to an exit or crossing area by platform edges or fencing.

STEP 7 After reaching the fare-gate or concourse level, while maintaining awareness of his direction of travel and orientation, the learner listens to the sound of the fare gates and exits the station. If necessary, he usually can follow a wall, and possibly some type of fence, to the fare gates.

Rationale Fare-gate positioning can vary in different stations, but the gates typically are quite audible as people pass through them. If the learner is not able to hear them, he can follow a wall to get to them because the area will usually be enclosed by the gates.

CONSIDERATIONS FOR DISEMBARKING FROM A RAIL VEHICLE AND LEAVING THE STATION

- Gaps between cars and between the platform edge and the car vary from system to system and from station to station. Learners should be aware of those differences and have experience during lessons in disembarking at different times of the day and with different passenger loads.
- The movement and sound of other passengers can provide excellent cues about the direction of the station exit. Learners need to be aware that there can be several sets of stairs or escalators and that each one may go to a different location.
- Systems have various configurations of entrances, exits, and payment systems. O&M specialists should include lessons to orient their learners to the nuances of their local system.

■ The direction of travel on the train provides orientation information for learners. Reorienting immediately after exiting the train is essential to maintaining orientation in the station. It may take practice for learners to easily make the correct determinations; for example, when exiting a northbound train on a side platform the learner will be facing east, whereas on a center platform the learner will be facing west.

NEGOTIATING RAILROAD CROSSINGS

Purpose: To enable the learner to cross railroad tracks safely and efficiently.

PROCEDURE AT A GLANCE

1 The learner approaches the tracks using constant-contact technique and listens and looks for cues that a train is approaching.

2 If a train is approaching, the learner stops at a predetermined landmark and waits for the train to pass.

3 If no train is approaching, or after the train has passed, the learner crosses the tracks, traveling parallel to traffic on the roadway.

METHOD

STEP 1 The learner approaches the tracks using constant-contact cane technique to detect a slight incline or decline before the tracks and the different texture of trackway gap filler, if present. He listens and looks for an approaching train, the sound of the crossing warning bells or the train whistle, or the lights flashing at the crossbucks (the term for the traditional railroad-crossing sign). At a familiar crossing, he looks for predetermined landmarks.

Rationale Constant-contact cane technique is used to detect small differences in footing. The learner wants to stop before the tracks if a train is coming and needs to be aware on his approach to the tracks.

STEP 2 If the learner hears or sees an approaching train or warning bells and lights, he stops a safe distance back from the tracks and waits for the train to pass. A predetermined landmark should be chosen at familiar locations, which will help to ensure the learner is far enough back for the train to clear. It is best for the learner to familiarize himself to the crossing at a time when a train is not nearby.

Rationale Some trains travel at high speeds through crossings, so it is important for the learner to wait far enough back to be outside the train envelope, which is the full space the train may sway into as it moves through the crossing.

STEP 3 If no train is approaching, or after the train has passed, the learner confirms that no train is coming from the other direction, crosses the tracks, and travels parallel to traffic on the roadway, if present.

Rationale Sometimes trains pass in close succession, so it is important to allow a train to clear the trackway and then check for another train before continuing.

Variation If there is no parallel traffic, the learner may be able to trail the edge of the raised walkway or roadway over the tracks, or travel perpendicular to the tracks.

CONSIDERATIONS FOR NEGOTIATING RAILROAD CROSSINGS

- There may be one set of tracks or more. Two sets are quite common.
- The counterweight from the vehicle gate (that comes down across the roadway before the train crosses) may protrude into the sidewalk. If warning bells are heard, the learner needs to be aware of that possibility.
- Vehicle gates may extend across the sidewalk as well as the roadway, however, the lowest part of the gate may extend at 36 inches above the roadway or sidewalk, which is not detected well with a cane and may be contacted at waist level upon approach.
- Sometimes there is a pedestrian gate (that is at a different location and height than the vehicle gate) for the sidewalk or pedestrian path. Most often, however, there is no gate for pedestrians to indicate a safe distance back from the tracks. Waiting 15 feet or more from the nearest rail will place the learner outside the train envelope. When familiarizing to a location, a landmark should be located at that distance if there is no gate or detectable warning surface before the tracks.

Other Transportation Systems

Other transportation systems include paratransit, ride sharing and commuter van pools, and taxis and taxi-like services such as Uber and Lyft. Paratransit services are part of the public transit system and usually operate only in the area served by the transit system. There are federal rules (as part of the Americans with Disabilities Act) that provide basic service requirements, but local operations may vary. In some cities, taxi services provide paratransit services for those who do not require a lift or special vehicle. O&M specialists should investigate the services available in their teaching area in order to provide their learners with accurate information and instruction.

Ride-sharing services and commuter van pools also vary greatly from city to city. They can be an effective transportation option for daily work or school trips in some areas, particularly between suburbs, or for a suburb-to-downtown commute.

Taxis and taxi-like services such as Uber and Lyft are available in most cities. Most have options to request service via the Internet, apps, or text messages and will send a text message when the ride arrives.

USING TAXIS

Purpose: To enable the learner to effectively use taxis and taxi-like services.

PROCEDURE AT A GLANCE

1. The learner obtains his destination address, along with the nearest cross street.
2. The learner calls or texts a taxi company and requests a taxi, either in advance by scheduling a pickup time, or at the time of need. The learner confirms the precise pickup or waiting location.
3. When the taxi arrives, the learner confirms the taxi name and driver and the destination.
4. The learner enters the taxi. He may use GPS or other mapping tools, or knowledge of the route, to follow the taxi's path.
5. At the destination, the learner confirms the proper location by asking a few key questions.
6. The learner pays the fare and gets a receipt.
7. The learner exits the taxi safely, maintaining awareness of traffic that may be present.

METHOD

STEP 1 The learner obtains his destination address, along with the nearest cross street. He also gets an approximate trip time or distance. This information can be obtained by calling the destination or through use of some type of online mapping program.

Rationale The learner needs the exact address to give to the taxi driver and the nearest cross street will usually result in finding the destination more quickly. He gets the approximate trip time and distance so he can plan effectively for the trip and to make sure that he is not being "taken for a ride."

STEP 2 The learner calls or texts a trusted taxi company and requests a taxi, either in advance by scheduling a pickup time, or at the time of need. He should allow extra time for the taxi to travel to his location if calling at the time of need. When calling, he should confirm a waiting location; for example, "I'll be waiting inside the front door of the building." In some cases, it's possible to arrange for the driver to come to the door or text when he arrives.

Rationale Calling or texting the company provides a cab sent in response to the call. The pickup time can be prearranged to reach a destination at a specific time. When calling for a taxi as needed, the nearest cab will usually be sent, but it may take some time to reach the learner.

Variations In some cities, taxis can be hailed on the street. Doing this may be difficult for a person who is totally blind, but some people do so efficiently with practice. Alternatively, the learner can go to a location where taxis are known to congregate, such as outside a major hotel. Hotel staff can assist in summoning a taxi. Taxi stands are located at specified locations outside many transit stations or airport exits. Soliciting aid is often the best way to find a taxi stand.

STEP 3 When the taxi arrives, the learner confirms the taxi name and driver and the destination.

Rationale Confirming information ensures that the learner is getting into the correct taxi. Particularly when waiting along a street, it is possible to have another cab stop and try to pick up a fare. If the learner has called a particular company or driver, it is best to wait for the expected cab.

STEP 4 The learner enters the taxi. He may use GPS or other mapping tools, or knowledge of the route, to follow the taxi's path.

Rationale For familiar routes or a regular trip, the learner may be able to follow the route based on his knowledge. He may need to give directions to the driver if the destination is his own residence. If the learner uses a GPS device to follow the route, he can learn more about the area. All taxi riders should maintain awareness about the route being taken by the driver to ensure that the driver does not take a longer than necessary route or drives to an isolated location.

STEP 5 At the destination, the learner can confirm the proper location by asking a few key questions (e.g., "Are you at the curbside?" "Are we in front of the main entrance?").

Rationale Knowing the position of the vehicle can make it easier to disembark from the taxi efficiently and continue the trip. If the taxi is not at curbside, the learner can ask other questions about the position in relation to lanes of traffic and other safety aspects before getting out. If the taxi drops the learner at a different entrance than anticipated, there may be disorientation.

STEP 6 The learner pays the fare and gets a receipt.

Rationale The fare must be paid before disembarking. A receipt usually provides taxi company information as well as payment information and can be useful for documenting the trip.

STEP 7 The learner exits the taxi safely, opening the door slowly and maintaining awareness of traffic and the possibility of other vehicles traveling in the same direction on either side of taxi, especially at an airport and especially if the taxi was unable to pull up to the curb.

Rationale The learner needs to be aware of other traffic that could be passing the taxi. Opening the door slowly (if the driver has not opened it) prevents opening the door into people or vehicles. Even if the taxi is curbside, there may be pedestrians or bicyclists traveling by within the swing of the car door.

CONSIDERATIONS FOR USING TAXIS

- Many taxis have identification materials on the back of the seat or other location within the taxi. This may include a picture of the driver and his name mounted over the front mirror, which may be readable by individuals with low vision. There may be braille information providing the taxi number. If there are problems with service, this information may be necessary to correctly identify the trip.
- Taxis in some cities have accessible fare devices that provide trip information, as well as allow for payment, including tips, with a credit card from the backseat. Some devices are not fully accessible.
- When using a taxi to travel home, the learner should know some landmarks and other features to describe his residence to the driver. The learner may ask the driver to drop him at a particular place, such as beside the mailbox, or to pull into the driveway.

Airport Terminals

A large segment of the population travels by air and learners who are blind or who have low vision will need to learn skills for airport travel. Due to increased security measures at airports, O&M specialists will rarely have the opportunity to teach learners how to apply skills for travel in airports unless they are traveling together on a field trip. Unless the learner uses the same airport frequently, it may be less important to self-familiarize to a specific airport. It can be judicious to learn about common features and airport travel guidelines and then to solicit assistance since it is readily available at most airports.

It is helpful if learners understand the general layout of the airport, including drop-off and skycap (porter) areas. Learners may find it worthwhile to check luggage with the outdoor skycaps to avoid the need to negotiate more crowded areas inside the airport while handling luggage. Ticket counters with baggage checks are typically located in a direct line from the entrance, but finding the ticket counter for the correct airline can be challenging. Security screening lines may be located in a wide variety of locations. Airports may have numerous concourse areas, which can be conceptualized as long intersecting hallways with shops, restaurants, and gates

on either side. Most restaurants are often found in the center of the airport where concourses intersect.

While O&M specialists may not have the opportunity to familiarize learners to the inside of airplanes, they can review the general seating arrangements and locations of restrooms, door latches, and flushing mechanisms. Specific models of airplanes (727, 747, and so on) have a fixed number of seats on either side of the aisle or center portion of the plane. The learner should be familiar with overhead luggage compartments, under-seat storage, and food trays. Seatbelts are somewhat similar to those found in other vehicles.

Planning flights is typically done online, but reservation agents can provide assistance for a small additional fee. Tickets can be printed from a computer before arriving at the airport or a confirmation number can be presented at the check-in counter along with appropriate photo identification. Alternatively, learners may choose to use their mobile devices for use with an e-ticket. Many aspects of the check-in process, including requests for preapproved security clearance from the Transportation Security Administration, can be completed online or done in advance of travel to reduce stress at the airport. Luggage should be clearly labeled and flight information and paper or e-tickets neatly organized prior to arriving at the airport.

Tips for Teaching Transportation Systems

Integrating Orientation

O&M specialists should arrange for orientation to buses or trains when they are not in service to review layout and parts of the vehicle, and to practice communicating with the driver or train operator, boarding, finding a seat, and disembarking. This can be an excellent group activity with several O&M specialists and learners exploring together to make it more fun for the learners. Also, some learners will be more outgoing than others about asking questions of bus or train operators and the entire group can learn from those questions. Transit agencies in several cities coordinate regular orientation sessions with groups and school systems.

Tactile or large-print maps of bus routes, transit systems, or rail stations can be helpful to learners' orientation and understanding of the routes and stations. Using a simple tactile map of the bus route, and following along on that map during the ride, can provide orientation information and help the learner understand routes better. Some O&M specialists also effectively use computer street-view mapping programs with low vision learners for orientation to the route and to destinations.

When calling for information from transit companies, learners may benefit from using some type of recording device to record the calls and responses so they have more time to transcribe information into braille, large print, or electronic storage for future use. These types of recordings can also be helpful for O&M specialists in role-playing and working with their learners on appropriate follow-up questions or clarifications. It takes practice to develop proficiency in obtaining accurate information about routes and bus and transit stops. Learners also may find they get different information if they call back and speak to a different customer service representative. They may need to ask more or different questions to clarify their route and plans. Premade route worksheets (in braille or large print) can aid learners in telephone communication for route planning.

There are many web-based routing services for vehicle, transit, and pedestrian trips, either through mapping programs or transit agencies. While their accuracy in terms of bus and train routing may vary from city to city, some good information can be gained in this manner. Most transit systems provide schedule information online, although some systems still do not provide such information in accessible formats.

Tactile models of intersections can be used to address typical locations of bus stops. These models work best if combined with travel and exploration of locations on the street. Tactile models of transit stations can also be useful for understanding the location and types of platforms, bus transfer areas within stations, and other features.

Role-playing situations can be used to make instruction interesting and motivating for the learner. Group lessons with other learners can also be motivating, particularly in aspects of travel such as route planning, when learners can work together to think about what other questions they should have asked, laugh about the unhelpful answers provided by some customer service representatives, and problem solve their route plan together.

Self-familiarization to the various areas of rail and transit stations can be a useful way to learn about various features, such as seating, fare gates, fare machines, bus stop bays and signage, information kiosks, and emergency call boxes. It can also provide excellent practice in maintaining orientation in large spaces. Rapid transit stations can usually be subdivided into the fare-gate entry area; the entry concourse; the steps, escalators, and elevators to platform areas; platform areas; and connecting bus areas. Bus transfer stations may have more than one entry area, passenger waiting area, driveway, crosswalk, or bus stop bay (a designated spot within a transfer area or on the side of the road where buses pull out of the flow of traffic to pick up and drop off passengers).

Sequencing

Orientation to the bus or rail vehicle before taking an independent trip contributes to smooth boarding and confidence in traveling on the bus or train. Learners who are accustomed to riding school buses may need to understand the difference in driver roles and interactions with other passengers. Learners need some awareness of basic personal safety information (for example, not giving too much information to strangers).

If the learner has not ridden public transit buses before, the first trip may be to familiarize the learner with the basics of riding the bus. If the learner is familiar with public transit buses, the first couple of trips might be the same route. On the first independent trip, the O&M specialist may trail close behind the learner, sitting with the learner and talking about things the learner should notice, such as turns, railroad tracks, stops where many passengers board, stop announcements, and other information that may help the learner keep track of progress on the route. The O&M specialist, depending on the learner's experience, may assist at various points on the first independent ride, but the learner should board and pay the fare, request stop information from the driver, and find a seat as though traveling alone, if possible. On subsequent trips, the O&M specialist will board separately and sit apart from the learner or follow the bus in a separate vehicle, as appropriate. The O&M specialist may intervene or join the learner during those trips if a need arises. After each trip, the O&M specialist should allow time to review the trip and discuss any questions or issues.

The first independent ride, if possible, should be a simple route with stops at nearside corner locations and simple street crossings to return on the bus traveling in the opposite direction. For most learners, a destination, and a task at the destination (e.g., getting coffee, buying gum), can improve their interest in the trip and provide an opportunity to discuss the first trip before returning.

After some experience traveling routes that have been preselected, and discussion of the details of those routes, route planning is introduced. With practice and experience, the learner develops additional skill at routes that are more and more complex, involving transfers from bus to bus and from bus to rail.

In rail travel, the first route should be between side platform stations and the next route from side platform to center and center platform to side, with simple transfers (those that do not require a lot of platform walking). Later lessons should incorporate transferring between train lines at the station and using stations that require travel on the platform level.

O&M Specialist Positioning

As noted earlier, the O&M specialist may closely accompany the learner on initial trips and follow further back on later routes. The O&M specialist may, at times, follow the bus in a car and meet the learner when he disembarks.

In rail travel, the same principles apply, with the O&M specialist close on earlier trips and trailing further behind on subsequent trips. It is important to stay close enough to ensure that the O&M specialist gets on the same train as the learner, but also be cautious not to precede the learner onto a train that the learner then misses. In rail stations with drop-offs, the O&M specialist must stay alert to the movement of other passengers that may disrupt the learner's travel near the edge of the platform.

Strategies for Different Populations

For individuals with low vision who use wheelchairs, practice backing onto the bus lift, using the lift, and traveling to the wheelchair securement location is necessary before attempting to take the bus on a regular route. In most systems, the drivers are not allowed to help position the wheelchair, although they often assist in securing the wheelchair in its space. Entering elevators in train stations and the doorways to train cars also needs to be practiced and can be scheduled at off-peak times.

Routes and trips can be practiced in segments for learners with poor stamina.

Advancements in technology may provide more opportunities to provide feedback and specific route-based information to all travelers, particularly travelers with cognitive disabilities, when using transportation systems.

Self-Advocacy

Traveling on public transit requires a good bit of self-advocacy and interaction with the public, customer service representatives, and bus drivers or train operators. All serve as opportunities to develop skills in refusing assistance when it is not needed, asking detailed questions to obtain needed information, and asking follow-up questions. There are also many opportunities to inform others about the capabilities of people who are blind or who have low vision. Learners will find that their skills improve with practice. Feedback and suggestions from the O&M specialist can help learners recognize better ways to phrase questions and identify additional questions that could have been asked.

Learners should be knowledgeable about the complaint (and compliment) system of their local transit agency and utilize it to provide feedback to the agency. They may be able to request modifications such as accessible signals to make street crossings on a route more usable or request accessible bus or train schedules or more information about stop locations. They may even have the opportunity to assist the agency in training bus drivers on appropriate interactions with people with disabilities.

O&M specialists can also work with learners to explore discounts that may be available for monthly passes, such as for individuals who have visual impairments or other disabilities, or for senior fares. Another part of self-advocacy may include discussing ride-sharing costs and taxi fares and how to handle situations in which a driver may not be charging the right amount. Developing a ride-sharing or carpool network, whether it be on a college campus or in a work environment, also requires self-advocacy on the part of the learner who wishes to be a part of the group. Each of these aspects of using transportation can be addressed within the O&M curriculum.

Special Situations

This chapter provides procedures for special situations that will be part of most orientation and mobility (O&M) programs. O&M specialists may insert special lessons or integrate these procedures at different points of the program for learners depending on the learner's age, previous experience, circumstances, and access to facilities.

SOLICITING ASSISTANCE

Purpose: To enable the learner to obtain information from other individuals about a current location, destination, or route features.

PROCEDURE AT A GLANCE

1. The learner determines that she needs additional information and localizes on available sound clues that indicate the presence of nearby individuals.

2. The learner turns toward the sound clue, maintaining awareness of her original facing direction, and calls out, "Excuse me, can you assist me please?" or "Excuse me, I need some directions."

3. If the person responds, the learner approaches, if necessary, and asks for additional information while remaining aware of her orientation and assessing the consistency of the other person's responses.

4. The learner asks specific, direct questions related to the directions provided.

5. The learner thanks the person and proceeds to her intended objective.

METHOD

STEP 1 The learner determines that she needs additional information and localizes on available sound clues that indicate the presence of nearby individuals. These clues might include footsteps, conversations, a telephone ringing, or the sound of a cash register.

Rationale Sound clues provide information about the location of individuals who may be able to provide assistance.

Variation If the learner is in an area with no nearby aid, she may choose to reposition herself to an area where she thinks help may be available. Other methods, such as phone apps, may also be used to request remote assistance.

STEP 2 The learner turns toward the sound clue, maintaining awareness of her original facing direction, and calls out, "Excuse me, can you assist me please?" or "Excuse me, I need some directions."

Rationale Turning toward the person or sound source makes it more likely that the person will notice and realize that the learner is talking to him. The learner needs to be continuously aware of her original facing direction to avoid becoming disoriented.

STEP 3 If the person responds, the learner approaches, if necessary, and asks for additional information, such as: "Is Joe's Diner located along this block?" or "Have I passed the entrance to the Hilton Hotel?" When approaching the person, the learner should remain aware of her orientation and assess the quality and consistency of the other person's responses.

Rationale Approaching the person facilitates communication. Maintaining orientation is important to understanding the directions the learner receives. Assessing the quality and consistency of the other person's responses is important for personal safety and to determine if the directions are accurate.

STEP 4 The learner asks specific, direct questions related to the directions provided. For example, "Is Joe's Diner the third door or the fourth door?" or "When you say over there, do you mean in that direction [pointing in the direction]?"

Rationale Other pedestrians may not provide accurate directions or assistance without additional questioning by the learner. The learner needs to clarify directions while she has the person's attention.

STEP 5 The learner thanks the person and proceeds to her intended objective.

Rationale Showing appreciation is a social grace that should be extended to the person for his assistance.

Variation If the person offers to guide the learner to the destination, the learner may choose to accept, using appropriate guide technique, but should remain aware of her route and continue to clarify directions in order to return from the destination or find the destination again on a later trip.

CONSIDERATIONS FOR SOLICITING ASSISTANCE

■ The learner may need to solicit assistance along a sidewalk, within stores or other facilities, or via telephone in advance of travel. Soliciting assistance is a necessary part of independent travel and learners should be reminded that any person in an unfamiliar location frequently needs to ask for directions from others.

- A learner may need to ask leading questions to obtain accurate directions. The learner also may need to assess whether her source of information was valid before following the given directions. It can be helpful to repeat the directions and follow up with additional questions to solicit more details. (The section on Route Planning in Chapter 8 also includes suggested questions that can be used for soliciting assistance.)

- The learner should be sure that directions are given relative to her body position. The learner may find it necessary to convert directions given as "right," "left," "straight," and "behind" into cardinal directions.

- At times the person responding may include landmarks in the directions. The learner must determine whether these are valid for her use.

- Occasionally it may be necessary to solicit aid twice, first when far away from the objective and once again when in the general vicinity of the objective.

- Learners will benefit from practicing how to solicit assistance from their O&M specialists prior to applying the skills in real situations. For learners who are less communicative, some basic utility questions can be scripted and practiced, such as "Can you tell me if X is on my right?"

- A variety of apps are available in which learners may request assistance regarding current or desired locations from individuals who are trained to provide that information. The learner still needs to be able to ask pertinent questions to obtain the necessary information.

NEGOTIATING ESCALATORS

Purpose: **To enable the learner to utilize escalators safely, efficiently, and independently.**

PROCEDURE AT A GLANCE

1. The learner locates the escalator and tries to determine, visually or through listening, whether the escalator is traveling up or down, and whether it is moving toward or away from her.

2. The learner uses constant-contact or touch-and-slide technique to detect the metal plate at the entry to the escalator, contacts the right side of the escalator with her cane, and transfers the cane to her left hand.

3. The learner locates the handrail with her right hand and confirms that the escalator steps are moving away from her by lightly touching the handrail and letting it slide through her fingers.

4. The learner grasps the handrail and steps forward to locate the edge of the moving steps with her cane tip.

5. The learner steps onto the escalator, repositioning herself as necessary onto the flat portion of the stair and maintaining a secure grip on the handrail.

6. The learner positions the cane tip on the edge of the step ahead, waiting for the handrail to level out and the cane tip to be at the same height as her lead foot to anticipate the escalator landing.

7. Upon reaching the escalator landing, she takes a normal step, clearing quickly with her cane and continuing for several steps to get out of the way of other people coming off the escalator.

METHOD

STEP 1 The learner detects the escalator by localizing available sound and visual clues. She tries to determine, visually or through listening, whether the escalator is traveling up or down, and whether it is moving toward or away from her. If the learner hears or sees the escalator steps moving at head height, she can expect that the steps are either moving up and away from her or down from the floor above and toward her. If the sounds are coming from below her feet, the escalator is either going down to or up from the floor below (Jacobson, 2013). The sound of the movement of people on the escalator can provide additional information about the escalator's direction.

Rationale Localizing on sound or visual clues facilitates locating the correct escalator. The learner must determine whether the escalator is going up or down and traveling toward her or away from her to decide if it is the escalator she needs.

STEP 2 After determining that it is the correct escalator, the learner uses constant-contact or touch-and-slide cane technique to detect the metal plate, or floor plate, at the entry to the escalator. The learner contacts the right side of the escalator with her cane and transfers the cane to her left hand.

Rationale The metal plate at the entry to the escalator provides a distinctive sound and texture change when contacted with a cane. Transferring the cane to the left hand facilitates grasping the handrail with the right hand. Some transit systems in the United States have a "stand right, walk left" rule on escalators or moving walkways, so this positions the learner appropriately for standing and allows other pedestrians to pass.

STEP 3 The learner locates the handrail with her right hand and confirms that the escalator is moving away from her by lightly touching the handrail and letting it slide through her fingers.

Rationale The escalator handrail moving away from the learner confirms that the stairs are moving away from her since the handrail moves in the same direction as the stairs. If the learner detects that the handrail is moving toward her, then she should prepare to move away from the current escalator to locate the correct escalator or solicit assistance as needed.

STEP 4 The learner grasps the handrail with her right hand and steps forward, locating the edge of the moving steps with her cane tip by quickly and gently pulling the cane in toward her. She walks forward to the edge of the moving stairs in preparation to step on.

Rationale The learner grasps the handrail for support in negotiating the moving steps. Locating the edge of the moving steps with the cane tip establishes the learner's position relative to the first step. Moving up to the edge of the stairs positions the learner to step onto the escalator. An inexperienced traveler may benefit from exploring the movement of the stairs with the cane tip to confirm the direction of the escalator (up or down) as it moves away from her.

Variation At times when the escalators are not crowded, the learner may modify this procedure by locating the first step with the cane tip, rather than just the edge. The learner should maintain a loose grasp on the handrail and confirm the escalator movement with her cane. If the escalator is traveling up, the extended cane will drop as each riser passes; if traveling down, the cane will be pulled forward somewhat. The learner perceives the rhythm of the stair movement so that she can step directly and firmly onto a flat stair when she is ready. At newer transit stations and other locations, escalators may have a longer, flatter step at the entrance and the movement of the cane tip will not provide as much information.

STEP 5 The learner steps onto the escalator, repositioning herself as necessary onto the flat portion of the stair and maintaining a secure grip on the handrail.

Rationale Maintaining a standing position on a flat step increases balance and better prepares the learner to transition to the landing at the end of the escalator. Holding the handrail steadies the learner if she happens to place a foot between steps. Moving forward or backward properly positions the learner on the step.

STEP 6 The learner positions the cane tip on the edge of the step ahead, waiting for the handrail to level out and the cane tip to be at the same height as her lead foot to anticipate the escalator landing.

Rationale The cane tip is positioned on the step ahead to facilitate detecting the leveling at the end of the escalator.

Variation The learner may stand with one foot forward on the edge of the step ahead to easily detect the change in level and be prepared to step off the escalator.

STEP 7 Upon reaching the escalator landing, the learner takes a normal step forward, clearing quickly with congested-area constant-contact cane technique, and continues for several steps to get out of the way of other people coming off the escalator. The escalator landing can be confirmed when the cane tip or foot contacts the comb plate (the portion between the stationary floor plate and the moving step) at the end of the escalator. The learner may wish to lift her toes up slightly on approach to the comb plate.

Rationale The learner moves off and quickly clears the area to avoid congestion and to ensure an open area for traveling. Lifting the toes up slightly helps to reduce the chance of tripping on the comb plate and eases the transition of the foot moving onto the stationary landing.

CONSIDERATIONS FOR NEGOTIATING ESCALATORS

- If possible, begin with an escalator traveling up. Going up is less daunting for most people and it is easier to hear the escalator and the movement of the steps going up from the level where the learner is standing.

- If the learner is traveling with a guide, she may need to traverse the steps independently because of the narrow width, with the guide positioned behind her; or in front using a narrow-passageway guide technique. On wider escalators the guide positions the learner at the handrail and verbally indicates when the learner should begin the first step. Coordinating the first step is important and the guide can adjust his position once on the escalator, if needed.

- Some learners may have a fear of escalators, which may be alleviated with practice at times when the escalators are not busy, and by fully explaining the nature and characteristics of an escalator. If the learner is inexperienced with escalators, practice first using the escalator with the O&M specialist as a guide. While allaying their fears, learners also should be made aware of potential issues with untied shoelaces, long skirts, open-toed shoes, or dangling small items that can get caught in escalator treads.

- The learner should be aware of the movement patterns of escalators (toward or away, up or down) as well as their placement. For example, some department stores may place the up and down escalators on opposite sides of the center of the store while in larger areas, such as airports or hotel lobbies, escalators or moving walkways may be located alongside one another.

- At busy escalators the movement of other people can provide information about the escalator direction. However, when transit stations are noisy and busy it can sometimes be difficult to make these determinations.

- The learner should remain aware of her orientation while traveling on escalators.
- If the learner will be using the escalator frequently, she can establish landmarks for locating it in the future.
- Escalators are quite common in transit stations and in large shopping malls.
- Escalators are usually the easiest way to move from level to level, but they can be very crowded. Learners should practice contacting the escalator, boarding quickly, and walking a few feet forward to clear the escalator area when disembarking.

NEGOTIATING ELEVATORS

Purpose: To enable the learner to utilize elevators safely, efficiently, and independently.

PROCEDURE AT A GLANCE

1 The learner listens and looks for clues to the location of the elevator or bank of elevators. In unfamiliar buildings, security personnel or other individuals may provide directions.

2 The learner locates the elevator door and searches near the doorway for the appropriate button. She calls the elevator by pushing the upper button to go up or the lower button to go down.

3 The learner positions herself to one side of the elevator door.

4 The learner listens and looks for the elevator to arrive. There often is a small light that illuminates above the elevator that is arriving. Usually there is a voice announcement, "going up" or "going down," or one bell for up and two bells for down, when the elevator arrives. If the elevator is traveling in the direction the learner desires, the learner pauses, then enters using the congested-area touch technique.

5 The learner locates the button panel, usually on one or both sides of the door, determines the arrangement, and presses the appropriate button.

6 When the desired floor is reached, the learner verifies the floor number and exits quickly using the congested-area technique.

METHOD

STEP 1 The learner listens and looks for clues to the location of the elevator or bank of elevators, such as a bell, the sound of the door opening, or movement of pedestrians. When entering an unfamiliar building or hotel, security personnel or other individuals may be available to provide directions.

Rationale In most buildings the movement of others and the characteristic sounds of the elevator are available to assist in locating the elevator bank.

STEP 2 The learner locates the elevator door and searches near the doorway for the appropriate button to call the elevator. If there are several elevators, there may be just one button to summon an elevator, located on the wall between cars. The learner presses the upper button if she desires to go up and the lower button if she desires to go down.

Rationale The learner must find the elevator and the button to call the elevator. The learner presses the appropriate button to summon the elevator.

Variations The top and bottom floors of buildings usually have only one button for summoning the elevator.

Destination-control or destination-oriented elevators are being used in some larger high-rise buildings. They have only one keypad outside the bank of elevators (usually four elevator cars or more), on which users must enter the desired floor number. The display then shows a message, such as "Floor 15, use Elevator C." Destination-only elevators usually have accessible features (speech) that can be activated by pressing a certain key or key combination, but determining which elevator is "Elevator C" may require searching for labels on each elevator. Individuals who are blind may need familiarization to the specific features of those elevators to use them efficiently. There is no keypad inside the elevator; if a person gets on the wrong elevator, he or she must exit at the predetermined floor and reenter the desired floor number on the keypad.

STEP 3 The learner positions herself to one side of the elevator door.

Rationale The learner's position to one side will avoid congestion from people exiting the elevator.

Variation If there are two or more elevators, the learner should position herself between the elevators to facilitate entering the first available one.

STEP 4 The learner listens and looks for the elevator to arrive. There often is a small light above the elevator that indicates it is arriving. Usually there is a voice announcement, "going up" or "going down," or one bell for up and two bells for down, when the elevator arrives. If the elevator is traveling in the direction the learner desires, she pauses to allow people to exit the elevator, then enters the elevator using the congested-area touch technique.

Rationale The learner must be alert and aware because the elevator may only open for a few seconds on each floor. The learner pauses to allow riders to exit first. Using constant-contact technique increases safety by confirming the presence of the elevator compartment floor and detects any elevation changes between the elevator and the floor. On rare occasions an elevator encasement door may open when the elevator compartment is not present.

Variation See the variation under Step 2 for destination-control elevators.

STEP 5 The learner locates the button panel, usually on one or both sides of the door, determines the arrangement, and presses the appropriate button. Braille and large-print labels are required beside the elevator buttons and are available inside most elevators now.

Rationale Pressing the appropriate button enables the learner to reach the desired objective. The learner positions herself to allow enough room for other individuals to board easily.

Variation If other individuals are entering or are already inside the elevator, the learner may ask someone to push the button for the floor she desires.

STEP 6 When the desired floor is reached, the learner exits quickly using the congested-area cane technique. If other individuals are present, the learner can verify her floor number with them before exiting. If there are no other riders, the learner can trail her hand out the doorjamb—while still in the elevator—to find a braille and tactile number indicating the floor number, which should be mounted on the doorframe 60 inches above the floor.

Billie Louise Bentzen

Rationale The congested-area technique increases safety and minimizes contact with other individuals. The learner exits quickly because elevator doors often reclose quickly and she needs to clear the door area to allow others to enter. Tactile floor numbers are required on the doorjamb to enable individuals to confirm the floor before exiting. The number will be mounted just past the door and the door will bounce back if it starts to close while the learner's hand is extended in front of it.

Variation When alone in the elevator and still positioned near the button panel, the learner can keep her finger resting lightly on the button for the floor that she desires. Once the door opens, she can wait until the door begins to close and press the button a second time to confirm that the door is opening on the desired floor. If the door reopens, she has confirmed her destination and can quickly exit the elevator (Jacobson, 2013).

CONSIDERATIONS FOR NEGOTIATING ELEVATORS

- Destination-control or destination-oriented elevators are likely to become more common in larger buildings. See the variation under Step 2 for a description. O&M specialists may wish to find destination-control elevators in their area to familiarize themselves with the elevator features and introduce their learners to their use.

- Elevators are usually recessed in the wall and may be located near the main entrance of a building.

- Floor buttons inside the elevator may be arranged vertically or in two or more horizontal rows. The learner should note that other buttons, such as alarm, open door, close door, and emergency stop, are usually positioned on the same panel with the floor buttons. Elevator buttons are usually labeled in braille.

- The learner should be aware that most elevators have intercom systems or emergency telephones.

- Some learners may be fearful of the elevator door closing on them, so the O&M specialist should demonstrate how contact with the rubber casing on the door will prevent the door from closing.

- In most newer buildings, elevators either announce floors verbally or provide a tone as each floor is passed, so the learner can determine when she has reached the desired floor. If there are other passengers in the elevator, asking them may be easiest. If there are no other passengers, the learner can follows the variation described under Step 6. Alternatively, in buildings with fewer floors, the learner may push all the floor buttons and count each stop. However, if additional people get on, they may express impatience with the fact that each floor button has been pushed.

- If the learner will be using the elevator frequently, she can establish landmarks for locating it in the future.

NEGOTIATING REVOLVING DOORS

Purpose: To enable the learner to utilize revolving doors safely, efficiently, and independently.

	PROCEDURE AT A GLANCE
1	The learner utilizes audible, visual, and tactile clues to locate the revolving doors. If possible, the learner approaches the doors from the right side, parallel to and near the wall.
2	The learner trails the wall, using congested-area touch technique or touch-and-drag technique, with her cane in her right hand.
3	When the learner detects the opening, she positions herself so that her right shoulder is next to the revolving door encasement and she is facing toward the revolving doors, raises her left hand in upper-body protective technique to contact the revolving door, makes a right turn, and follows the door inward.
4	The learner trails the wall of the encasement with her cane, and when contact is lost she exits and resumes the preferred cane technique.

METHOD

STEP 1 The learner uses audible, visual, and tactile clues to locate the revolving doors. Temperature changes, pedestrian traffic, or landmarks can also be used to locate the revolving doors. If possible, the learner approaches the doors from the right side, parallel to and near the wall.

Rationale Approaching near the wall positions the learner away from pedestrian traffic and facilitates location of the door.

STEP 2 The learner trails the wall, using congested-area touch technique or touch-and-drag technique, with her cane in her right hand.

Rationale Trailing the wall facilitates locating the revolving doors and using congested-area touch technique reduces the chance of the cane tip getting caught in the revolving doors.

STEP 3 When the learner detects the opening, she positions herself so that her right shoulder is next to the revolving door encasement and she is angled toward the revolving doors. The sound of the rubber flap of the revolving doors contacting the encasement wall will make the opening more prominent. She raises her left hand in upper-body protective technique and contacts the revolving door, makes a right turn, and quickly follows the door inward. The learner may slide her hand down to locate the push bar of the door. The learner may choke up on the cane and hold it in a vertical position to facilitate movement while traversing the door.

Rationale Contacting the door with the left hand provides leverage for negotiating the door. The learner makes a right turn and quickly follows the door inward to maintain the door's rhythm and avoid pedestrian congestion. Revolving doors in the United States are generally set to revolve in a counterclockwise direction and the right turn inward ensures that the learner is going in the same direction that the door is moving.

Variation If the panels of the revolving door are not in motion, the learner quickly steps inside, locates the push bar, and applies pressure to negotiate the door. For revolving doors that are in constant motion, the learner may prefer to let several openings pass before stepping into the door to become familiar with the size and timing of the movement of the door. If so, she should be careful that her cane does not extend into the walkway or into the doorway area where it may get caught.

STEP 4 The learner trails the wall of the encasement with her cane, and when contact is lost she exits, quickly turning slightly to the right while using appropriate cane technique. Temperature, air pressure, and auditory clues may inform the learner that she has traversed the door.

Rationale The learner trails the wall of the encasement to detect the appropriate time to exit. The learner exits quickly to avoid pedestrian congestion and turns slightly to the right to reestablish her intended line of travel.

Variation The learner may utilize her right elbow or hand for trailing the inside of the revolving door.

CONSIDERATIONS FOR NEGOTIATING REVOLVING DOORS

- If possible, the learner should approach the door from the right side to avoid injury to herself or others who may be exiting on the left because of the door's counterclockwise movement.
- Revolving doors are usually located in larger buildings.
- Automatic or manually operated doors may be located on either side of the revolving door, and the learner may prefer to use them.
- When walking with a guide, because of the narrow width of the door opening, the learner may break contact and negotiate the door independently.
- Some learners may have fears of getting a hand trapped between the rubber flap and the wall. The learner should be introduced to revolving doors at a time when pedestrian traffic through the revolving door is light. After examining the door, the O&M specialist may push the door and have the learner negotiate it independently for practice.
- Some hotels have very large automatic revolving doors intended to accommodate several pedestrians and their rolling suitcases in each section.

Commercial Facilities

A major aspect of O&M and independent travel is accessing shops and other commercial facilities in order to purchase items, eat dinner out at a restaurant, go to a show, or attend a meeting. These activities usually involve locating the entry to the facility, traveling to a destination within the facility, and interacting with staff at the facility to purchase an item, gather additional information, or locate a seat.

The simplest type of facility for most learners is a small business with a doorway facing the sidewalk that has one or two clerks. This can be a convenience store, coffee shop, ice-cream shop, small clothing store, specialty shop, drugstore, or other similar small facility.

ACCESSING COMMERCIAL FACILITIES

Locating the Entrance

Purpose: To enable the learner to locate the doorway to a facility that she needs to visit.

PROCEDURE AT A GLANCE

1 The learner gathers basic information from a passerby or through a phone call to the business about its location.

2 When the learner is near the location, she trails the building line using constant-contact or touch-and-drag technique.

3 When the doorway is located, the learner turns toward the door and finds the handle or doorknob to open the door and enter the building.

METHOD

STEP 1 The learner gathers basic information from a passerby or through a phone call to the business about its location, including exact address, nearest cross street, location within the block, and any distinguishing features regarding the doorway or signage.

Rationale Calling the business provides direct information, which can be more effective than relying on maps or mapping programs or general knowledge of address systems. Details about the entrance features can help the learner locate the business more efficiently.

STEP 2 When the learner is near the location within the block where she expects to find the business, she trails the building line using constant-contact or touch-and-drag cane technique.

Rationale Trailing the building line allows the learner to contact each door and locate the destination without passing it by.

Variation In some situations the learner may use three-point-touch technique, lifting the cane tip slightly to tap the building, in order to hear the change in sound of a doorway—such as differentiating between a brick or concrete wall, wooden doorframe, and glass door—or trail the building with one hand while using the cane in the other hand to help distinguish textures and changes.

STEP 3 When the doorway is located, the learner turns toward the door and extends her cane arm. She positions her cane vertically against the door and moves it back and forth to locate the handle or doorknob. She may also use her other hand in upper-body protective technique. She opens the door to enter the building.

Rationale The learner turns toward the door to prepare to enter. She will usually find the handle more quickly by searching with the cane rather than her hand since handles may be located at different heights. Doors usually open outward toward the street and sidewalk and the upper-body protective technique is used to protect the head in case someone opens the door quickly when coming out of the building.

CONSIDERATIONS FOR LOCATING THE ENTRANCE

- The learner and O&M specialist can discuss common characteristics of entrances, such as doors recessed into the building line, a change in wall texture or color, a doormat, signs or planters located near the door, as well as possible cues provided by sounds, such as the door opening or closing. For some types of businesses or in some areas of the country, doors may be open in mild weather and sounds from inside the business or odors such as the smell of bread baking or coffee brewing may provide additional cues.
- At first, the O&M specialist may provide information about the destination to be located. After the learner has gained some experience, she can call the destination or ask a passerby and gain additional experience by asking appropriate questions to gather the necessary information.
- Some questions that may be asked in gathering information from the business include: What is your nearest cross street? Which side of [insert name of street] are you on? Are you near a corner or in the middle of the block? Is your entrance recessed (set back from building line)? Are there any planters, doormats, or signs near your entrance?
- O&M specialists and their learners can consider questions that can be asked of nearby pedestrians, or a bus driver as they disembark from the bus, to help locate the destination, such as: Can you help me find [business name]? Is that to my right [point in direction]? How many doors from this one? Or from this corner? (See the procedures for Soliciting Assistance earlier in this chapter).
- Finding the entrance is much more difficult at facilities like grocery stores, where the doors may face a parking lot rather than open onto a sidewalk. Various strategies may be employed to cross a parking lot, but learners will want to get as much information as possible ahead of time about the layout by calling

the facility or requesting additional information from nearby pedestrians, if available. Some parking lots have walkways to the storefront, which are sometimes just painted lines on the pavement; others have no designated place for pedestrians to walk. Trailing alongside a driveway, until close to the building, can work in some locations but may also lead to an area where trucks are parked and unloaded.

- As technology advances, the ability to preview routes on global positioning systems (GPS) and other devices or search for specific sites using the street view on online maps may make calling the destination less necessary. However, calling is a good way to confirm information gathered from other sources.
- A variety of apps are available in which learners may request assistance regarding current or desired locations from individuals who are trained to provide that information. The learner still needs to be able to ask pertinent questions to obtain the necessary information.

Entering a Business and Locating a Clerk or Other Personnel

Purpose: To enable the learner to appropriately and safely enter a store or business and locate the clerk or other personnel to assist.

PROCEDURE AT A GLANCE

1 The learner enters and checks with her cane to find a clear space just inside and to one side of the doorway.

2 The learner stops and listens for the sound of cash registers, conversations, or other indications of activity or store personnel.

3 If the sound is close by, the learner turns toward the sound and confirms that she has arrived at her destination by asking someone. If further away, she moves toward the sound or clue using congested-area technique while maintaining awareness of the location of the exit.

4 The learner travels independently or solicits assistance as necessary to complete her shopping or other task. She either follows the clerk or uses appropriate guide techniques, maintaining awareness of her location within the store.

METHOD

STEP 1 The learner enters and checks with her cane to find a clear space just inside and to one side of the doorway.

Rationale The learner needs to find a place that is not in the path of travel to be able to listen and orient herself before traveling further. There are often displays and various types of shelving near store entrances, so she should check with her cane before stepping to one side of the doorway.

STEP 2 The learner stops and listens for the sound of cash registers, conversations, or other indications of activity or store personnel.

Rationale The sound of a cash register or a conversation taking place can provide information about the location of store personnel.

STEP 3 If the sound is close by, the learner turns toward the sound and confirms that she has arrived at her destination by asking someone. If further away, she moves toward the sound or clue using congested-area technique while maintaining awareness of the location of the exit.

Rationale The learner first needs to confirm she is at her destination before continuing with any further tasks. Congested-area cane technique is used inside the store because there are often other shoppers, temporary or permanent merchandise displays, or narrow aisles bordered by shelves.

STEP 4 The learner travels independently or solicits assistance as necessary to complete her shopping or other task. If the task involves travel within the business, she may travel independently, follow the clerk, or use appropriate guide techniques. She maintains awareness of her location within the store and uses the door as a reference point for orientation.

Rationale The learner may ask store personnel to locate items in unfamiliar areas. She maintains awareness of her location to become familiar with the store layout and to be able to exit efficiently.

CONSIDERATIONS FOR ENTERING A BUSINESS AND LOCATING A CLERK OR OTHER PERSONNEL

- Learners who have had little independent experience of this type may benefit from discussion and role-playing methods to learn how to get the attention of store personnel and request appropriate assistance.

- At grocery stores or larger stores, such as department stores, the learner may need to travel around carts and other obstacles near the doorway, or travel across a wide aisle to get to a location where assistance is available. At grocery stores that a learner will frequent regularly, the learner may familiarize herself with the entrance area and location of customer service counters or other needed facilities, or request detailed directions before visiting.

- A variety of apps are available in which learners may request assistance regarding current or desired locations from individuals who are trained to provide that information. The trained individuals can describe the surroundings, identify shopping items, or even read price tags. The service is not free, but may be a viable option for some individuals.

- The learner can be encouraged to think about the type of business or facility she will be visiting and what features she may need to access or use, and develop a mental map of the relationships among those features. For example, at a hotel the learner will need to be able to travel from the front door to the registration desk, and then to the elevators in the lobby area. There may be other facilities that she makes use of, such as a restaurant or bar, waiting area, or the concierge desk, but the learner may orient to those facilities from one of the other reference points mentioned (e.g., door, elevator, registration desk). She also obviously needs to get to her room from the elevators as a separate orientation and travel task.

Drop-Off Lessons

Drop-off lessons are often used to assess learners' ability to establish orientation in an unfamiliar area, or in a familiar area from a disoriented state, and to locate an assigned objective, using previously taught O&M skills. Drop-off lessons also reinforce (for the learner's benefit) that properly applied O&M skills allow for greater travel independence. The cognitive process needed to complete a drop-off lesson involves integrating various points of information to establish the learner's possible location in relation to a desired destination or objective, verifying hypotheses related to her location, and eliminating alternatives as the learner analyzes the environment. These orientation processes are updated at various points as the learner travels—using appropriate techniques—and verifies existing ideas or gathers new information.

In the traditional drop-off lesson, a residential neighborhood with a regular grid pattern may be used. A grid area of approximately six square blocks with both one- and two-way streets with different traffic patterns and blocks that contain irregular construction patterns can be used to provide environmental variability for the learner to use for re-orientation. The grid should be bounded by streets with noticeable characteristics, such as heavy traffic or lack of sidewalks, to keep the learner from leaving the grid area.

Drop-off lessons are typically conducted in very familiar areas for the learner, where the learner has a thorough understanding of the geographic area in which the drop-off will take place, including:

- Boundaries of the area
- Traffic directionality of each street

- Traffic volume, which involves labeling each street with regard to the amount of traffic on that street (i.e., heavy, moderate, light)

- Knowledge of the traffic control and pattern of traffic movement at intersections

- Physical characteristics and general clues that might help the learner distinguish certain streets (e.g., lack of sidewalks, presence of parking meters, long or short blocks, presence or absence of traffic signals, or any other distinguishable physical landmarks)

DROP-OFF LESSONS

Purpose: To assess the learner's ability to establish orientation and to locate an assigned objective using previously taught O&M skills.

PROCEDURE AT A GLANCE

1 After disorienting the learner, the learner is brought to the starting point of the lesson, where the O&M specialist assigns her a destination or objective.

2 The learner stands still and uses all her senses to gather information that will aid in establishing initial orientation, then locates a sidewalk.

3 The learner gathers any available information regarding the location of surrounding streets, including traffic directionality, volume, traffic controls, signage, and other physical clues and characteristics to help in the identification of the street along which she is standing.

4 The learner hypothesizes the direction to travel along the sidewalk to reach an intersection and walks to an intersection.

5 At the intersection, the learner gathers information and attempts to name the possible intersection(s).

6 The learner walks in the direction in which she feels the objective is located, listening to traffic and examining landmarks as needed or desired to confirm or reject the hypothesis.

7 At the next intersection, the learner analyzes the intersection and the information she knows about the area. If the intersection characteristics match what the learner expected, she continues toward her objective. If observations at this intersection are not consistent with her expectations, she reevaluates the information gathered so far and replans the route to her objective based on the new information.

8 The learner continues with Steps 4–7 until the objective is located and the learner verifies that she has reached her assigned destination.

METHOD

STEP 1 After disorienting the learner, the learner is brought to the starting point of the drop-off lesson, where the O&M specialist assigns her a destination or objective. The O&M specialist uses a variety of distractions to ensure that the learner is disoriented before beginning the drop-off lesson. The starting point for the drop-off may be on the sidewalk or in a parking lot or other non-sidewalk area, depending on the skill level of the learner.

Rationale Since the drop-off lesson is intended to test the learner's skill at reorienting herself, initial disorientation is needed. The destination is assigned after arrival at the starting point to make it more difficult for the learner to figure out details or study the area in advance.

STEP 2 The learner stands still and uses all her senses to gather information that will aid in establishing initial orientation. She locates a sidewalk (if she is not on a sidewalk) by using traffic sounds, systematic search patterns, or other strategies, such as used in street-corner familiarization or in recovery from a veer (see Chapters 6 and 7).

Rationale Determining the location of the street and finding the sidewalk are the first steps needed to reach the learner's destination. Starting on the sidewalk is a safe location to gather other available information for orientation purposes.

STEP 3 The learner gathers any available information regarding the location of surrounding streets, including traffic directionality, volume, traffic controls, signage, and other physical clues and characteristics to help in the identification of the street along which she is standing.

Rationale While standing on the sidewalk, the learner can use a variety of sensory information to learn more about nearby streets, which can further confirm her relative location and lead to a data-informed hypothesis about which direction to travel along the sidewalk.

STEP 4 The learner hypothesizes the direction to travel along the sidewalk in order to reach an intersection for further information gathering for orientation purposes. She walks in one direction along the sidewalk—noting any usable landmarks or characteristics of the sidewalk that may help identify her location—until she reaches the intersection.

Rationale The learner needs to move to another location in order to gather additional information to identify the location and determine a route to travel to her destination. Intersections usually have distinct traffic patterns that can provide additional location information.

STEP 5 At the intersection, the learner gathers information and attempts to name the possible intersection(s) at which she might be located. Through available clues, the learner should make an educated guess about the intersection at which she is located.

Rationale By figuring out the nature of an intersection, the learner can begin to reasonably deduce her possible position within the area.

STEP 6 The learner sets out to prove or disprove her location hypothesis by walking in the direction in which she feels the objective is located, listening to traffic and examining landmarks as needed or desired to confirm the hypothesis along the way.

Rationale Walking in the expected direction of her objective allows the learner to gather additional information to confirm or reject her hypothesis.

STEP 7 Upon arriving at the next intersection, the learner analyzes the intersection and reviews the information she knows about the area. If the intersection characteristics match what the learner expected, she continues toward her objective. If her observations at this intersection are not consistent with her expectations, she reevaluates the information gathered so far and replans the route to her objective based on the new information.

Rationale By gathering additional information at the next intersection, the learner has further details that she can use to confirm that she is headed toward her destination. The features need to be reevaluated to determine if her hypothesis about the location is correct and to further inform her next steps in traveling to the destination.

STEP 8 **The learner continues with Steps 4–7 until the objective is located and the learner verifies that she has reached her assigned destination.**

Rationale The learner needs to reevaluate the intersections and landmarks at each decision point as she travels to the destination to confirm that she is on the correct route. Repeating these steps will allow the learner to gather more information about her current location in order to plan a route to reach her objective.

CONSIDERATIONS FOR DROP-OFF LESSONS

- The difficulty of the drop-off lesson should be dictated by the ability and confidence of the learner. For example, a learner who lacks confidence can be given an easy drop-off in order to build her skill set and self-image.
- Drop-off lessons can also be completed in home, school, or indoor community locations. Orientation skills must also be reinforced in irregular grid patterns and indoor environments. Some large school or university campuses are extremely complex and a well-timed drop-off lesson can help the learner to apply orientation skills in an environment in which she will be traveling frequently. These drop-offs would follow the same general format described.
- The O&M specialist can attempt to disorient the learner on the way to the starting point of the drop-off lesson by driving the learner on a route with many turns, talking to the learner while traveling to the location, playing the radio, and stopping occasionally.
- During the drop-off lesson, the O&M specialist usually remains a good distance away from the learner to allow her freedom of movement, moving close to the learner only when a dangerous situation is anticipated. However, for some learners, anxiety may be reduced if the O&M specialist checks in with the learner at predetermined times, or if they prearrange a signal to use for when the learner feels overwhelmed by the task.
- Drop-off lessons may also be conducted in less familiar areas, challenging the learner to analyze new intersections, solicit information from other pedestrians or shopkeepers, and figure out a new location and route. This type of drop-off lesson may overlap with route-planning lessons, possibly moving from a more familiar area to a less familiar one.
- Practicing orientation questions can support skills for soliciting assistance during independent travel (see Soliciting Assistance earlier in this chapter). By integrating this skill within the drop-off lesson, real-life situations as well as O&M and communication skills can be practiced. However, some O&M specialists plan for drop-off lessons in which the learner is not allowed to solicit assistance during the drop-off. By doing so, the O&M specialist ensures that the learner doesn't travel the entire route with a guide and encourages the learner to engage in independent problem-solving during the lesson. In some situations, the O&M specialist may allow the learner to solicit assistance once during the drop-off, as long as the learner doesn't allow the individual to physically assist her.
- Giving the learner a "phone-a-friend" (O&M specialist) card to be used during the drop-off lesson can add an element of fun and strategy. The learner may ask only five yes-or-no questions on the call and should be prompted in advance of the types of questions that can be asked. The phone-a-friend variation enables learners to integrate mainstream technology into their travel and may reduce levels of anxiety for some learners.
- On days when travel to an outdoor area is not possible, route-planning activities or verbal drop-off lessons can be used for problem-solving practice. The O&M specialist may present verbal drop-offs, in which he may describe a hypothetical situation within the grid area and ask the learner how she would react. These practice opportunities can be used in preparation for an actual drop-off lesson.

■ In route planning and traveling or in drop-off lessons, it may be helpful for the O&M specialist and learner to record the lesson. This will assist the learner in recalling and understanding the experiences she encountered and facilitate further discussions of the lessons.

TRAVEL IN AREAS WITHOUT SIDEWALKS (RURAL OR SUBURBAN)

Walking along Roadways without Sidewalks

Purpose: To enable the learner to travel safely along streets where there is no sidewalk.

	PROCEDURE AT A GLANCE
1	The learner positions herself along the side of the roadway, facing oncoming parallel traffic (on the left in the United States), and aligns herself parallel to the edge of the roadway and traffic movement.
2	The learner walks on the roadway, close to the edge, using constant-contact or touch-and-drag technique.
3	The learner mentally projects a straight line of travel and maintains orientation.
4	As a vehicle approaches, the learner stops, checks the terrain at the edge of the road, and then steps out of the roadway.
5	After the vehicle has passed, the learner repositions herself, as in Step 1, and continues.

METHOD

STEP 1 The learner positions herself along the side of the roadway, facing oncoming parallel traffic (on the left in the United States), and aligns herself parallel to the edge of the roadway and traffic movement. She uses her cane to explore the features of the edge of the roadway.

Janet M. Barlow

Rationale Facing traffic conforms with traffic laws in most states and provides a better opportunity for drivers to see the learner's long cane. The learner explores the edge features of the roadway to be prepared for travel; some locations have curbs along the roadway and some are an irregular junction of dirt and grass, occasional ditches, and the roadway pavement.

Variation It may be necessary for the learner to walk for short distances with her back to traffic in order to reach an appropriate crossing point or to find a destination. She should be aware that drivers will not see her long cane and should plan to step off the roadway when a car approaches in the near lane.

STEP 2 The learner walks on the roadway, close to the edge, using constant-contact or touch-and-drag cane technique.

Rationale Constant-contact or touch-and-drag cane technique helps the learner keep a consistent distance close to the edge of the roadway and provides tactile information about uneven terrain.

STEP 3 The learner mentally projects a straight line of travel and maintains orientation, particularly paying attention to curves or turns.

Rationale If the learner does not maintain good orientation, she may, without realizing it, follow a rounded corner and begin walking on a different street.

STEP 4 As a vehicle approaches, the learner stops, checks the terrain at the edge of the road, and then steps out of the roadway.

Rationale Moving off the roadway provides more clearance for the vehicle. It is also important to check the area the learner is about to step onto to ensure that she is not stepping off into a ditch.

Variation If the lanes of the roadway seem wide, vehicles are not too close, and traffic movement is slow, the learner may choose to stop and hold her position within the roadway, close to the edge of the street, as the vehicle passes.

STEP 5 After the vehicle has passed, the learner repositions herself, as in Step 1, and continues moving along the roadway.

Rationale Repositioning in relation to the roadway provides an opportunity to reorient and realign before walking further.

CONSIDERATIONS FOR WALKING ALONG ROADWAYS WITHOUT SIDEWALKS

- Some very busy roads with signalized crossings do not have sidewalks and there may be times these techniques are needed to travel a short distance to a bus stop or other destination. Other locations without sidewalks may include residential subdivisions with very little traffic.

- Some locations without sidewalks, particularly suburban neighborhoods, may have a curb and gutter that are intersected by many driveways. The curb may be what is usually referred to as a rolled curb, which allows cars to drive over it. These curbs are slightly rounded and raised about 3 inches, as opposed to a 6-inch-high right-angle curb at the edge of the street.

- The edge of the street, usually called the shoulder by traffic engineers, may be irregular and may contain a deep rut at the edge of the pavement caused by water or vehicle tires running off the road, particularly on curves and hills.

Determining Street-Crossing Location without Sidewalks or Curb Ramps

Purpose: To enable the learner to determine where to begin crossing while maintaining orientation when there is no sidewalk or curb ramp.

	PROCEDURE AT A GLANCE
1	The learner detects a corner or a consistent, sharp curve of the street edge that indicates a cross street.
2	The learner follows the street edge until she is at a 90-degree angle from her original path of travel.
3	The learner turns and squares off to the edge of the street.
4	The learner evaluates traffic as described in Chapter 7, uses appropriate methods to decide when to begin crossing, and crosses.
5	After contacting the opposite edge of the street, the learner realigns with the edge of the street, as described in Steps 1 and 2 of the previous procedure on Walking along Roadways without Sidewalks.

METHOD

STEP 1 The learner detects a corner or a consistent, sharp curve of the street edge that indicates a cross street.

Rationale Detecting the street is the first step before crossing. Changes in the street edge need to be identified or the learner may veer from her planned travel route and walk into a lane of traffic or down the wrong street.

STEP 2 The learner follows the street edge until she is at a 90-degree angle from her original path of travel.

Rationale Traveling around the corner positions the learner to align more accurately to cross. Crossing just as the street begins to curve away can result in angling out and into the parallel street.

Variation At a familiar location or where there is adequate traffic to use as an alignment cue, the learner may choose to cross without traveling around the corner and squaring off.

STEP 3 The learner turns and squares off with her back to the edge of the street.

Rationale Squaring off with the edge of the street helps the learner to turn back to face her original travel direction in preparation for crossing the street. Usually the curb can be used for alignment at this point.

STEP 4 The learner evaluates traffic as described in Chapter 7, uses appropriate methods to decide when to start crossing, and crosses. If her position seems too far around the corner to be adequately visible to drivers and to be able to hear approaching cars, she may need to move back around the corner to be closer to parallel traffic.

Rationale Traffic on streets without sidewalks varies and the intersection must be appropriately analyzed to determine when it is safe to cross. If the learner is positioned too far around the corner from the parallel street, it can be dangerous due to limited visibility and lack of anticipation on the part of drivers, particularly if there is a lot of traffic.

STEP 5 After contacting the opposite edge of the street, the learner realigns with the edge of the intended street, as described in Steps 1 and 2 of the previous section on Walking along Roadways without Sidewalks.

Rationale The learner needs to reorient herself and align close to the edge of the street to continue on her route.

CONSIDERATIONS FOR DETERMINING STREET-CROSSING LOCATION WITHOUT SIDEWALKS OR CURB RAMPS

- Some very busy roads with signalized crossings do not have sidewalks and there may be times these techniques are needed to travel a short distance to a bus stop or other destination. Other locations without sidewalks may include residential subdivisions with very little traffic.
- Recognizing the difference between a driveway and cross street may require practice for some learners and in some areas, depending if they have similar widths or textures. Design can vary greatly in different parts of the country. Driveways often slope up slightly from the street while a cross street will generally be at the same level. Driveways may or may not be paved.
- Using an accessible GPS device may help in identifying approaching cross streets. In some cases, the compass of the device or a separate compass may provide information that can be helpful for aligning. Learners should recognize that accuracy can vary and that it might be necessary to start moving in a certain direction to get an accurate reading of direction.

Travel in Adverse Weather

Adverse weather, including winter conditions such as snow and ice, rain, wind, and fog, and extreme heat and hot weather can affect travel and may require modification of some techniques described in this book. In addition, the O&M specialist may need to consider adaptations to lessons, and both the learner and O&M specialist must consider and be prepared with appropriate clothing for the weather conditions. O&M lessons may continue regardless of weather conditions for the learner to understand how to deal with different environments. (See Kim, Wall Emerson, & Gaves, 2016, for recommendations about cane tips that are most effective in snow conditions and Couturier & Ratelle, 2010, and Wall, 2001, for more detailed information about travel in adverse weather.)

Personal Safety

Personal safety is an area of concern for many learners and their family members, and it should be discussed in O&M lessons. Some individuals express resistance to using a cane, saying they think they are more of a target when using a cane. There are resources (David, Kollmar, & McCall, 1998) as well as personal safety and self-defense courses available

for individuals who are blind. Learners can benefit from a discussion of their concerns and thinking through personal safety issues ahead of time. Planning routes on well-traveled streets and knowing which businesses may provide assistance are two obvious strategies.

Tips for Teaching Special-Situation Lessons
Integrating Orientation

Skillful questioning and use of information gathered when soliciting assistance is an essential part of orientation and reorientation in a variety of environments and special situations. In instances where directions provided by the general public may not be specific enough to provide the information needed by the learner, follow-up questions and clarifications are often necessary and important to staying oriented and using the information efficiently. Shopping or utilizing escalators, elevators, or revolving doors all include orientation elements.

Drop-off lessons are intended to provide opportunities to integrate orientation and O&M skills and can be inserted at various points in the learner's O&M program. While drop-offs have traditionally been used as a concluding lesson in an area, they can also act as motivators for learners or used as confidence-building opportunities. In any case, drop-off lessons can help develop problem-solving skills in learners. Although the procedure described refers to blocks and intersections, the O&M specialist can design drop-off lessons in other environments, such as a school campus or a shopping mall.

When traveling in rural or suburban areas without sidewalks, orientation may be more challenging, especially if traffic is not available or consistent enough to provide alignment cues. The learner will need to pay careful attention to slight turns of the roadway and other orientation cues, such as the sun or prominent landmarks. Electronic orientation aids and digital maps can be helpful in establishing and maintaining orientation in rural and suburban areas when connectivity is available.

Sequencing

The lessons in this chapter are intended to be incorporated into an O&M program as needed or desired by the O&M specialist and learner. For example, some learners will need instruction in the use of elevators or escalators early in their program due to the facilities they visit or their school or work environments. Others may benefit from early instruction in travel without sidewalks because of the location of their home. Soliciting assistance and drop-off lessons may be revisited several times in different environments and travel situations throughout the course of an O&M program.

O&M Specialist Positioning

When teaching the learner skills needed for soliciting assistance, the O&M specialist should be positioned in a manner that does not communicate to the public that he is working with the learner. Whether that may include standing a slight distance from the learner or taking a nonchalant and disinterested stance while remaining close to the learner, the O&M specialist must be inconspicuous in order for the general public to interact freely and naturally with the learner.

Teaching O&M for special situations such as escalators or elevators provides unique challenges in busy or congested areas. O&M specialists may need to be positioned close to learners to ensure they are not separated when stepping onto a crowded escalator or elevator. Initial instruction may need to be

planned for a time when minimal pedestrian traffic is expected.

Inclement weather also poses challenges for the O&M specialist in terms of positioning. For example, rainy weather may make it difficult for the O&M specialist and learner to hear each other, especially if the learner is wearing a raincoat with a hood or carrying an umbrella. Wet pavement can also increase the noise level of vehicle tires and may require the O&M specialist to remain closer to the learner on street-crossing lessons.

Rural and suburban areas without sidewalks may require the O&M specialist to vary his position based on how flat or level the terrain may be or how much room he may have to walk alongside the road. The same general principles for street crossings should apply, including avoiding positioning that might block the learner's visual or auditory information.

Regardless of the technique being presented or reviewed, O&M specialists must always be positioned so that they are physically and mentally able to react to the environment on behalf of their learners, based on their learners' abilities, ages, and physical capabilities. The goal is to encourage learners to problem solve and react with increasing independence to the travel environment. Ultimately, learners will have independent travel experiences so they must learn to deal with unexpected situations in dynamic travel environments. O&M specialists should collaborate with learners and their families—making sure to operate within school or agency risk-management policies—to ensure that learners have a full repertoire of appropriate travel experiences to prepare them for increased levels of independence.

Strategies for Different Populations

Learners Who Have Low Vision
Learners who have low vision can be encouraged to practice visual skills such as systematic scanning to locate areas where they may be able to solicit assistance from various individuals, such as customer service kiosks, bus stops, or storefronts. Learners can practice visually identifying environmental features associated with elevators, including locating and using the call button or reading the floor numbers on the panel buttons. Exploring a variety of elevator layouts can help the learner who has low vision to generalize primary and secondary areas to look for

important information such as where to find the floor number to visually confirm she is exiting the elevator at the correct floor. This can include observing illuminated information located above the elevator doors or examining high-contrast, tactile numbers on the doorframe. Learners can practice visually tracking people as they use the escalator and learn to identify the direction of the escalator visually. In travel in areas without sidewalks, visual skills for locating landmarks or tracing a hedge to follow a line of travel can assist with orientation and safety.

Low vision devices, including handheld magnifiers and monocular telescopes, can be incorporated into lessons for negotiating elevators to help orient the learner to a specific elevator that will be used frequently or to analyze a variety of elevators for concept development and greater exploration. These same devices can be used effectively in stores and shopping malls to view signage and packaging information.

Age Differences

For young learners, early experiences in soliciting assistance may start with familiar adults in school and community environments. By interacting with familiar adults initially, learners can practice the type of questions to ask and how to clarify information, building their confidence for future experiences with less-familiar individuals. O&M specialists can prepare school personnel for O&M lessons that will incorporate interpersonal and communication skills in gathering information from others, and let them know what types of questions may be asked. For example, asking the cafeteria staff what is on the menu for lunch is a meaningful question that holds immediate relevance for the young learner. These types of interactions can be integrated into a learner's daily or weekly routine to help build a foundation for later requests for information and assistance in the community.

Young learners may need concept development to understand the mechanics and layouts of escalators and elevators; creating or obtaining a three-dimensional model may be helpful. On occasion, when elevators or escalators are being serviced in a mall or office building, learners may be able to see or touch some of the internal mechanisms to gain a better understanding of the parts required to run an elevator or escalator.

In preparation for drop-off lessons, O&M specialists will need to create lessons that are highly motivating for younger learners, such as building a map together of familiar or unfamiliar blocks, planning treasure hunts, or creating challenges for small groups of young learners to embark upon together, as a lead-up to a semi-independent drop-off lesson. (For further ideas and information about teaching O&M to children, see Fazzi & Naimy, 2010; Fazzi & Petersmeyer, 2001; Knott, 2002.)

Teens may also need prompting or reinforcement for interacting with others in the community. O&M specialists can provide them with general locales where they may be able to solicit assistance from various people as well as sample scripted questions to build their confidence.

Adult learners may be interested in exploring apps for trained assistance. It is useful for travelers to have ready access to such technology and resources so they can quickly and easily access them while traveling.

Older adults, who may have mobility and balance concerns, may not be able to travel safely during inclement weather due to a fear of slipping, or in areas without sidewalks due to the uneven footing. O&M specialists may need to familiarize older learners with using paratransit or other transportation services that might be available in their community. These services usually require advanced planning for travel and may be somewhat limited in rural areas. Older adults living in rural areas may also need to utilize delivery services for groceries and pharmaceuticals. Older adults living in an assisted-living facility may need to ask for assistance for orientation. O&M specialists can work with facility personnel to assist them in providing good orientation information to learners with visual impairments who reside there.

Learners with Additional Disabilities

Learners with additional disabilities may benefit from a variety of assistive technologies that promote as much independent travel as is desired and possible. For example, a learner who uses a hearing aid may need adjustments based on the noise levels in the travel environment, such as at a loud mall or arcade. O&M specialists will need to work with learners, families, and audiologists to ensure that learners maximize their use of hearing for travel in special situations.

Learners who use communication cards or devices may need to have their phrases and communication requests expanded to include brief statements and questions that can be applied to travel in special situations, such as, "Can you help me with my shopping list?" for soliciting assistance from a store clerk prior to handing him the list of items, or "I don't need help, thank you" for declining assistance when negotiating drop-offs. Learners with a hearing impairment may also use a video-relay service to communicate with others via telephone. (For a discussion of assistive technology in O&M for learners with hearing loss, see Lolli, Sauerburger, & Bourquin, 2010; and Pogrund et al., 2012.)

Learners who use mobility devices for balance or to aid with limited physical stamina may need additional practice in negotiating elevators and escalators. Depending on the type of mobility device being used, the learner may want to avoid escalators altogether and seek out elevators. Learners who use wheelchairs may want to practice making a 180-degree turn after entering an elevator, while remaining cognizant of others who may be sharing the elevator space. The panel of elevator buttons is usually positioned at a height that learners who use wheelchairs can easily reach. Travel in areas without sidewalks presents an additional mobility challenge for learners who use mobility devices. Learners may easily get their wheels stuck in drainage areas that are often found to the side of the road. O&M specialists may need to familiarize learners with using paratransit or other transportation services that might be available in their community. These services usually require advanced planning for travel and may be somewhat limited in rural areas. Learners living in rural areas may also need to utilize delivery services for groceries and pharmaceuticals. (See Rosen & Crawford, 2010, for a discussion of O&M for learners with physical impairments.)

Learners with intellectual or learning disabilities who have challenges with memory functions may benefit from a memory aid during travel in special situations. For example, homemade flip maps with photos or tactile cues representing a sequence of landmarks can be used to help a learner with orientation during travel at a mall. Commercially available recording and memory devices can serve a similar purpose. Mainstream technologies such as smartphones also have apps or tools for taking notes or setting points of interest that can be used to further enhance travel. (For additional ideas and strategies for teaching O&M to learners with additional disabilities, see Ambrose-Zaken, Calhoon, & Keim, 2010; Herrera, Cmar, & Fazzi, 2016; Lolli et al., 2010; and Rosen & Crawford, 2010.)

Self-Advocacy

Learning to solicit information and assistance when needed, and to politely and assertively refuse assistance and end conversations with strangers, are important self-advocacy skills that learners will need to develop during travel in special situations and as they begin to interact with individuals in the community with whom they are not familiar. Knowing how much assistance is desired of another person is a matter of personal choice and risk assessment. Some learners will have the confidence and prior experience necessary to interact with and maintain appropriate boundaries with other individuals they may encounter. O&M specialists can work with learners to understand how moments of disorientation, such as those that may be experienced during a drop-off lesson, may attract greater interaction with the public than other aspects of travel. Being prepared to interact in these situations, through role-play and practice, can help learners advocate for themselves.

10

Travel Techniques for Learners Who Have Low Vision

Ideas and suggestions for teaching orientation and mobility (O&M) techniques to learners who have low vision have been incorporated throughout earlier chapters of this book, as the coordinated use of vision in conjunction with hearing, other senses, and use of the long cane are essential to O&M instruction for many learners. This chapter is intended to provide a supplement to those earlier chapters and variations, considerations, and tips for teaching that have been addressed throughout. While many of the O&M techniques have important similarities for learners who are blind and learners who have low vision, the skills addressed in this chapter provide greater detail, procedures, and possible sequencing for O&M specialists to teach visual skills that may supplement and fundamentally benefit independent travel for learners who have low vision.

Basic Low Vision Skills

Learners who have low vision may benefit from various levels of instruction in, and selective use of, guide techniques, protective techniques, and hand trailing in conjunction with cane techniques. The techniques chosen for any given situation depend on the learner's ability to visually interact with the

travel environment under changing conditions and should to be assessed on an individual basis. (See Chapters 3 and 4 for detailed procedures that can be used to teach these techniques, along with strategies for incorporating use of vision.) A unit on basic skills, which is typically conducted indoors, can also be a perfect time to work on visual skills that learners can then apply throughout their O&M training. Visual spotting (using visual cues to detect an object that can be used as a reference point or examined for more detail), localization (aligning visual gaze with a desired object to perceive the object in relation to the location of other objects), *tracing* (following single or multiple stationary lines in the environment), *tracking* (following a moving object), and systematic visual scanning, while stationary or while moving, are useful in both indoor and outdoor environments and can be integrated with use of the long cane for many learners who have low vision. Eccentric viewing is a useful visual skill for learners who have a central *visual field* loss (the area seen when looking straight ahead) or *scotoma* (blind spot) and need to look around that area in their field of vision during travel. Once visual skills are refined, magnification devices like monocular telescopes can be introduced and used for specific tasks during travel, such as reading street signs or viewing traffic signals.

SCANNING

Systematic Scanning: Static Procedure for Open Areas

Purpose: To enable the learner to use a systematic approach to visually scan an open area while standing still in order to determine the overall layout or the location of key points of interest.

PROCEDURE AT A GLANCE

1 The learner visually traces a stationary line that follows a given pattern.

2 The learner applies the same scanning pattern on a wall, whiteboard, or other flat surface to search for desired items posted on the surface.

3 The learner uses the same scanning pattern in a regularly shaped open space to search for desired items found in the area.

4 The learner uses the same scanning pattern in an open space that is irregularly shaped to search for desired items found in the area.

METHOD

STEP 1 The learner visually traces a stationary line that follows a given pattern. The overall pattern can initially be illustrated with a high-contrast line drawn on a note card so that the learner can readily follow it and refer to it as needed. Sample static scanning patterns that can be used to view open spaces are depicted in Sidebar 10.1.

Rationale Visually tracing a stationary line enables the learner to practice the scanning pattern before applying it to an open area that may be more visually complex to view and more challenging to maintain

---

Sidebar 10.1

Static Scanning Patterns for Open Spaces

Horizontal Grid Pattern
Starting from the left side and top of the open area, the learner follows an imaginary line or physical feature across to the right side of the open area, lowers the point slightly before following an imaginary line back to the left, then lowers the point again and follows the line back to the right. The pattern is repeated until the full open area has been surveyed and important elements of the environment viewed in sequence.

Vertical Grid Pattern
Starting from the left side and bottom of the open area, the learner follows an imaginary line or physical feature up to the top of the area, moves the visual line slightly toward the right before following an imaginary line back to the bottom,

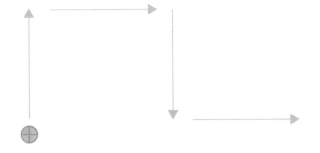

Sidebar 10.1

then moves the visual line to the right and follows the line back up to the top. The pattern is repeated until the full open area has been surveyed and important elements of the environment viewed in sequence.

Full Grid Pattern
Combines the horizontal and vertical grid patterns into one full view of the open area.

Linear Overlap
Starting from the left side of the open area and dividing the space into four segments, the

learner overlaps views as he shifts his gaze to the next area of the open space until the entire open space has been surveyed and important elements of the environment viewed in sequence.

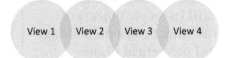

for the exact pattern. Using a systematic pattern in an open space can be more challenging because there may be no natural lines to follow or there may be visual distractions that cause the learner to lose track of the intended pattern.

STEP 2 To practice the skill, the learner applies the same scanning pattern on a wall, whiteboard, or other flat surface to search for desired items posted on the surface.

Rationale Learning and practicing a static scanning pattern on a wall, whiteboard, or other flat surface enables the learner to apply the scanning pattern to a more complex area with greater confidence. The O&M specialist can hang, write, or post items on the surface to better assess how effective the learner is in using the scanning pattern.

STEP 3 The learner uses the same scanning pattern in a regularly shaped open space, such as a classroom, conference room, or enclosed yard, to search for desired items found in the area.

Rationale Starting in an open space that has a regular shape will enable the learner to apply the scanning pattern more easily.

STEP 4 The learner uses the same scanning pattern in an open space that is irregularly shaped, busy, or cluttered, such as a lobby, arena, or restaurant, to search for desired items found in the area.

Rationale Many open areas are irregularly shaped; scanning patterns should be practiced in such areas so the learner can generalize the skill to a variety of areas. Once the learner can apply the scanning pattern to a variety of open areas, he will have greater ability to use the technique in daily situations that may arise.

Systematic Scanning: Static Procedure to Search for Vertical and Horizontal Objects

Purpose: To enable the learner to use a systematic approach to visually scan an area while standing still to locate objects of interest that may be oriented along a horizontal or vertical plane.

PROCEDURE AT A GLANCE

1 The learner uses a static scanning pattern by visually tracing a stationary line that follows the desired pattern; that is, a vertical pattern for objects to be found along a horizontal plane and a horizontal pattern for objects to be found along a vertical plane.

2 The learner practices the same scanning pattern on a wall, whiteboard, or other flat surface to search for desired items posted on the surface.

3 The learner uses the same scanning pattern in a regularly shaped, well-lit open space to search for vertical and horizontal items found in the area.

4 The learner uses the same scanning pattern in an open space that is irregularly shaped to search for desired items found in the area.

METHOD

STEP 1 The learner uses a static scanning pattern by visually tracing a stationary line that follows the desired pattern; that is, a vertical pattern for objects to be found along a horizontal plane and a horizontal pattern for objects to be found along a vertical plane (see Sidebar 10.1 for sample scanning patterns).

Rationale The scanning pattern can be readily taught by having the learner visually trace a stationary line that outlines the desired pattern. Using a vertical pattern for objects to be found along a horizontal plane, such as street signs, addresses, and tabletops or countertops, increases the likelihood that the object will be found and not skipped over. Using a horizontal pattern for objects to be found along a vertical plane, such as traffic control signs, traffic signals and signal poles, and doors and doorways, increases the likelihood that the object will be found and not skipped over.

STEP 2 The learner practices the same scanning patterns on a wall, whiteboard, or other flat surface to search for desired vertical and horizontal items posted on the surface.

Rationale Learning and practicing static vertical and horizontal scanning patterns prior to scanning in open areas to locate objects enables the learner to refine the skill and build confidence prior to applying the pattern in a more complex area.

STEP 3 The learner uses the same scanning patterns in regularly shaped, well-lit open spaces to search for vertical and horizontal items found in the area. Indoor environments with good lighting and contrast may be a good starting place, and a combination of two- and three-dimensional items can be searched for. As learners become more proficient, the skills can be applied in outdoor areas and areas with less ideal lighting and contrast.

Rationale Applying visual skills in areas that are regularly shaped and have good lighting and contrast helps to promote success with visual scanning lessons early on.

STEP 4 The learner uses the same vertical and horizontal scanning pattern in spaces that are irregularly shaped, busy, or cluttered, such as a lobby, arena, park, or restaurant, to search for desired vertical and horizontal items found in the area.

Rationale Once the learner can apply the scanning pattern in a variety of open areas, he will have greater ability to use the technique in daily travel situations.

Systematic Scanning: Dynamic Patterns for Visual Planning While Walking

Purpose: To enable the learner to use a systematic and dynamic approach to visually scan and preview the travel environment ahead, while walking, to plan a path of travel between and around objects in the environment and to increase the distance at which he consistently identifies overhangs, obstacles, and drop-offs.

PROCEDURE AT A GLANCE

1. While stationary, the learner uses a three-level vertical scanning pattern by looking at head-level, mid-level, and lower-level areas.

2. The learner describes what is seen at head-level, mid-level, and lower-level areas.

3. The learner incorporates three-level vertical scanning with the use of the long cane while moving forward and negotiating obstacles along the travel path.

4. The learner scans to the left and right as needed for perpendicular walkways, driveways, or pedestrians approaching from the side.

METHOD

STEP 1 While stationary, the learner uses a three-level vertical scanning pattern by looking at head-level, mid-level, and lower-level areas (Ludt & Goodrich, 2002). The pattern is repeated from top to bottom and then bottom to top. At each level, the learner looks as far into the distance as he can resolve images in the area.

Rationale The three-level vertical scanning ensures that the learner has a consistent *field of view* and focuses vision in the distance at each level to identify overhangs, obstacles, and drop-offs from the furthest distance possible. The pattern goes from top to bottom and bottom to top to ensure there are no gaps in what is being viewed.

STEP 2 The learner describes what is seen at head-level, mid-level, and lower-level areas. In some instances, the learner may recognize changes in lighting or shadows that may be interpreted as obstacles or changes in surface level as he gets closer to the object to resolve the image.

Rationale By describing what is seen at each level, the learner can focus more energy on resolving images and the O&M specialist can assess the distance and accuracy at which the learner is able to recognize overhangs or obstacles at mid-level and changes in surface level.

STEP 3 The learner incorporates three-level vertical scanning with the use of the long cane while moving forward and negotiating obstacles along the travel path.

Rationale Incorporating the use of the long cane provides the learner with consistent information for immediate surface preview, including level and texture changes, freeing the learner to use three-level vertical scanning to preview the travel path in advance and select a clear path for travel as he detects and negotiates around obstacles.

STEP 4 The learner scans to the left and right as needed for perpendicular walkways, driveways, or pedestrians approaching from the side.

Rationale While the three levels of vertical scanning can be sufficient to confirm visual information to the left and right sides of the learner at greater distances, a purposeful scan to the left and right is indicated when there is an immediate possibility of intersecting pedestrian movement from either side, which can be anticipated by the presence of a perpendicular walkway or hallway, increased noise, or detection of movement from the visual periphery.

ECCENTRIC VIEWING

Training learners to use eccentric viewing, utilizing paramacular or *peripheral vision* to substitute for a central field loss, has been found to be effective in supporting the use of vision for daily activities such as reading, food preparation, shaving, and makeup application (Hong, Park, Kwon, & Yoo, 2014). For individuals who have age-related macular degeneration or other central field losses, research has focused on clinical training on near-distance vision tasks, especially reading. More research is needed on eccentric viewing training related to O&M tasks for individuals who have central field losses.

Purpose: To enable the learner to use his peripheral vision to look around a scotoma (blind spot) in his central vision and direct his most clear vision forward to preview the travel path, read signage with the use of a magnification device, or determine the overall layout or the location of key points of interest.

PROCEDURE AT A GLANCE
1 The learner locates the most acute peripheral vision to accommodate central field loss or to view around a centrally located blind spot or scotoma.
2 The learner determines the necessary position of the eye (eccentric viewing angle) so that the most acute peripheral vision is directed forward for travel.
3 The learner maintains the eccentric viewing angle to view the path of travel.
4 The learner may make use of a magnification device to view finer details.

METHOD

STEP 1 The learner locates the most acute peripheral vision (*preferred* or *trained retinal locus* [PRL or TRL]) to accommodate central field loss or to view around a centrally located blind spot or scotoma. Some learners will naturally locate a functional PRL, but through clinical or functional assessment it may be determined that a better area is available for viewing. O&M specialists can review clinical reports or consult with the learner's optometrist or certified low vision therapist to identify the TRL to be used and work with learners to incorporate the use of this area.

Rationale Taking time to identify the optimum viewing area for O&M purposes will help the learner to adjust and locate the PRL or TRL. Eccentric viewing training, which requires practice, has been found to increase performance in some activities of daily living (Hong et al., 2014).

STEP 2 The learner determines the necessary position of the eye (*eccentric viewing angle*) so that the clearest peripheral vision is directed forward for travel. Some learners may think about looking past rather than directly at the desired target or area. This viewing angle may require the learner to appear to be looking above, below, or to the side of the target or viewing area.

Rationale In order to make use of the PRL or TRL, the learner will need to move his eye to the side or up or down to direct the most clear vision forward for travel. The physical position of the eye may cause others to perceive that the learner is looking above, below, or to the side of the target, when the clearest vision is actually being directed toward the target.

STEP 3 The learner maintains the eccentric viewing angle to view the path of travel. A clock face analogy can be used to conceptualize the eccentric viewing angle, such as looking at ten o'clock for an angle that is up and slightly to the left or five o'clock for an angle that is down and to the right.

Rationale The eccentric viewing angle needs to be maintained somewhat consistently to be used effectively for viewing the travel path.

STEP 4 The learner may combine eccentric viewing with use of a magnification device, such as a handheld *magnifier* or monocular, to view finer details while stationary. The learner will need to be able to view eccentrically prior to adding the magnification device so that the clearest vision is used to look through the device.

Rationale While the PRL may assist the learner with using another area of his vision for certain tasks, the acuity may be such that finer details may not be easily resolved. Magnification can supplement the use of eccentric viewing for detailed tasks such as reading a directory or viewing a pedestrian signal. If the learner cannot maintain an eccentric viewing angle, then he will have a difficult time viewing through the magnification device.

USE OF A MONOCULAR (TELESCOPE)

Purpose: To enable the learner to use a low vision magnification device for viewing targets at a distance.

PROCEDURE AT A GLANCE

1	The learner identifies the parts, care, and capabilities of the device.
2	The learner grasps the monocular with the ocular piece held near his eye and the objective lens pointed toward the target, using his thumb, index, and middle fingers to hold the device at the ocular lens. The learner may hold his other hand near the objective lens to assist in stabilizing the monocular.
3	The learner positions the monocular to his face and eye by pressing the index finger curved atop the ocular lens against the bone above his eye and the thumb curved underneath the ocular lens against his nose or cheek.
4	Initially the learner visually spots the target without the device, then brings the device slowly and directly to his eye, and localizes the device by aligning his eye and device with the desired target.
5	The learner rests his elbow on a table or other flat surface to stabilize the device during initial viewing.
6	The learner focuses the device by twisting the housing initially set at infinity (the most closed position), then twists the focusing ring to bring the image into focus, move past focus, and back to focus again.
7	The learner traces or follows a stationary line, contour, or edge by smoothly moving his head in the direction of the line, with the monocular continuously aligned with the edge in order to locate a target area or determine the layout of an area.
8	While viewing vertically and horizontally with the monocular, the learner scans using a smooth movement of his head, with the monocular aligned in a systematic search pattern.
9	The learner tracks a moving object by smoothly moving his head, with the monocular continuously aligned with the moving object, to keep track of the object as it moves.
10	The learner integrates the use of the device with other O&M tasks.

METHOD

STEP 1 The learner identifies the parts (including ocular and objective lenses, housing, neck strap, lens cap, and focusing ring), care and cleaning, and capabilities of the device. The learner can describe what the device specifications are related to the power of the device, focusing range, field of view, and size of the objective lens. The learner can make a list of indoor and outdoor items that he may be able to view with the device. The learner should also understand that due to the restricted field of view, exaggerated movement, and loss of depth perception when looking through a monocular, the device should only be used while stationary. Good care of the device includes using the neck strap to avoid dropping the monocular. Using the neck strap also makes the device easy to reach when needed.

Rationale Device familiarization is a good starting point so that the learner and O&M specialist can share terminology for teaching the skills needed. It is also important for the learner to know how to care for the device for long-term use. Understanding the device properties helps the learner develop realistic expectations for what he will be able to accomplish and not accomplish with a given device.

STEP 2 The learner grasps the monocular with the ocular piece held near his eye and the objective lens pointed toward the target, using his thumb, index, and middle fingers to hold the device at the ocular lens. He should use the hand that is on the same side as the monocular eye so that his nose does not get in the way. The learner may hold his other hand near the objective lens to assist in stabilizing the monocular as needed.

Rationale Cupping his thumb, index, and middle fingers around the ocular lens provides the learner with a stable grasp of the device. Using the hand that is on the same side as the monocular eye is more comfortable and efficient.

STEP 3 The learner positions the monocular to his face and eye by pressing the index finger curved atop the ocular lens against the bone above his eye and the thumb curved underneath the ocular lens against his nose or cheek. The position can be practiced first without the monocular and then with the monocular with the lens cap on so that the learner is not visually distracted. Remove the cap and repeat until the learner can align the monocular with correct positioning to catch the light through the objective lens to localize on a desired target.

Rationale The thumb and index finger provide a concrete reference point and act as stabilizers so that the learner does not poke himself in the eye when positioning the monocular.

STEP 4 Initially the learner visually spots the target without the device, then brings the device slowly and directly to his eye, and localizes the device by aligning his eye and device with the desired target.

Rationale Initially spotting the target without the device and with the full field of view makes it easier for the learner to find the general location of the target. Bringing the device slowly and directly to his eye allows for easier alignment of his eye, the device, and the target for detailed viewing.

STEP 5 The learner rests his elbow on a table or other flat surface to stabilize the device during initial viewing.

Rationale Initial stabilization on a flat surface can help the learner hold the device steady while practicing next steps, including focusing the device.

Variations One of the following methods may be used to stabilize the monocular while standing:

- Press both elbows against the chest, forming a stable brace. (Some learners are able to maintain stabilization without any bracing.)
- Use the free hand to support the elbow of the arm and hand grasping the monocular. (*Note:* Some individuals are able to twist the focusing ring with the same hand that is grasping the monocular. If the learner finds this too difficult, he can shift the free hand from providing stabilization to focusing the monocular as needed.)
- Lean against a wall or pole, if one is near, for balance and stabilization.

Diane L. Fazzi

STEP 6 The learner focuses the device by twisting the housing initially set at infinity (the most closed or shortest length position), then twists the focusing ring to bring the image into focus, move past focus, and back into focus again. Demonstrate twisting the housing while reviewing that the monocular at its shortest length is focused at infinity for the furthest focal distance and at its longest length is focused at the closest focal distance. Alternatively, the device can be fully opened at its longest length, with the focusing ring turned counterclockwise until the image is brought into focus, then moved past focus, and back into focus again (Pogrund et al., 2012). The O&M specialist may prefocus the device initially.

Rationale Starting with the monocular at infinity enables the learner to begin focusing from the same starting point each time. Continuing to twist the focusing ring past the optimum focus ensures that the learner has gone far enough to have the clearest focus. A prefocused monocular may help the learner recognize the clarity to expect when the monocular is focused properly.

STEP 7 The learner traces or follows a stationary line, contour, or edge by smoothly moving his head in the direction of the line, with the monocular continuously aligned with the edge in order to locate a target area or determine the layout of an area.

Rationale Teaching learners to trace a stationary line while using the monocular enables the O&M specialist to introduce various scanning patterns that can be used later in open spaces or areas in a simple-to-complex sequence.

STEP 8 While viewing vertically and horizontally with the monocular, the learner scans using a smooth movement of his head, with the monocular aligned in a systematic search pattern (see Sidebar 10.1 earlier in this chapter).

Rationale The smooth movement of the learner's head with the monocular held in alignment reduces the impact of a perceived exaggeration of movement caused by the magnification power of the device. Similar scanning patterns are used with and without a low vision device and should be taught as a visual skill prior to introducing the use of a low vision device with a reduced field of view.

STEP 9 The learner tracks a moving object by smoothly moving his head, with the monocular continuously aligned with the moving object, in order to keep track of the object as it moves.

Rationale Tracking a moving object while using a monocular can be challenging unless the object is moving slowly and in an expected direction. The smooth movement of the learner's head with the monocular held in alignment reduces the impact of a perceived exaggeration of movement caused by the magnification power of the device.

STEP 10 The learner integrates the use of the device with other O&M tasks.

Rationale Unless the learner integrates the use of the device into other O&M tasks (such as reading a street sign or identifying the Walk signal) and daily routines (such as leisure activities), the learner may not have the necessary practice and experience to optimize use of the device. If the learner does not regularly use the device and have it easily accessible, he may not have it handy when needed unexpectedly. When using the long cane and monocular simultaneously, the cane strap can be held over the learner's thumb, pinkie finger, or wrist to keep firm control of the cane at all times.

CONSIDERATIONS FOR BASIC LOW VISION SKILLS

- Visual skills such as tracing, scanning, and eccentric viewing can be most successfully taught in a simple-to-complex sequence as related to the following:
  - □ Position of the learner (e.g., seated versus standing)
  - □ Lighting conditions (e.g., indirect versus direct lighting, presence of glare)
  - □ Position of viewing targets (e.g., at head level versus above the head)

☐ Level of contrast present

☐ Level of visual complexity and clutter (e.g., regular spacing patterns versus irregular spacing patterns as may be found on a classroom bulletin board)

☐ Familiar versus unfamiliar viewing targets

☐ Size and distance of the viewing target

- Following a simple-to-complex instructional approach, visual skills should first be taught without a low vision optical device to develop essential skills that can then be applied with an optical device with magnification and reduced field of view.

- Low vision optical devices are commonly prescribed by optometrists who specialize in low vision. O&M specialists should review eye reports to determine which eye the device was prescribed for and if it should be used with or without corrective lenses. On many monocular devices, the rubber eyecup can be rolled back so that the monocular can be lightly pressed against the prescription lens of the learner's eyeglasses, if needed.

- While use of a low vision device may be introduced in a clinical setting, O&M specialists have the opportunity to provide a full sequence of instruction, progressing from simple to complex, in indoor and outdoor environments.

- To learn tracing skills and scanning patterns, learners can start by using a finger to trace a high-contrast, thick line on a piece of paper or a whiteboard, first without a low vision device, and then with the device. Give or ask for examples of tracing side to side, up and down, near and far, and diagonally, or any combination of these.

- Incorporate numbers or letters along lines to be traced and have the learner read or identify them while tracing to ensure that the line is being traced accurately. Once the learner is more proficient, have him trace broken lines or unusual patterns.

- Have the learner practice using the low vision device outdoors with real environmental elements when possible, making sure to position the learner to avoid looking directly toward the sun.

- Tracking a moving object with or without a monocular is most effective when the line of motion is predictable and the motion being tracked is relatively slow. Learners who become proficient with the skill may be able to use tracking for leisure viewing or daily activities such as slower-moving sporting events, bird-watching, keeping track of young children, and so on. Visual tracking can be achieved by moving the eyes and the head as needed to maintain visual contact with the object being tracked. Visual tracking with a monocular requires a smooth head movement to maintain alignment of the eye, device, and visual target.

- In general, tracking with a monocular is difficult and sometimes inefficient. For example, tracking an approaching bus to determine its number using a monocular may be very frustrating for the learner. It may be easier and more efficient for him to wait until the bus stops and ask the bus driver or other waiting passengers for the bus number.

- Due to relative speed, tracking moving traffic is easier without a monocular and will yield enough needed information about the flow and order of the traffic cycle. The monocular can be used to confirm the types of traffic signals present, such as a left-turn arrow.

- Learners should not use a monocular for tracking traffic during a street crossing, but can use it to confirm the pedestrian signal display, if needed. Learners wearing a monocular on a neck strap should drop it from their hands after seeing the Walk signal and use full visual scanning with head movements as they prepare to step off the curb. This needs to be completed relatively quickly since walk signals may be as short as a few seconds.

- Learners who have low vision often experience discomfort from glare as a result of sudden changes in lighting levels, overhead lighting (indoor and outdoor), veiling glare from reflective surfaces (such as a bright sun reflecting off of shiny marble flooring), and dazzling glare (produced by excessive illumination in the peripheral field), which affects individuals who are very sensitive to light (Ludt, 1997). Glare occurs when the type or amount of light or the change in light entering the eye is greater than the eye's ability to manage or adapt to that light. A hat or visor with a 3-inch brim or wider can provide some protection from overhead glare. Well-selected light-absorptive lenses and filters (e.g., sunglasses with good optical quality that protect against ultraviolet rays) that include coverage that extends from the temple and over the eyes can help to reduce the most disabling glare during travel.

- Other devices, from a simple handheld magnifier to a video magnification device, can be incorporated into O&M lessons as tools to prepare routes, preview maps, and review transportation schedules for daily travel.

Visual Skills with Guide Techniques

Learners who have low vision may benefit from various levels of instruction in and selective use of guide techniques, protective techniques, and hand trailing in conjunction with cane techniques. Required techniques depend on the learner's ability to interact visually with the travel environment on a reliable basis under changing conditions, and should be assessed on an individual basis. For example, a learner may benefit from using protective techniques in a dimly lit environment or from traveling with a guide in an unfamiliar, congested area. Some visual skills (such as scanning and eccentric viewing) can be introduced and practiced in a focused manner while walking, with the O&M specialist serving as a guide. In this case, the guide is responsible for drop-off detection and orientation while the learner focuses on viewing the travel path using a systematic approach. This scenario presents the learner with an opportunity to practice identifying depth-perception cues for impending drop-offs (such as the slope of a railing to indicate stairs) or locating visual landmarks along a route (such as a bright red lobby carpet) without distractions. (See Chapter 3 for detailed procedures for teaching guide techniques.)

Visual Skills with Cane Skills

Learners who have low vision may benefit from various levels of instruction in and use of cane techniques. Required techniques depend on the learner's ability to interact visually with the travel environment on a reliable basis under changing conditions, and should be assessed on an individual basis. (See Chapter 5 for detailed procedures that can be used to teach cane techniques, including verification cane technique, as well as strategies for in-

corporating vision during cane use.) A unit on cane skills, which commonly spans both indoor and outdoor environments, can also be a perfect time to integrate basic visual skills that apply throughout O&M training. Systematic visual scanning, while stationary and while moving, is useful in both indoor and outdoor environments and integrated with the use of the long cane for many learners who have low vision. Eccentric viewing is a visual skill for learners who have central field loss or scotoma and need to look around the central scotoma to view items of interest during travel. The use of the long cane to provide detection of lower-level obstacles and changes in level and terrain complements the use of scanning and eccentric viewing. These visual skills are described earlier in this chapter. For learners who will use an optical device such as a monocular during travel, O&M specialists will want to work on coordinating the use of devices and absorptive sun filters or quality sunglasses with the long cane. The neck strap of the monocular should be worn so that the learner can let go of the device as needed when he starts walking. Similarly, sunglasses with neck chains afford the learner easy access to them when switching between using the monocular and the sunglasses. The need to efficiently switch between the use of the monocular and sunglasses is especially important for initiating a street crossing with the Walk signal or a green vehicular signal.

Visual Skills for Block Travel

Techniques needed for block travel depend on the learner's ability to interact visually with the travel environment on a reliable basis under changing conditions, and should be assessed on an individual basis. (See Chapter 6 for detailed procedures that can be used to teach block travel, including strategies for incorporating use of vision.) A unit on block travel, which is commonly conducted in residential areas, can also be a perfect time to work on basic visual skills that learners can then apply throughout their O&M training. For example, the learner can practice three-level vertical scanning to detect overhangs, lower-level obstacles, and changes in level and terrain along the sidewalk to be traveled. Visual depth-perception cues, such as parked cars, detectable warning surfaces, or contrasting crosswalk lines, can be identified as tools for anticipating curbs. Changes from light to dark along the sidewalk can indicate broken or uneven pavement and reflections from the walking surface might indicate an upcoming puddle. Practice can also help learners understand that changes from light to dark may just be a shadow of a tree or pole or a change in paving material rather than an uneven surface, and may help to reduce learners' confusion when they do not find an irregularity with their cane. Learners can also practice establishing and locating visual landmarks within block travel, such as a unique and brightly colored fence to locate a specific home or a unique shape such as an ornate fountain in front of an office building.

Visual Skills for Street Crossings

Learners who have low vision may benefit from using a variety of visual skills, in combination with auditory skills, for intersection analysis and street crossings. Required techniques depend on the learner's ability to interact visually with the travel environment, recognize parked and moving vehicles on a reliable basis under changing conditions, and possess a conceptual understanding to know what to look for. (See Chapter 7 for detailed procedures that can be used to teach street-crossing and analysis techniques, along with strategies for incorporating use of vision.) A unit on intersection analysis or street-crossing skills, which is commonly conducted in residential and small business areas, can also be a perfect time to work on visual skills that learners can then apply throughout their O&M training. At intersections where streets stand out in contrast to surrounding sidewalks, corners, and crosswalks, learners may use vision to determine the geometry of the intersection by tracing, in sequence, contrast-

ing crosswalks at each cross street. Visually tracing the crosswalk to the opposite corner can establish a reference point for scanning for the pole with the pedestrian signal. Monocular skills can be used to identify traffic controls that are too far away to identify visually without magnification.

Visual Skills for Intersection Analysis

Visual skills can be paired with auditory skills to perform intersection analysis. Learners may incorporate the following visual cues as part of intersection analysis:

- **Intersection geometry:** In addition to listening to and looking at traffic-movement patterns to determine if the intersection is four-leg, three-leg, or multi-leg, the learner can look for marked crosswalks and observe the angle of the crosswalk line to the opposite corner to determine if the intersection is skewed or offset.
- **Traffic controls:** In addition to listening to and looking at traffic-movement patterns to determine traffic controls, the learner can look for marked crosswalks, stop or limit lines or words such as STOP painted on the street, stop signs, traffic signals, and pedestrian signals. If the learner can see the traffic signals (with or without a monocular), he can observe the changes in the signals while listening to the movement of traffic to confirm the pattern of the controls at the intersection.
- **Width of the crossing or size of the intersection:** The learner can count the lanes of traffic by noting the lane markings or by counting cars that are stopped at the intersection. He can also observe and visually track other pedestrians making the crossing and mentally time how long it takes them to complete the crossing.
- **Visibility:** The learner can scan the corner to determine if there are any objects, parked cars, trees, or large hedges that may block the visibility of the traffic to the learner or the visibility of the learner to drivers. Hilly or curved roads can also negatively impact visibility for drivers and pedestrians.

Scheffers and Myers (2012) provide detailed coverage of intersection analysis and lane-by-lane scanning for learners who have low vision, along with strategies for teaching school-age learners.

Visual Skills for Locating and Tracking Moving Vehicles

In making street crossings at uncontrolled, stop sign–controlled, or signal-controlled intersections, the learner who has low vision can practice tracking the movement of vehicles through various intersections to determine whether he can consistently follow movement and discern turning vehicles from those continuing through the intersection (Geruschat & Smith, 2010).

Learners who use vision to watch for vehicles need to understand how lighting, sight lines, and features of vehicles can affect their ability to see them. For example, they may notice that

- certain vehicle features (e.g., color, size, headlights, reflection of the sun off the surface, etc.) make vehicles easier or more difficult to see;
- they can detect a vehicle more easily if they see its movement, so it is easier to see vehicles approaching at an angle than to see vehicles moving directly toward them;
- lighting conditions (e.g., sunny, cloudy, nighttime) can affect their ability to see vehicles;
- their line of sight may be blocked temporarily by passing vehicles; and
- their vision fluctuates, and they can see better in some instances and worse in others (Sauerburger, n.d.).

Practice in scanning for vehicles may improve the ability of learners with low vision to detect approaching vehicles in each lane. Visual tracking of vehicles should be practiced from multiple directions, corner locations, and in different lighting conditions, with learners describing what they see and the O&M specialist providing feedback until consistency and accuracy are reached (see Sauerburger, n.d., for examples).

Visual Skills for Lane-by-Lane Scanning

Visual skills are also used during the initiation and completion of a street crossing in a systematic manner by carrying out lane-by-lane scanning at traffic signal–controlled streets to visually clear each lane prior to stepping into the potential path of an oncoming vehicle. The scanning procedure is dependent on the learner understanding the phases of traffic and where possible traffic danger points exist

during the crossing. Scheffers and Myers (2012) recommend starting by introducing left-right scanning, a simplified approach that includes looking left for the start and first half of the crossing, switching to looking right as the learner approaches the midpoint of the crossing, and continuing until it is time to locate the place to step up on the opposite corner. Practice should take place with all aspects of scanning as described in the lane-by-lane scanning procedures outlined in Sidebar 10.2.

Visual Skills for Detecting Vehicles at Uncontrolled Crossings

In order to use vision to detect approaching vehicles at uncontrolled crossings, learners need to practice tracking vehicles through the intersection and quickly scanning in all directions to determine if approaching vehicles can be detected to allow enough time to complete a crossing. Cheong, Geruschat, and Congdon (2008) found that individuals with peripheral field loss made errors in judging gaps in traffic, resulting in risky crossing decisions at a mid-block uncontrolled crossings. Differences in abilities to judge traffic gaps might be explained by smaller fixation areas and fewer fixations (maintaining visual gaze on a single location) distributed to the relevant tasks for individuals with peripheral field losses. Training for individuals with peripheral field loss to safely manage independent street crossings should include considerations for smaller fixation areas, utilizing auditory skills whenever possible, and finding safe street-crossing locations (Cheong et al., 2008).

Visual Skills for Using Transportation

Incorporating visual skills into transportation units for learners who have low vision can be of tremendous benefit. Required techniques depend on the learner's ability to interact visually with the travel environment on a reliable basis under changing conditions, and should be assessed on an individual basis. (See Chapter 8 for detailed procedures that can be used to teach techniques for using transportation, along with strategies for incorporating use of vision.)

Sidebar 10.2

Lane-by-Lane Scanning

The following sequence can be used for lane-by-lane visual scanning at intersections for students who have low vision (see Figures 7.4 and 7.5 for illustrations of these situations). Learners should combine visual scanning with listening and cane skills.

Counterclockwise Crossing

1. Check the crosswalk area for uneven or broken pavement, vehicles extending into the crosswalk area, and alignment within the crosswalk in preparation for the crossing. Observing pedestrians may help to indicate the location of pedestrian pushbuttons or the opposite corner.
2. Scan the entire intersection prior to initiating the crossing to confirm traffic patterns, traffic controls, and the movement of pedestrians, and to note any unusual occurrences.
3. As the crossing is initiated, look over the left shoulder to the near-lane-parallel traffic for cars turning right on red.
4. Continue looking directly left to the near-lane-perpendicular traffic to ensure that no cars are moving straight through the intersection and coming across the path of travel.
5. Look ahead and to the left to see if cars in the far-lane-parallel traffic are making a left turn into the path of travel.
6. Just before reaching the midpoint of the crossing, look to the right to the far-lane-perpendicular traffic to see if vehicles are stopped, to look for potential vehicles attempting to make a right turn on red, and to negotiate around any vehicles that may be stopped or parked across the crosswalk.
7. Look ahead to the curb to locate a clear space to quickly step up onto the curb.

Clockwise Crossing

1. Check the crosswalk area for uneven or broken pavement, vehicles extending into the crosswalk area, and alignment within the crosswalk in preparation for the crossing. Observing pedestrians may help to indicate the location of pedestrian pushbuttons or the opposite corner.
2. Scan the entire intersection prior to initiating the crossing to confirm traffic patterns, traffic controls, the movement of pedestrians, and to note any unusual occurrences.
3. As the crossing is initiated, look left to make sure that no cars are trying to make a right turn on red from the near-lane-perpendicular traffic prior to stepping off the curb. Continue on to make sure that no cars are stopped across the crosswalk.
4. Continue looking left during the first half of the crossing to confirm that all vehicles are stopped or stopping.
5. Just before reaching the midpoint of the crossing, look over the right shoulder to check for cars coming from the far-lane-parallel traffic that may potentially turn left into the path of travel.
6. Look to the right to the far-lane-perpendicular traffic to ensure that no cars are moving straight through the intersection and coming across the path of travel.
7. Look ahead to the right to see if cars in near-lane-parallel traffic are making a right turn into the path of travel.
8. Look ahead to the curb to locate a clear space to quickly step up onto the curb.

The learner can incorporate visual skills such as spotting a target with or without a low vision device, tracing, scanning, and tracking for use in locating bus stops, buses, light rail stations, and information signage. The depth-perception cues practiced earlier can be of benefit in crowded areas of public-transportation hubs. The learner can observe the movement of other pedestrians in a light rail station to locate stairs and entrances. For example, the learner may notice that the height of pedestrians is lowering, which would indicate a set of descending stairs or escalators. A crowd of moving people slowing down may indicate the entrance to a turnstile. Detectable warning surfaces and contrasting guidance tiles (tiles used to provide visual guidance) may provide markings for train platforms or for expected door openings of railcars. The monocular can come in handy for reading well-placed signage for orientation or fare information.

Visual Skills in Special Situations

Familiar or unfamiliar special environments can provide opportunities to apply visual skills in novel situations. (See Chapter 9 for detailed procedures that can be used to teach techniques for these situations, along with strategies for incorporating use of vision.) Grocery stores with regularly spaced aisles and signage provide opportunities to practice eccentric viewing, tracing, scanning, as well as using a magnification device. The learner may use tracing to locate an item typically found along the top shelf of the canned-goods aisle. Scanning may help the learner navigate around the produce section, which may have numerous fruit and vegetable displays. The monocular can be used to read aisle signs for locating certain items and handheld magnifiers can be used to correctly identify price markings.

Tips for Teaching Travel Techniques for Learners Who Have Low Vision

Integrating Orientation

Once learners have mastered the use of specific visual skills in a variety of travel environments, they can be expected to use them systematically to help with orientation tasks. Vision can be used together with other sensory information to identify and locate landmarks along a route or to find a point of interest. When applicable, vision can also be used to access print signage that will assist the learner with wayfinding, such as locating and reading a street sign or an office directory of adequate size and contrast. Developing a systematic approach for the use

of vision during travel may help a learner become actively engaged in route-path preview and support spatial updating by keeping track of the changing object-to-object relationships as he moves along a route. Learners who have low vision can also benefit from printed, uncluttered diagrams that convey the overall shape or layout of a building or area as well as visual maps of areas for the purposes of route planning and overall orientation.

Sequencing

Sequencing of instruction for travel techniques for learners who have low vision must take into account each learner's individual goals and abilities. While some visual skills and practice in the use of low vision devices may take place outside of the more traditional sequence of O&M instruction in order to learn and develop confidence in the use of these skills, it is important that visual skills be embedded throughout O&M training. See Table 10.1 for an outline of how visual skills may be integrated throughout travel in various environments and corresponding considerations for O&M specialists.

O&M Specialist Positioning

The O&M specialist's position for learners who have low vision may vary slightly from that of other learners. For example, while some O&M specialists may choose to walk in front of their learners who are blind during initial cane instruction, doing so for a learner who has low vision could be distracting in some instances and would not be effective when the lesson objective involves having the learner establish and maintain a straight line of travel or locate a destination, as it would provide the learner with a clear visual clue and possibly hinder the use of vision. When working on specific visual skills, the O&M specialist may benefit from walking alongside the learner to more closely observe the pattern of eye and head movements for eccentric viewing or scanning. Systematic scanning or eccentric viewing can also be assessed by asking the learner to say out loud what items or areas of significance he is seeing along the route so that the O&M specialist can determine if particular aspects of the visual field are being missed during travel.

O&M specialists can also include aspects of visual modeling of various techniques for using the long cane or a low vision device for learners who have low vision. For example, when teaching cane

Table 10.1   Incorporating Low Vision Training into an O&M Sequence
Brenda J. Naimy

This sample outline emphasizes the incorporation of visual aspects of training into O&M units and does not address conceptual training needs or other O&M skills and techniques. The content and sequence are to be adapted for individual learners' needs.

Unit and Skills	Notes and Considerations
Indoor Instruction	
Basic Skills ■ Guide techniques ■ Protective techniques ■ Trailing techniques ■ Locating lost objects	■ Are there selective use needs? ■ Is eye pathology actively progressive? ■ Is there poor adjustment to lighting changes? ■ Does vision fluctuate day to day? ■ Does the learner experience night blindness? ■ Is there a need or benefit to train the learner to serve as a guide?
Visual Skills Taught **before** monocular training and verification cane technique ■ Systematic scanning patterns for indoor environments: 　□ Hallways (vertical and horizontal) 　□ Three-level vertical scanning 　□ Visual room orientation 　□ Visual identification of landmarks ■ Eccentric viewing	■ Emphasize what learner should be looking for during use of each scanning pattern. ■ If learner has central field loss or scotoma.
Cane Skills Typically, one of the following cane skills would be most appropriate for an individual: ■ Touch technique (with selective use of constant-contact, touch-and-drag, etc.) ■ Constant-contact as primary technique ■ Verification cane technique (taught in conjunction with visual skills)	If learner has weak or inconsistent functional vision abilities, such as night blindness, fluctuating vision, or active progression of eye pathology. Functional vision abilities include the following: ■ Having good visual line of travel ■ Visually adjusting line of travel to navigate around obstacles ■ Visually identifying obstacles; suspecting surface changes ■ Functioning consistently with day or night travel abilities ■ Having stable vision
Stair Travel Cane Techniques	Same techniques for travelers who are blind are taught to learners with low vision.
Monocular Skills ■ Familiarization with and care of device ■ Stabilization ■ Spotting indoor targets ■ Tracing to locate indoor targets ■ Scanning to locate indoor targets ■ Tracking ■ Practical applications for indoor environments (e.g., locating/reading room numbers, reading whiteboards, seeing overhead projections)	

(continued on next page)

Table 10.1 (continued)

Unit and Skills	Notes and Considerations
Concepts and Orientation Skills ■ Landmarks, cues ■ Compass directions ■ Use of large-print maps ■ Cognitive mapping skills (e.g., use of five-point travel system) ■ Spatial updating emphasis for route travel	■ Landmarks for travelers with low vision may be distinctly different than for travelers who are blind (i.e., visual versus tactile) but must still be unique, permanent, distinctive, and give location information. Consider day versus night ability to visually identify landmarks. ■ Compass directions: N, S, E, and W; concept that hallways may run N–S; offices or classrooms may be placed on the E–W side and vice versa.

Residential Environments
Note: Night travel functional assessment and training are recommended upon completion of residential travel training.

Unit and Skills	Notes and Considerations

Visual Skills
■ Assess for best glare remediation (tints and visors)
■ Systematic scanning patterns for sidewalk travel (vertical and horizontal)
  □ Vertical, check for:
    ● Head-level obstacles (e.g., branches)
    ● Obstacles in travel path
    ● Uneven surfaces, curbs
    ● Location of driveways, walkways
  □ Horizontal, check for:
    ● Cars entering or exiting driveways
    ● Pedestrians and bicyclists crossing walkways and intersecting sidewalks
    ● Identification of landmarks
■ Visual identification of landmarks to aid cognitive mapping and orientation
	■ For tints, recommend the lightest the traveler can tolerate (when assessing, introduce lightest tints first, then gradually introduce darker tints if needed).
	■ Travelers may need tints of varying darkness and colors for different lighting conditions.
	■ The repeated cycle of the scanning pattern can be adjusted to the learner's maximum distance thresholds. For example, if the learner's maximum distance threshold is 25 feet to see surface changes, obstacles, and curbs, the pattern should be completed repeatedly at least every 25 feet.
	■ Emphasize slow, smooth, and continuous scanning patterns.
	■ Most desired landmarks may still need to be near the learner's path of travel (to ensure visual ability to see in different lighting conditions, such as day versus night).

Cane Skills Transfer cane technique skills to outdoor environments: ■ Practice sidewalk travel skills ■ Emphasize scanning skills ■ Focus on using constant-contact technique to "verify" curbs and uneven areas	

Table 10.1

Unit and Skills	Notes and Considerations

Street-Crossing Skills
■ Cane mechanics:
  □ Curb detection
  □ Clearing of gutter
  □ Cane "on display"
  □ Long arc (flagging)
  □ Using constant-contact technique with consistent arc movement during crossing
  □ Up-curb approach and clearing of curb
■ Lane-by-lane scanning patterns (introduced after cane mechanics are mastered):
  □ Counterclockwise scanning pattern
  □ Clockwise scanning pattern
■ Systematic scanning to analyze intersections (consider using monocular to aid when static):
  □ Static analysis (initially)
  □ Dynamic analysis (upon approach to increase visual efficiency)
■ Key intersection characteristics to analyze (visual approach):
  □ Shape or geometry of intersection
  □ Traffic controls
  □ Traffic patterns
  □ Visibility
	■ Learners with low vision will be aligning visually (e.g., with parkways and curbs), thus time spent on auditory direction-taking (e.g., with traffic) may not be needed.
	■ Clearing the gutter allows the learner with low vision to check the depth of curb drop-off.
	■ Curb approach, both ascending and descending, is often problematic for learners with low vision due to poor contrast; consider use of the same approach as that used for learners who are blind.
	■ Other street-crossing cane techniques increase safety by emphasizing "high visibility" to traffic.
	■ Timing options for safe crossings are the same as those taught for learners who are blind.
	
	Intersection analysis for learners who have low vision:
	■ Assists learner in making decisions about whether to cross, when to cross, and where to cross.
	■ Give same considerations relating to timing of crossings for learners who have low vision as for learners who are blind.
	■ Start intersection analysis with simple, quiet residential intersections, gradually progressing to those with more traffic volume and varying shapes or geometry.
	■ Learner's ability to see road markings may aid in intersection analysis. Consider the use of a monocular for this purpose if beneficial.

Monocular Skills ■ Locating addresses ■ Reading street signs ■ Analyzing intersections	
Concepts and Orientation Skills ■ Expand use of compass directions ■ Use the sun to establish which direction traveler is facing ■ Use address system ■ Increase use of enlarged, high-contrast maps ■ Expand the integration of visual skills for cognitive mapping and spatial updating for route travel ■ Expand visual identification of landmarks for residential environments	■ Use of compass directions for sides of the street (e.g., N–S streets have an east and a west side) and corners of intersections (NW, NE, SW, SE). ■ Use of monocular may allow for introduction of an address system in residential neighborhoods. ■ Use of print maps can include more sophisticated representations of residential neighborhoods.

(continued on next page)

243

Table 10.1 (continued)

Unit and Skills	Notes and Considerations
Route Travel ■ Application of all the skills previously identified for residential route travel (simple to complex)	
Business Environments *Note:* Night travel functional assessment and training is recommended upon completion of business travel training.	
Visual Skills ■ Sidewalk scanning ■ Lane-by-lane scanning for street crossings	■ Sidewalk scanning incorporates the same patterns, but more obstacles, pedestrians, and driveway traffic may be present. ■ Systematic use of visual skills can help to confirm the presence of two bus stops or multiple buses using a shared stop.
Cane Skills ■ Transfer of cane technique to business environments	
Monocular Skills ■ Locating and reading business signage ■ Locating and reading addresses ■ Reading street signs ■ Using for intersection analysis ■ Using for traffic and pedestrian light changes	■ Give same considerations relating to timing of crossings for learners who have low vision as for learners who are blind; however, learners who have low vision may be able to see pedestrian control signals to aid their timing (with or without monocular).
Concepts and Orientation Skills ■ Expand use of compass directions ■ Introduce address system if not done in residential area	■ Bus travel will require advanced use of compass directions. For example, a learner may need to identify the location of the bus stop on the SW corner where he might locate a southbound bus, and be aware that an eastbound bus may be in a different spot on the same corner.
Locating Businesses ■ Finding entrances ■ Conducting small business transactions	
Route Travel ■ Application of all the skills previously identified for residential route travel	
Route-Planning Skills ■ Making phone calls to businesses, bus companies, etc. ■ Using video magnifier with print maps and GPS, online, and mobile technology for route mapping ■ Using online tools for bus travel planning	

Table 10.1

Unit and Skills	Notes and Considerations

Shopping Strategies
■ Assisted versus independent shopping:
  ☐ Monocular use (to read aisle signs)
  ☐ Magnifier use (to read product packaging and prices)
  ☐ Systematic scanning for travel in aisles and to avoid displays and obstacles
  ☐ Systematic visual tracing to locate items on shelves or along a produce counter
■ Blur interpretation for details that may not be clearly visible; using environmental context, location, past experiences, and educated guessing to identify products by packaging color, size, or shape	

Mall Travel ■ Ability to get to and from the mall ■ Independent travel within the mall using the same visual skills noted for shopping strategies ■ Use of the monocular to locate shops within the mall or restaurants at a food court ■ Escalator travel ■ Elevator travel (may be inserted into curriculum earlier)	
Transportation	
Bus Travel Instructional Sequence ■ Use same instructional sequence as for learners who are blind	Visual skills and low vision devices can be used to: ■ Read bus stop information ■ Identify bus number ■ Aid in visual identification of landmarks along the route or at bus stops ■ Locate an empty seat on the bus
Other Public Transit Options ■ Rail systems ■ Commuter rail services ■ Taxis and taxi-like services (e.g., Uber)	Visual skills and low vision devices can be used to: ■ Read transit stop and fare information ■ Locate the opening door of a light rail car ■ Visually identify landmarks at light rail stops ■ Locate an empty seat ■ Locate a taxi
Paratransit Options ■ Access services ■ Dial-A-Ride, Access-A-Ride, Senior Ride, City Ride	

(continued on next page)

Table 10.1   (continued)

Unit and Skills	Notes and Considerations
Metropolitan Travel	
Application of skills in heavy business environment: Apply all skills in heavier traffic and pedestrian volume, including dealing with pedestrian congestion.	
Visual Skills ■ Addressing needed changes in lane-by-lane scanning at intersections with one-way streets	
Cane Skills ■ Use of cane technique in crowded pedestrian environments (e.g., sidewalk travel and positioning at corners with multiple pedestrians) ■ Use of revolving doors	

techniques to a learner who has low vision, the O&M specialist may carry her own long cane to model the technique for the learner. Typically, this modeling would occur alongside the learner so that the view of the cane is the same, rather than providing a mirror image by facing the learner.

Strategies for Different Populations

General Strategies

O&M specialists may use a variety of strategies to promote the use of visual skills during travel. For those learners who will be using cane techniques, visual modeling or demonstration of cane techniques may be used in conjunction with verbal instruction. When using visual modeling, O&M specialists should be sure to select an environment that is well lit and free from glare and visual clutter, and provide contrast as needed to make sure that the key aspects of the techniques are easily seen. For example, the correct position of the cane for diagonal technique can be shown to the learner. The long white cane and its position across the instructor's body will be more visible if the O&M specialist is wearing dark-colored pants. O&M specialists should be careful, however, not to overly rely on the use of demonstration for teaching mobility techniques, as learners with low vision may miss important aspects of positioning and rationale if not paired with clear explanation and practice.

Learners who have low vision can be encouraged to practice visual skills while traveling with the long cane. Skills such as scanning, eccentric view-

ing, visual path preview, distance vision recognition, or distance estimation can be combined with cane techniques so that learners integrate information from multiple senses to enhance travel experiences. Some of these skills can be taught in an indoor environment initially and then applied to outdoor environments. For example, if a learner has mastered the touch technique, the O&M specialist can introduce visual path preview and planning using three levels of vertical scanning: head level at the greatest distance at which the learner can resolve images, mid-level at the greatest distance at which the learner can resolve images, and lower level at the greatest distance at which the learner can resolve images. Once the learner has practiced this scanning pattern, he can use it to plan his path of travel around obstacles that may be present in indoor hallways or lobby areas. These same skills can be applied in outdoor environments, such as parking lots or along sidewalks, and later used to anticipate drop-offs, obstacles, and overhangs in a variety of travel environments. In pairing visual skills with cane techniques, O&M specialists may notice an initial reduction in the quality of cane skills exhibited while the learner is concentrating on something new. However, with practice, both skills can be readily mastered in conjunction with each other.

Similarly, O&M specialists will want to consider the incorporation of optical and nonoptical low vision devices during instruction in cane techniques. Nonoptical means for reducing glare, such as wearing a hat or visor with a minimum 3-inch brim or appropriate tint, can be incorporated into lessons on cane techniques as needed. Introducing a device such as a monocular telescope may need to be done in a separate unit and then paired with the use of the cane in indoor and outdoor environments.

Age Differences

Younger learners may learn visual skills through age-appropriate activities and games that challenge them to look and listen and pique their curiosity for further environmental exploration and learning. For example, a preschool-age learner may learn searching patterns through games of "I Spy" or pretending the monocular is a telescope on a pirate ship as a lead-up to learning how to use low vision devices at home, in the classroom, and during O&M lessons.

Older adults can also benefit from the use of systematic visual skills in their home or community travel environments. For those with health limitations or problems with stamina, instruction may need to be broken down into meaningful steps and other nonphysical activities planned during rest breaks.

Learners with Additional Disabilities

Learners with intellectual disabilities who have low vision will also benefit from O&M instruction that integrates the use of vision along with other senses and mobility devices. High-interest items can be used to encourage use of visual skills and initial lessons may be conducted in areas that are relatively free from distractions.

Learners who have low vision and who use wheelchairs or other support devices for mobility may also benefit from O&M instruction that integrates the use of vision and low vision devices. It is important to work collaboratively with physical and occupational therapists to ensure that correct positioning is maintained so that the learner can focus on using visual skills.

Self-Advocacy

O&M specialists teach their learners visual skills in conjunction with cane techniques as needed to ensure maximum access to environmental information that can be applied to independent travel in a variety of environments. As learners develop the confidence to explain their visual needs to others, they can advocate for accommodations for lighting, color, contrast, accessible signage, or seating in classrooms or at work as needed. The end goal is to ensure that learners can maximize use of vision and other sensory perception along with O&M tools needed to travel in a variety of home, school, work, or community environments.

References

Allman, C. B., & Lewis, S. (Eds.). (2014). *ECC essentials: Teaching the expanded core curriculum to students with visual impairments*. New York, NY: AFB Press.

Ambrose-Zaken, G. (2005). Knowledge of and preferences for long cane components: A qualitative and quantitative study. *Journal of Visual Impairment & Blindness, 99*(10), 633–645.

Ambrose-Zaken, G., Calhoon, C. R., & Keim, J. R. (2010). Teaching orientation and mobility to students with cognitive impairments and vision loss. In W. R. Wiener, R. L. Welsh, & B. B. Blasch (Eds.), *Foundations of orientation and mobility: Vol. II. Instructional strategies and practical applications* (3rd ed., pp. 624–666). New York, NY: AFB Press.

Americans with Disabilities Act of 1990, Pub. L. No. 101-336 (1990).

Barlow, J. M., Bentzen, B. L., & Franck, L. (2010). Environmental accessibility for students with vision loss. In W. R. Wiener, R. L. Welsh, & B. B. Blasch (Eds.), *Foundations of orientation and mobility: Vol. I. History and theory* (3rd ed., pp. 324–385). New York, NY: AFB Press.

Barlow, J. M., Bentzen, B. L., Sauerburger, D., & Franck, L. (2010). Teaching travel at complex intersections. In W. R. Wiener, R. L. Welsh, & B. B. Blasch (Eds.), *Foundations of orientation and mobility: Vol. II. Instructional strategies and practical applications* (3rd ed., pp. 352–419). New York, NY: AFB Press.

Barlow, J. M., Scott, A. C., Bentzen, B. L., Guth, D. A., & Graham, J. (2013). Effectiveness of audible and tactile heading cues at complex intersections for pedestrians who are blind. *Transportation Research Record: Journal of the Transportation Research Board, 2393*, 147–154.

Bentzen, B. L., & Marston, J. R. (2010a). Orientation aids for students with vision loss. In W. R. Wiener, R. L. Welsh, & B. B. Blasch (Eds.), *Foundations of orientation and mobility: Vol. I. History and theory* (3rd ed., pp. 296–323). New York, NY: AFB Press.

Bentzen, B. L., & Marston, J. R. (2010b). Teaching the use of orientation aids for orientation and mobility. In W. R. Wiener, R. L. Welsh, & B. B. Blasch (Eds.), *Foundations of orientation and mobility: Vol. II. Instructional strategies and practical applications* (3rd ed., pp. 315–351). New York, NY: AFB Press.

Bourquin, E. A., Wall Emerson, R., Sauerburger, D., & Barlow, J. M. (2014). Conditions that influence drivers' yielding behavior in turning vehicles at intersections with traffic signal controls. *Journal of Visual Impairment & Blindness, 108*(3), 173–186.

Bourquin, E. A., Wall Emerson, R., Sauerburger, D., & Barlow, J. M. (in press). Conditions that influence drivers' behavior at a roundabout: Increasing yielding. *Journal of Visual Impairment & Blindness*.

Bozeman, L., & McCulley, R. M. (2010). Improving orientation for students with vision loss. In W. R. Wiener, R. L. Welsh, & B. B. Blasch (Eds.), *Foundations of orientation and mobility: Vol. II. Instructional strategies and practical applications* (3rd ed., pp. 27–53). New York, NY: AFB Press.

Cheong, A. M., Geruschat, D. R., & Congdon, N. (2008). Traffic gap judgment in people with significant peripheral field loss. *Optometry and Vision Science, 85*(1), 26–36.

Couturier, J.-A., & Ratelle, A. (2010). Teaching orientation and mobility for adverse weather conditions. In W. R. Wiener, R. L. Welsh, & B. B. Blasch (Eds.), *Foundations of orientation and mobility: Vol. II. Instructional strategies and practical applications* (3rd ed., pp. 486–518). New York, NY: AFB Press.

Crudden, A. (2015). Transportation issues: Perspectives of orientation and mobility providers. *Journal of Visual Impairment & Blindness, 109*(6), 457–468.

Cutter, J. (2004). Parents: blind children's first mobility teachers. *Future Reflections, 23*(2). Retrieved from https://nfb.org/images/nfb/publications/fr/fr14/fr04se13.htm

David, W., Kollmar, K., & McCall, S. (1998). *Safe without sight: Crime prevention and self-defense strategies for people who are blind*. Boston, MA: National Braille Press.

Dodson-Burk, B., Park-Leach, L., & Myers, L. (2010). Teaching the use of transportation systems for orientation and mobility. In W. R. Wiener, R. L. Welsh, & B. B. Blasch (Eds.), *Foundations of orientation and mobility: Vol. II. Instructional strategies and practical applications* (3rd ed., pp. 420–461). New York, NY: AFB Press.

Fazzi, D. L., & Naimy, B. J. (2010). Teaching orientation and mobility to school-age children. In W. R. Wiener, R. L. Welsh, & B. B. Blasch (Eds.), *Foundations of orientation and mobility: Vol. II. Instructional strategies and practical applications* (3rd ed., pp. 208–262). New York, NY: AFB Press.

Fazzi, D. L., & Petersmeyer, B. A. (2001). *Imagining the possibilities: Creative approaches to orientation and mobility instruction for persons who are visually impaired.* New York, NY: AFB Press.

Federal Highway Administration. (2000, June). *Roundabouts: An informational guide* (Publication No. FHWA-RD-00-067). Washington, DC: US Department of Transportation. Retrieved from https://www.fhwa.dot.gov/publications/research/safety/00067/00067.pdf

Federal Highway Administration. (2004, August). *Signalized intersections: Informational guide* (Publication No. FHWA-HRT-04-091). Washington, DC: US Department of Transportation. Retrieved from https://www.fhwa.dot.gov/publications/research/safety/04091/04091.pdf

Federal Highway Administration. (2008). *Designing pedestrian facilities for accessibility.* Washington, DC: US Department of Transportation.

Federal Highway Administration. (2009). Chapter 4E: Pedestrian control features. In *Manual on uniform traffic control devices for streets and highways.* Washington, DC: US Department of Transportation. Retrieved from https://mutcd.fhwa.dot.gov/pdfs/2009r1r2/mutcd2009r1r2edition.pdf

Geruschat, D. R., & Smith, A. J. (2010). Improving the use of low vision for orientation and mobility. In W. R. Wiener, R. L. Welsh, & B. B. Blasch (Eds.), *Foundations of orientation and mobility: Vol. II. Instructional strategies and practical applications* (3rd ed., pp. 54–90). New York, NY: AFB Press.

Griffin-Shirley, N., & Bozeman, L. (Eds.). (2016). *O&M for independent living: Strategies for teaching orientation and mobility to older adults.* New York, NY: AFB Press.

Guth, D. A., Rieser, J. J., & Ashmead, D. H. (2010). Perceiving to move and moving to perceive: Control of locomotion by students with vision loss. In W. R. Wiener, R. L. Welsh, & B. B. Blasch (Eds.), *Foundations of orientation and mobility: Vol. I. History and theory* (3rd ed., pp. 3–44). New York, NY: AFB Press.

Harkey, D. L., Carter, D., Bentzen, B. L., & Barlow, J. M. (2007). *Accessible pedestrian signals: A guide to best practices* (National Cooperative Highway Research Program Document 150). Washington, DC: The National Academies of Sciences, Engineering, and Medicine, Transportation Research Board.

Herrera, R., Cmar, J., & Fazzi, D. (2016). Orientation and mobility programs. In S. Z. Sacks & M. C. Zatta (Eds.), *Keys to educational success: Teaching students with visual impairments and multiple disabilities* (pp. 294–335). New York, NY: AFB Press.

Hill, E., & Ponder, P. (1976). *Orientation and mobility techniques: A guide for the practitioner.* New York, NY: American Foundation for the Blind.

Hong, S. P., Park, H., Kwon, J. S., & Yoo, E. (2014). Effectiveness of eccentric viewing training for daily visual activities for individuals with age-related macular degeneration: A systematic review and meta-analysis. *NeuroRehabilitation, 34*(3), 587–595.

Hunter, R. (2004). *Madeline Hunter's mastery teaching: Increasing instructional effectiveness in elementary and secondary schools* (Updated ed.). Thousand Oaks, CA: Corwin Press.

Jacobson, W. H. (1993). *The art and science of teaching orientation and mobility to persons with visual impairments.* New York, NY: AFB Press.

Jacobson, W. H. (2013). *The art and science of teaching orientation and mobility to persons with visual impairments* (2nd ed.). New York, NY: AFB Press.

Kim, D. S., & Wall Emerson, R. (2012). Effect of cane length on drop-off detection performance. *Journal of Visual Impairment & Blindness, 106*(1), 31–35.

Kim, D. S., Wall Emerson, R., & Curtis, A. (2009). Drop-off detection with the long cane: Effects of different cane techniques on performance. *Journal of Visual Impairment & Blindness, 103*(9), 519–530.

Kim, D. S., Wall Emerson, R., & Curtis, A. (2010). Ergonomic factors related to drop-off detection with the long cane: Effects of cane tips and techniques. *Human Factors: The Journal of Human Factors and Ergonomics Society, 52*(3), 456–465.

Kim, D. S., Wall Emerson, R., & Gaves, E. (2016). Travel in adverse winter weather conditions by blind pedestrians: Effect of cane tip design on travel on snow. *Journal of Visual Impairment & Blindness, 110*(1), 53–58.

Kirschbaum, J. B., Axelson, P. W., Longmuir, P. E., Mispagel, K. M., Stein, J. A., & Yamada, D. A. (2001). *Designing sidewalks and trails for access, Part II of II: Best practices design guide.* Washington, DC: US Department of Transportation, Federal Highway Administration. Retrieved from http://www.fhwa.dot.gov/environment/bicycle_pedestrian/publications/sidewalk2/sidewalks207.cfm

Knott, N. I. (2002). *Teaching orientation and mobility in the schools: An instructor's companion.* New York, NY: AFB Press.

LaGrow, S. J. (2010). Improving perception for orientation and mobility. In W. R. Wiener, R. L. Welsh, & B. B. Blasch (Eds.), *Foundations of orientation and mobility: Vol. II. Instructional strategies and practical applications* (3rd ed., pp. 3–26). New York, NY: AFB Press.

LaGrow, S. J., Blasch, B. B., & De l'Aune, W. (1997). The effect of hand position on detection distance for object and surface preview when using the long cane for nonvisual travel. *RE:view, 28*(4), 169–175.

LaGrow, S. J., & Long, R. G. (2011). *Orientation and mobility: Techniques for independence* (2nd ed.). Alexandria, VA: Association for Education and Rehabilitation of the Blind and Visually Impaired.

LaGrow, S. J., & Weessies, M. (1994). *Orientation and mobility: Techniques for independence.* Palmerston, New Zealand: Dunmore Publishing Limited.

Lolli, D., Sauerburger, D., & Bourquin, E. A. (2010). Teaching orientation and mobility to students with vision and hearing Loss. In W. R. Wiener, R. L. Welsh, & B. B. Blasch (Eds.), *Foundations of orientation and mobility: Vol. II. Instructional strategies and practical applications* (3rd ed., pp. 537–563). New York, NY: AFB Press.

Long, R. G., & Giudice, N. A. (2010). Establishing and maintaining orientation for mobility. In W. R. Wiener, R. L. Welsh, & B. B. Blasch (Eds.), *Foundations of orientation and mobility: Vol. I. History and theory* (3rd ed., pp. 45–62). New York, NY: AFB Press.

Ludt, R. (1997). Three types of glare: Low vision O&M assessment and remediation. *RE:view, 29*(3), 101–113.

Ludt, R., & Goodrich, G. L. (2002). Changes in visual perceptual detection distances for low vision travelers as a result of dynamic visual assessment and training. *Journal of Visual Impairment & Blindness, 96*(1), 7–21.

National Center for Statistics and Analysis. (2016, May). *Traffic safety facts: 2014 data. Pedestrians* (Report No. DOT HS 812 270). Washington, DC: US Department of Transportation, National Highway Traffic Safety Administration.

Penrod, W. M., Smith, D. L., Haneline, R., & Corbett, M. P. (2010). Teaching the use of electronic travel aids and electronic orientation aids. In W. R. Wiener, R. L. Welsh, & B. B. Blasch (Eds.), *Foundations of orientation and mobility: Vol. II. Instructional strategies and practical applications* (3rd ed., pp. 462–485). New York, NY: AFB Press.

Pogrund, R. L., & Fazzi, D. L. (Eds.). (2002). *Early focus: Working with young children who are blind or visually impaired and their families* (2nd ed.). New York, NY: AFB Press.

Pogrund, R. L., Sewell, D., Anderson, H., Calaci, L., Cowart, M. F., Gonzalez, C. M., . . . Robserson-Smith, B. (Eds.). (2012). *TAPS—Teaching age-appropriate purposeful skills: An orientation and mobility curriculum for students with visual impairments* (3rd ed.). Austin: Texas School for the Blind and Visually Impaired.

Rodgers, M. D., & Wall Emerson, R. (2005). Human factor analysis of long cane design: Weight and length. *Journal of Visual Impairment & Blindness, 99*(10), 622–632.

Rosen, S. (2010a). Improving sensorimotor functioning for orientation and mobility. In W. R. Wiener, R. L. Welsh, & B. B. Blasch (Eds.), *Foundations of orientation and mobility: Vol. II. Instructional strategies and practical applications* (3rd ed., pp. 118–137). New York, NY: AFB Press.

Rosen, S. (2010b). Kinesiology and sensorimotor functioning for students with vision loss. In W. R. Wiener, R. L. Welsh, & B. B. Blasch (Eds.), *Foundations of orientation and mobility: Vol. I. History and theory* (3rd ed., pp. 138–172). New York, NY: AFB Press.

Rosen, S., & Crawford, J. S. (2010). Teaching orientation and mobility to learners with visual, physical, and health impairments. In W. R. Wiener, R. L. Welsh, & B. B. Blasch (Eds.), *Foundations of orientation and mobility: Vol. II. Instructional strategies and practical applications* (3rd ed., pp. 564–623). New York, NY: AFB Press.

Sauerburger, D. (1999). Developing criteria and judgment of safety for crossing streets with gaps in traffic. *Journal of Visual Impairment & Blindness, 93*(7), 447–450.

Sauerburger, D. (2005). Street crossings: Analyzing risks, developing strategies, and making decisions. *Journal of Visual Impairment & Blindness, 99*(10), 659.

Sauerburger, D. (2006). Instructional strategies for teaching judgment in detecting gaps for crossing streets with no traffic controls. *RE:view, 37*(4), 177–188.

Sauerburger, D. (n.d.). Self-study guide: Preparing visually impaired students for uncontrolled crossings. Retrieved from http://www .sauerburger.org/dona/crosscredit.html

Scheffers, W., & Myers, L. (2012). Part 4: Supplement: Street crossings for travelers who are visually impaired. In R. L. Pogrund, D. Sewell, H. Anderson, L. Calaci, M. F. Cowart, C. M. Gonzalez, . . . B. Robserson-Smith (Eds.), *TAPS—Teaching age-appropriate purposeful skills: An orientation and mobility curriculum for students with visual impairments* (3rd ed.). Austin: Texas School for the Blind and Visually Impaired.

Schroeder, B., Rodegerdts, L., Jenior, P., Myers, E., Cunningham, C., Salamati, K., . . . Bentzen, B. L. (2016). *Crossing solutions at roundabouts and channelized turn lanes for pedestrians with vision disabilities: A guidebook* (National Cooperative Highway Research Program Report 834). Washington, DC: The National Academies of Sciences, Engineering, and Medicine, Transportation Research Board.

Scott, A. C., Barlow, J. M., Guth, D. A., Bentzen, B. L., Cunningham, C. M., & Long, R. (2011a). Nonvisual cues for aligning to cross streets. *Journal of Visual Impairment & Blindness, 105*(10), 648–661.

Scott, A. C., Barlow, J. M., Guth, D. A., Bentzen, B. L., Cunningham, C. M., & Long, R. (2011b). Walking between the lines: Nonvisual cues for maintaining headings during street crossings. *Journal of Visual Impairment & Blindness, 105*(10), 662–674.

Skellenger, A. C., & Sapp, W. K. (2010). Teaching orientation and mobility for the early childhood years. In W. R. Wiener, R. L. Welsh, & B. B. Blasch (Eds.), *Foundations of orientation and mobility: Vol. II. Instructional strategies and practical applications* (3rd ed., pp. 163–207). New York, NY: AFB Press.

Smith, D. L., & Penrod, W. M. (2010). Adaptive technology for orientation and mobility. In W. R. Wiener, R. L. Welsh, & B. B. Blasch (Eds.), *Foundations of orientation and mobility: Vol. I. History and theory* (3rd ed., pp. 241–276). New York, NY: AFB Press.

United States Access Board. (2011). *Proposed accessibility guidelines for pedestrian facilities in the public right-of-way.* Washington, DC: Author.

Wall, R. S. (2001). An exploratory study of how travelers with visual impairments modify travel techniques in winter. *Journal of Visual Impairment & Blindness, 95*(12), 752–756.

Wall, R. S., & Ashmead, D. H. (2002). Biomechanical movements in experienced cane users with and without visual impairments. *Journal of Visual Impairment & Blindness, 96*(7), 501–515.

Wall Emerson, R., & Sauerburger, D. (2008). Detecting approaching vehicles at streets with no traffic control. *Journal of Visual Impairment & Blindness, 102*(12), 747–760.

Wall Emerson, R. S., & De l'Aune, W. R. (2010). Research and the orientation and mobility specialist. In W. R. Wiener, R. L. Welsh, & B. B. Blasch (Eds.), *Foundations of orientation and mobility: Vol. I. History and theory* (3rd ed., pp. 569–595). New York, NY: AFB Press.

Wiener, W. R., Welsh, R. L., & Blasch, B. B. (Eds.). (2010). *Foundations of orientation and mobility* (3rd ed., Vols. I–II) New York, NY: AFB Press.

Willoughby, D. M., & Monthei, S. L. (1998). *Modular instruction for independent travel for students who are blind or visually impaired: Preschool through high school.* Baltimore, MD: National Federation of the Blind.

Wright, T. S., & Wolery, M. (2014). Evaluating the effectiveness of roadside instruction in teaching youth with visual impairments street crossings. *The Journal of Special Education, 48*(1), 46–58.

Glossary

Accessible pedestrian signal (APS) A device that provides information (audible, vibrotactile, or both) that is accessible to pedestrians who are blind or visually impaired about when the Walk signal is on. Additional features include a pushbutton locator tone, a tactile arrow aligned with the direction of travel on the crosswalk, and automatic volume adjustment.

Address system A systematic use of numbers to identify homes or buildings in an area or rooms within a building. *See also* **Numbering system**.

Adventitious Occurring or appearing later in life.

Affective component An individual's feelings about or comfort using an O&M technique, and the extent to which the individual will use that technique freely.

Alleyways Narrow lanes that usually run behind buildings; typically found in older parts of town and cities as rear-access or service roads.

Allocentric frame of reference An understanding of the location of objects or places as related to one another, independent of the individual's current location in space. *See also* **Object-to-object spatial relationships**.

Americans with Disabilities Act (ADA) Federal legislation defining the responsibilities of and requirements for municipalities and transportation providers to make public facilities and transportation accessible to individuals with disabilities.

Arc The semicircle created when the tip of the cane is moved from one side to the other.

Arc height The distance the cane lifts up from the walking surface at the apex, ideally less than 1 inch.

Arc width The distance between the furthest points of contact for the cane tip, ideally 2 inches beyond the widest part of the individual's body.

Ascending Going up or climbing, as in a set of stairs or a mountain.

Auditory alignment Using available auditory cues such as traffic sounds to establish or maintain a straight line for travel.

Behavioral-learning theory A set of principles that attempts to explain learning in terms of observable changes in the behavior of a person. Includes behavioral reinforcement principles.

Blended curb Transition to the street from the sidewalk that has a grade less than 5 percent, where the entire corner area may be level with the street. Also referred to as a depressed corner, blended transition, or fan-shaped ramp.

Blur interpretation Applying problem solving and prior knowledge about the size, shape, color, or typical location of an item to help interpret something that is viewed without clarity.

Body image Knowledge of the parts of the body, their labels, functions, spatial relationships to other body parts, and range of movements. Also referred to as body concepts.

Boulevard A type of street with wide medians separating lanes of traffic. *See also* **Median**.

Bus lift A platform that raises and lowers to assist people who use wheelchairs or who are otherwise unable to climb stairs move onto and off of buses.

Cane coverage The area previewed by the placement and movement of the cane while the individual travels.

Cane storage Techniques for stowing folding and rigid (nonfolding) canes in a variety of home, school, and work environments.

Cane tip drift A tendency for the cane tip to wander to the side, beyond the optimum extent of coverage.

Center platform station A transit station with a boarding platform that is between two trains or buses, with vehicles typically traveling in opposite directions on each side of the platform. *See also* **Side platform station**.

Channelized turn lane Lane for vehicles turning right that is separated from the main traffic lanes by a triangular island to allow right-turning vehicles to continue moving through an intersection.

Clue Information that, when paired with additional information, can be used by an individual to help in orientation or the location of objects, people, or places in the environment.

Cognitive component The understanding of why, when, and where an O&M technique should be used during travel in changing environments.

Cognitive-learning theory A set of principles that attempts to explain learning in terms of the mental processes that a person uses to more fully understand a concept or strategy.

Cognitive map A mental representation of a specific spatial layout, which includes object-to-object or survey-level relationships. *See also* **Survey-level frame of reference; Object-to-object spatial relationships.**

Cognitive mapping The ability to develop a mental representation or image of a physical space, specific location, geographic area, or travel route.

Cognitive orientation process A multistep process that includes utilizing sensory perception, analyzing perceived information, selecting relevant information to inform orientation, planning a course of action or next steps, and taking the planned course of action in travel.

Commuter rail An electric or diesel-powered urban passenger-train service consisting of local, short-distance travel operating between a central city and adjacent suburbs or nearby regional cities.

Comparative measurement A correlation of the length, size, or distance among two or more things.

Compass directions Specialized directions that are dictated by the magnetic polar fields of the earth. The four main directions are north, south, east, and west. Intermediate directions that can be used for orientation purposes include northwest, northeast, southwest, and southeast. Also known as *cardinal or polarcentric directions*.

Concept A mental representation, image, or idea of concrete objects, as well as of intangible notions such as feelings.

Congenital Present at birth.

Congested-area technique A modified cane technique in crowded areas or small spaces in which the cane is held closer to the body to temporarily shorten the extension of the cane tip into the immediate area.

Constant-contact technique A standard cane touch technique in which the cane tip remains in contact with the ground at all times.

Coordination The ability to use different parts of the body and muscles together smoothly and efficiently for purposeful movement.

Corner radius An indication of the roundness of a street corner. Also known as *curb radius*.

Cross slope A gradient in the walking surface that is perpendicular to the line of travel.

Crosswalk A marked or unmarked location near the intersection of two streets where pedestrians are supposed to make their crossing.

Cue A signal that something is about to happen or a certain location or object is about to be reached.

Curb feelers Functional modifications or attachments to wheelchairs that enable an individual to maintain tactile contact with a wall or other surface while moving.

Curb ramp A sloped area leading to a crosswalk to provide pedestrian and wheelchair access to the street crossing.

Cycle (traffic signal) One complete sequence of all possible traffic movements at an intersection.

Descending Moving downward or walking down a set of stairs or sloping walkway.

Detectable warning surface A walking surface of a specific texture that is detectable underfoot or with a long cane and standardized in the ADA as a warning for persons with visual impairments about their next step.

Diagonal technique A cane technique used in familiar indoor areas or with a guide in which the cane is held in one hand and is positioned diagonally across and in front of the body.

Direction taking A technique by which an individual can use a sound source or a tactile surface such as a wall to gain a straight line of travel from a parallel sound or surface or to square off to a perpendicular sound or surface.

Discovery learning A teaching strategy in which the material to be learned is uncovered by the learner in the course of solving a problem or completing a task. *See also* **Problem-based model of instruction.**

Disorientation Confusion related to not knowing one's location in the environment.

Drop-off A change in level found at curbs, sidewalks, and stairs.

Drop-off lesson A means to teach and assess the full integration of orientation and mobility skills and concepts, including information gathering and problem solving, in an environment that takes into account the learner's age and ability.

Dynamic scanning The systematic use of visual scanning while moving to preview the travel environment to plan for a clear path of travel or to look for landmarks, signage, and other information about the surroundings. *See also* **Scanning**.

Eccentric viewing Intentionally looking to one side of an object to focus the image with a functional portion of the retina; using peripheral vision to look around a blind spot in one's vision.

Eccentric viewing angle The necessary position of the eye to direct the clearest peripheral vision forward for travel.

Echolocation The use of reflected sound (including ambient sound) to detect the presence of objects, such as walls, buildings, doors, and openings.

Egocentric frame of reference An understanding of the location of objects or places in the environment as related to one's own body or body position.

Electronic orientation aid (EOA) A device used for orientation and navigation that may be external to the learner and mounted on a pole or wall, or that may be carried with the traveler.

Environmental features Characteristics found in the environment, such as the size, shape, color, and texture of landscapes, telephone poles, parking meters, and sidewalks, and of their spatial regularities in built environments.

Environmental flow The changes in perception during movement of various types of sensory information and distances and directions between the learner and surrounding objects.

Exclusive pedestrian phase A signal timing strategy that provides the pedestrian Walk signal and time to cross when all cars at the intersection have a red signal.

Expanded core curriculum (ECC) The body of knowledge and skills, beyond the core academic curriculum, that students with visual impairments need to learn to lead full, independent lives. This includes, among others, independent living skills, orientation and mobility, assistive technology skills, and sensory efficiency skills.

Experiential knowledge General or specific information and understanding gained from past experiences.

Express bus service A bus service that operates on a faster schedule than normal bus service between two destinations, either by making fewer stops or taking a quicker route; often found in major metropolitan areas during peak commuting hours.

Extension A movement of the joints that increases the angle between the bones of the joint. For joints that move forward and backward, extension refers to movement in the posterior direction. The opposite of flexed.

Familiar environment Any indoor or outdoor physical setting in which the learner has traveled previously, and is therefore consciously aware of the surroundings or layout.

Familiarization The organized process of learning the arrangement of a room, building, or other area by using systematic strategies to locate landmarks and relate their location to other locations or features in the environment. Also known as *self-familiarization*.

Fare Payment to ride in a public transportation vehicle, or a transportation system owned by a private entity. Means of payment include tickets, tokens, cash, transfers, passes, fare cards, and smart cards.

Field of view The extent of the surroundings that can be seen at any given moment without moving the eyes.

Fixed-route service Transit service provided on a repetitive, predetermined fixed-schedule basis along a specific route with vehicles stopping to pick up and deliver passengers to specific locations.

Flexed A movement of the joints that decreases the angle between the bones of the joint. For joints that move forward and backward, flexion refers to movement in the anterior direction. The opposite of extension.

Forearm The part of the arm between the elbow and wrist. Also known as *lower arm*.

Four-leg right-angle intersection A basic square-shaped intersection of two streets crossing at right angles (commonly referred to as a plus or plus-shaped intersection by O&M specialists).

Fully actuated signals Traffic signals at which the timing changes depending on presence of and the amount of traffic in each lane.

Gait A person's pattern of walking.

Geographic information system (GIS) An electronic database that stores, edits, analyzes, and displays spatial or geographic data.

Glare An uncomfortable sensation produced by too much light in the visual field that can cause both discomfort and a reduction in visual acuity.

Glare remediation Proactive methods used to reduce the damaging impact of glare on a learner's ability to function visually and travel in the environment.

Global positioning system (GPS) An electronic position-sensing technology based on orbiting satellites that communicate with portable transmitters and receivers that, in interaction with a GIS, can identify a person's exact location and relationship to landmarks or coordinates in the environment.

Grasp The way in which an entity, such as a cane or guide's arm, is held.

Grass line The area where the sidewalk meets the vegetation or dirt found along the edge of the sidewalk furthest from the street, usually detectable with a cane or underfoot.

Gridline pattern The systematic exploration of an area in which the learner moves back and forth across a space to locate landmarks and establish object-to-object relationships for future reference. *See also* **Perimeter pattern; Reference point; Systematic search pattern.**

Grip (cane) The top portion of the cane, which is grasped by the learner. It is typically black and made of rubber, but may come in other colors and materials. Also known as *cane grip*.

Grip strength The firmness of a learner's grasp of an object or a guide's arm.

Guided practice The opportunity to review a newly learned skill with observation and support from an O&M specialist, teacher, family member, or peer.

Guide team The active engagement in the travel process by both the guide and learner, who maintain awareness of surroundings and orientation and adjust positions or techniques as needed.

Guide technique Procedure for giving appropriate assistance to a person with a visual impairment to travel safely and efficiently with a guide.

Hand trailing A technique used to establish or maintain a line of travel or locate a specific destination by contacting and following a wall or other surface with the hand. Best used in conjunction with the long cane.

Heel strike The contact of the heel with the ground as the foot steps down.

Hines break A technique used to accept, correct, or refuse assistance from a potential guide.

Hyperextension (hyperextended) The movement or overstretching of joints beyond the normal range of motion.

Index finger grasp A cane hold in which the index finger is extended along the flat edge of the cane's grip, the thumb is up, and the remaining fingers are flexed around the grip so that the grip rests comfortably against the palm of the hand. *See also* **Pencil grasp; Thumb grasp.**

Information processing Learning that is a result of mental connections and associations among points of information that can be saved for later retrieval and use. *See also* **Cognitive-learning theory.**

In rhythm Walking with the cane tip striking the ground at the same time as the heel strike.

In step Walking with the cane tip striking the ground on the side opposite to where the lead foot is stepping.

Intersecting sidewalk A point at which two perpendicular sidewalks meet and a pedestrian can change travel direction.

Intersection analysis A process by which an individual examines intersection geometry, traffic volume and speeds, traffic controls and movement patterns, and visibility in preparation for making a crossing.

Intersection geometry The layout, design, and shape of the intersection, as well as slopes and curves or angles of the sidewalk and roadway surface.

Kinesthetic The awareness of movement that results from the interaction of tactile, proprioceptive, and vestibular inputs. *See also* **Proprioceptive.**

Label A name given to an object or place so that different individuals can consistently identify the same item or area.

Landing (curb ramp) A level area at the top or bottom of a curb ramp. Also referred to as a turning space.

Landing (stairs) A level area at the end of a flight of stairs or between flights of stairs.

Landmark An environmental feature that is easily detectable and recognized, constant, and has a known, permanent location in the environment that can offer specific information about an individual's location. Landmarks may be further delineated as *primary* (readily encountered along the travel path) or *secondary* (not readily encountered along the travel path due to their size or location).

Landscape strip A regional term used to describe the grass or other landscaping often found between the sidewalk and the street. Other names include collector strip, parking strip, planter strip, park strip, buffer, furniture zone, landscape area, greenway, parkway, and utility strip.

Leading pedestrian interval (LPI) A signal timing strategy that provides pedestrians a three to six second head start before the vehicular green signal to allow them to establish their presence in the crosswalk.

Learning styles The ways in which individuals absorb, process, comprehend, retain, and use information.

Light rail An electric railway typically loading from a low platform with rails in shared or exclusive right-of-way.

Linear measurement Determining the basic dimensions of length, width, and height using standard increments or units.

Local bus service The most common type of bus service in which buses stop every block or two along a route according to a timetable. Also referred to as circulator, feeder, neighborhood, or shuttle service.

Long cane The primary mobility device used by individuals with visual impairments to provide object and surface preview through the probe of the cane tip and the vibrotactile feedback conducted through the tip and shaft of the cane to the hand of the learner.

Low-floor bus A type of bus designed so that the front of the bus can be lowered to within 9.8 inches (25 cm) of the road surface, or about 3.9 inches (10 cm) from the sidewalk or curb to enable passengers who use wheelchairs or those who cannot use steps to board the bus.

Low vision A visual impairment, even after best correction, that is severe enough to interfere with an individual's ability to learn or perform tasks of daily life, but with the potential to use vision for some tasks along with multisensory approaches and compensatory strategies and devices to support visual input.

Magnifier A device used to increase the size of an image through the use of lenses or lens systems.

Map A multi-dimensional visual, tactile, or tactile-visual representation of spatial layout.

Measurement The act or process of determining the exact or approximate dimensions of an object or space using a given unit.

Median A traffic island in the center of a roadway intended to separate lanes of traffic traveling in opposite directions. It may also serve as a pedestrian safety area.

Midline An imaginary vertical line down the middle of the body separating the left and right sides.

Mnemonics Memory aids or learning techniques that incorporate acronyms or easily remembered phrases to assist in the recall of steps, lists, or formulas.

Mobility The process of moving from an individual's present location to a desired destination safely, efficiently, and as independently as possible. *See also* **Orientation; Orientation and mobility (O&M).**

Mobility device A device used to support movement, such as the long cane.

Mobility techniques A set of specific skills and strategies for travel developed for individuals who are visually impaired, including those with additional disabilities.

Model A three-dimensional representation of an object or spatial layout.

Models of instruction A framework or broad set of approaches to instruction stemming from a particular learning theory.

Motor Related to movement.

Motor component The physical ability to demonstrate or execute an O&M technique, incorporating strength, balance, coordination, and stamina.

Multi-leg intersection An intersection at which more than two streets meet, resulting in five or six legs converging at the intersection.

Nonverbal cue A physical cue used to signal the need to execute or change a technique without talking. May be used frequently with experienced guide teams.

Numbering system A systematic pattern or arrangement of numbers to identify buildings in an area or rooms within a building. *See also* **Address system.**

Object preview The detection of an object in the path of travel by a mobility device prior to reaching the object.

Object-to-object spatial relationships Spatial associations between objects or places as related to one another, independent of the individual's current location in space. *See also* **Allocentric frame of reference.**

Obstacle An object or item that obstructs the travel path and must be negotiated.

Occupational therapist A professional who focuses on maximizing an individual's potential for age-appropriate functional behaviors and fine motor skills through purposeful activities.

Offset intersection An intersection at which the junction of two segments of the same street are not directly opposite each other, as when two three-leg intersections are located in close proximity. *See also* **Three-leg (T) intersection.**

Orientation The process of using sensory information and conceptual understanding to determine one's location and destination in relation to significant objects in the environment. The knowledge of the distance and direction relative to things observed or remembered in the surroundings and ability to keep track of these spatial relationships as they change during movement or travel. *See also* **Mobility; Orientation and mobility (O&M).**

Orientation and mobility (O&M) The professional field dealing with systematic techniques by which individuals who are blind or who have low vision orient themselves to home, school, and community environments and move about independently. *See also* **Mobility; Orientation.**

Orientation and mobility (O&M) specialist A professional who specializes in teaching travel skills to individuals who are blind or who have low vision in home, school, and community environments, including use of sensory and cognitive skills, specialized cane techniques, adaptive and mainstream technology, and travel with guides.

Orientation and mobility (O&M) specialist positioning The position from which the O&M specialist monitors the travel techniques being taught and practiced.

Parallel Positioned alongside a feature or sound in the environment. *See also* **Perpendicular.**

Paratransit services A transportation system for persons with disabilities who are unable to use fixed-route bus and rail services. Trips are scheduled by riders.

Pedestrian hybrid beacon Traffic control device for pedestrian crossings at uncontrolled, marked crosswalks. The beacon has a specific sequence for vehicles: it is dark (not lit) until activated by a pedestrian pushbutton, after which it displays a stop signal for vehicles and a Walk signal for pedestrians.

Pedestrian phase The calculated time provided for pedestrian crossing in a traffic signal cycle, including the walk interval (Walk or walking-man symbol), the pedestrian clearance interval (Don't Walk or flashing orange hand), and buffer time. Each crosswalk may be timed differently depending on the phasing and timing plan for the intersection.

Pedestrian pushbutton An electronic control, typically located on a pole on the side of the sidewalk furthest from the parallel street, that enables pedestrians to change traffic signal timing and activate a Walk signal, providing adequate time to cross the intersection.

Pencil grasp A hold in which the cane is held in a manner similar to that of a pencil, with the cane grip resting between the middle and index fingers and the thumb applying light pressure to keep the grasp firm and the cane steady. *See also* **Index finger grasp; Thumb grasp.**

Perception The way in which a person receives, interprets, and organizes stimuli. The ability to obtain information about the characteristics, identity, and location of objects by looking, listening, touching, and using other forms of active, direct observation.

Perimeter pattern The systematic exploration of an area in which the learner moves along the outside border of a space and remembers the various features in order, starting from a salient reference point. *See also* **Gridline pattern; Reference point; Systematic search pattern.**

Peripheral vision The perception of objects, motion, or color outside the direct line of vision. Also referred to as side vision.

Perpendicular Positioned at a 90-degree angle to a feature or surface; intersecting. *See also* **Parallel.**

Phase (traffic signal) One segment of the traffic signal cycle for a specified movement of traffic at an intersection.

Physical prompt The use of touch to remind a learner to execute, change, or refine a technique or skill.

Physical therapist A professional who specializes in the development and functioning of gross motor skills.

Point of information Any perceived sensory stimulus that can be used by an individual to determine position, location, or line of travel. Can also refer to points of interest entered into a GPS for later reference and navigation.

Posture The vertical alignment of body parts over the body's center of gravity.

Preferred retinal locus (PRL) The most acute peripheral vision available to view around a blind spot. Also known as *trained retinal locus (TRL).*

Pre-timed signals Traffic signals that run on a predetermined cycle that provides a predictable amount of time for each crossing. Also known as *fixed time signals.*

Problem-based model of instruction An approach to instruction that incorporates authentic tasks or projects to engage learners in constructing new knowledge. *See also* **Discovery learning.**

Proprioceptive The sense or perception of the relative positions and movements of parts of the body received through the bones, joints, and skeletal system. *See also* **Kinesthetic.**

Protective techniques A combination of procedures in which the individual positions the hand to provide protection from objects that may come in contact with the upper or lower body. Best used in conjunction with the long cane.

Rapid rail transit An electric railway run on a dedicated line, with stations above or below street level.

Recovery from veer Techniques used to re-locate a desired sidewalk after realizing that the intended line of travel has been lost. *See also* **Veer.**

Reference point The fixed position used for orientation during familiarization from which the learner systematically explores a space. *See also* **Gridline pattern; Perimeter pattern.**

Roundabout An intersection where traffic moves around a circular island in the middle, with entering vehicles yielding to traffic traveling within the circulatory roadway.

Route A path followed to reach a destination.

Route planning Selecting a sequence of directions or path to follow to reach a given destination.

Route reversal Reversing a route from a destination to return to a point of origin.

Route shape The description of a travel path according to its basic shape, such as I, L, U, and Z-shaped.

Scanning The systematic use of eye movements to search for targets or overall layouts of open areas. Also referred to as *visual scanning. See also* **Dynamic scanning.**

Scotoma A gap or blind spot in the visual field that may be caused by damage to the retina or visual pathways.

Self-advocacy The ability of a person to communicate or assert to others his or her preferences or needs.

Self-familiarization *See* **Familiarization.**

Self-to-object spatial relationships Spatial associations between a learner and objects in the environment that change predictably with the individual's movement.

Semi-actuated signals Intersection signal at which the minor street has detectors to change the traffic signal on the major street. Signals can be activated by a pedestrian or a vehicle.

Sensory information Sensory input received from the environment that can be incorporated for the purposes of integration and problem solving.

Sensory integration The neurological process that organizes sensory input from one's own body and the environment to support effective movement.

Sequence for instruction The steps or order of skills taught as part of a unit of instruction.

Shaft (cane) The hollow length comprising the main body of the cane. Made of different materials, its length may vary according to the height of the individual. Also known as *cane shaft.*

Shoreline The border between the area being walked upon and the surrounding area.

Shorelining *See* **Touch-and-drag technique; Touch-trailing technique.**

Side platform station A transit station with two separated platforms, with trains or buses running on trackways between the platforms. *See also* **Center platform station.**

Skewed intersection An intersection at which two streets meet at an angle where one angle is 75 degrees or less.

Skip step A technique for getting back in step once out of step in which a learner inserts a skip into her step pattern to regain the in-step position.

Smart card A pocket-sized card with embedded integrated circuits that can be used for payment and ticketing on transit systems, among other uses.

Social-learning theory A set of principles that attempts to explain learning that develops in a social context, through observation, modeling, and social supports and exchanges.

Soliciting assistance Obtaining information from another individual about a destination or surrounding area.

Sound localization Determination of the direction of a sound source; may be used to orient oneself to the environment.

Sound shadow An area of diminished sound created by the blockage of background noise by a large object positioned between the listener and the sound.

Spatial concepts Mental representations of how people, places, and things are positioned and located in the environment.

Spatial orientation The process of establishing and maintaining one's position in space relative to objects; the process of learning the spatial relationships among objects in a place.

Spatial updating The ability to keep track of spatial relationships while moving to accurately know one's current location and the changing location of relevant objects in the environment, adjusting the travel path as needed.

Squaring off Aligning and positioning one's body in relation to an object to establish a line of direction, usually perpendicular to the object, and a definite position in the environment.

Stop announcements Automated or driver-spoken announcements made on transit vehicles stating the location of the bus or rail stop as the vehicle approaches a stop.

Stop request system A method by which a passenger calls for a stop on a transit system, such as using a pull cord or pushing a raised bar.

Stop sign–controlled street A crossing at which two streets meet, where one (two-way stop) or both streets (all-way or four-way stop) have stop signs at which vehicles must halt. For two-way stops, the streets without stop signs are considered uncontrolled crossings.

Street-corner familiarization A procedure to become familiar with the layout of a street corner to recognize it and make the best decisions regarding crossings, alignment for crossings, or recovery from veer during crossings.

Stride length The distance between successive steps of the same foot.

Support cane An ambulatory aid that consists of a single vertical post with a handgrip at hip height. The cane may have a single point of contact on the ground or may have a base consisting of three or four small legs.

Surface preview The detection of changes in the surface to be traveled with a long cane, most notably changes in the texture, density, slope, and level.

Survey-level frame of reference The connection of one place or location to another that spans a small or large geographic area, allowing for flexible route planning and travel.

Switching (transferring) sides with a guide A technique used to swap sides from one arm of the guide to the other as the learner and guide walk together.

Systematic search pattern A set configuration used to visually or tactilely search for a dropped or lost item or item of interest, such as concentric circles or a perimeter or grid pattern. *See also* **Gridline pattern; Perimeter pattern**.

Tactile alignment The use of tactile cues, the long cane, or a body part in proximity with a relatively flat-edged environmental feature to establish or maintain a straight line for travel.

Tactile map A three-dimensional representation of spatial layout using raised surfaces to provide information that is perceptible to touch.

Task analysis The division of an assignment or technique into smaller, attainable segments that are eventually combined to achieve full completion of the task.

Telescope An optical device that makes small objects appear closer and larger.

Three-leg (T) intersection An intersection at which two streets meet, with one street ending at the intersection with the other.

Three-point-touch technique A cane technique used to follow a raised surface to locate a desired objective on a higher-level surface.

Thumb grasp A cane hold in which the thumb is extended along the flat edge of the cane's grip. *See also* **Index finger grasp; Pencil grasp**.

Time-distance estimation The ability to judge a distance based on the time it takes to travel between two points at a consistent rate of walking.

Tip (cane) The bottom portion of the cane that provides contact with the walking surface. It comes in a variety of shapes and sizes and is frequently made of nylon or metal. Also known as *cane tip*.

Touch-and-drag technique A cane technique used to maintain a desired line of travel along a border or surface by dragging the cane tip from the opposite side of the surface to the surface to be followed. Also known as *shorelining*.

Touch-and-slide technique A cane technique used to detect subtle surface changes, such as blended curbs or expansion joints, by slowing the walking pace and sliding the tip further forward at each point of contact.

Touch-trailing technique A cane technique used to maintain a line of travel parallel to a border or trailed surface by alternating touching the surface being walked upon and the differing surface material to the side of the path. Also known as *shorelining*.

Two-point touch technique A cane technique used by travelers in a variety of indoor and outdoor environments. The cane is swung from side to side, low to the ground, touching down at each end of the arc. Also known as *touch technique*.

Tracing Visually following single or multiple stationary lines in the environment, such as hedge lines, roof lines, or baseboards.

Tracking Visually following a moving object.

Traffic controls The signs, signals, and markings that dictate the rules for vehicular traffic in a given area.

Traffic engineers Trained professionals who specialize in transportation systems, particularly the design and maintenance of streets and highways.

Traffic signal–controlled streets Streets where vehicular and pedestrian movement is controlled by some type of traffic signal, which can be pre-timed, semi-actuated, or fully actuated.

Trolley (streetcar) A transit mode composed of lightweight electric vehicles running on tracks along city streets and drawing power from overhead wires.

Uncontrolled street crossing A street crossing where traffic does not have a yield or stop sign or a signal at the crosswalk location.

Veer To divert from an intended, straight line of travel. *See also* **Recovery from veer**.

Vehicular traffic patterns The direction, pattern of movement, volume, and speed of traffic moving through an intersection.

Verbal prompt The use of spoken instructions to remind a learner to execute, change, or refine a technique or skill.

Verification technique A cane technique used in conjunction with systematic visual and auditory skills by individuals who have sufficient vision and can benefit from increased-distance visual awareness.

Visual field The area that can be seen when looking straight ahead, measured in degrees from the fixation point.

Walker An ambulatory aid generally consisting of a lightweight, U-shaped frame of four legs, with a waist-high grip.

Wayfinding Planning and strategic components that guide action, deliberate movement, and the ability to reach a goal while traveling.

Index

About the Authors

Diane L. Fazzi, PhD, a certified orientation and mobility (O&M) specialist and educator for over 30 years, is Associate Dean, Charter College of Education, and Coordinator of the Orientation and Mobility Specialist Training Program, California State University, Los Angeles. Dr. Fazzi is coeditor of *Early Focus: Working with Young Children Who Are Blind or Visually Impaired Children and Their Families* (2nd edition) and coauthor of *Imagining the Possibilities: Creative Approaches to Orientation and Mobility Instruction for Persons Who Are Visually Impaired.* Her research interests include early childhood development for children with visual impairments, including those with additional disabilities. Dr. Fazzi has authored numerous texts, books chapters, and journal articles on the topics of visual impairment and blindness, with an emphasis on O&M for young children, and has made numerous presentations at state, national, and international conferences in the field of visual impairment. Her most recent presentations have been on the topics of O&M for young children, O&M for students with multiple disabilities, and strategies for online instruction. Dr. Fazzi is a member of the Board of Trustees of the American Foundation for the Blind and previously served as chair of the California Advisory Commission on Special Education.

Janet M. Barlow, MEd, a certified orientation and mobility specialist, is president of Accessible Design for the Blind in Asheville, North Carolina. Ms. Barlow has over 40 years' experience in teaching, training, presenting, writing, and researching safe travel for pedestrians with disabilities and has worked extensively with adults who are blind or who have low vision in a rehabilitation center setting. Ms. Barlow is the coauthor of *Accessible Pedestrian Signals: A Guide to Best Practices* and *Detectable Warnings: Synthesis of U.S. and International Practice,* as well as numerous journal articles, papers, conference sessions, and seminars focusing on the accessibility of sidewalks and intersections. She has collaborated with technical committees of the National Committee on Uniform Traffic Control Devices and with transportation engineers and planners on developing standards and solutions to make travel environments safer and more accessible. Ms. Barlow served as chair of the Environmental Access Committee of the Orientation and Mobility Division of the Association for Education and Rehabilitation of the Blind and Visually Impaired and was a member of the Public Rights-of-Way Access Advisory Committee of the US Access Board.

CPSIA information can be obtained
at www.ICGtesting.com
Printed in the USA
LVOW05s1359170118
563080LV00012B/360/P